Linear Vibration and
Control System Theory

By the same author

Linear Vibration Theory: Generalized Properties aud Numerical Methods

Linear Vibration and
Control System Theory
WITH COMPUTER APPLICATIONS

James B. Vernon

University of Southern California
Los Angeles

JOHN WILEY & SONS, INC.   New York · London · Sydney

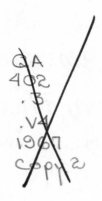

Preface

This book, with a companion volume, *Linear Vibration Theory: Generalized Properties and Numerical Methods*, is the outgrowth of notes written to explain the practical uses of "generalized" quantities, numerical methods, computers, and control system theory in the analysis of complex linear, mechanical systems. As a result of consulting and classroom experience, I became aware of an apparent discontinuity in the level of proficiency required to understand the idealized situations often discussed in the classroom and the complex problems encountered in practice. One objective has been to bridge this gap, and thus both volumes are addressed to the senior undergraduate or first-year graduate student, and to the practicing engineer.

Chapter 1 of this text reviews the portions of the companion volume which are of major interest in relation to this book. Chapters 2 to 7 relate useful topics in control system theory to the material usually associated with the study of vibration. I believe that control system theory contributes concepts which can be of great assistance in developing intuition and perception of factors which affect the vibration of complex systems. As an aid in the application of some of this theory, transparent overlays for frequency response analysis are provided in an appendix. Digital computer program listings are also provided for the determination of frequency response, complex plane, and root locus plots.

Chapters 8 and 9 explain the use of digital and analogue computers in the analysis of control systems or vibrating mechanical systems. In addition to the explanation of the FORTRAN coding method contained in Chapter 8, listings are provided for other frequently occurring problems in vibration analysis, including (besides those previously mentioned) programs for calculation of normal modes and frequencies, matrix inversion, redundant beam and unrestrained or partially restrained beam flexibility matrix, characteristic equation from a determinant having quadratic elements, factors of a polynomial, the analytical inverse Laplace transform of a function having real or complex poles of any order, response of such a system to an arbitrary forcing function, Fourier series coefficients, numerical Fourier transforms and inverse transform, and the shock spectrum for simple or complex shocks.

The problems which have been suggested often provide important extensions of the text material. Some are "project-type" problems requiring days or weeks to complete. The reader is urged to give his attention to these problems, as well as to the simpler ones, and at least to formulate a method of solution even if he does not actually complete the solution.

This book could be used either in a formal course or for self-instruction as a textbook for a first course in control system theory, and as a textbook for a first course in the use of computers in numerical analysis. However, the reader should be acquainted with the material contained in the companion volume and Chapter 1 of this volume or the equivalent.

In the companion volume, *Linear Vibration Theory: Generalized Properties and Numerical Methods*, emphasis is on theory pertaining to linear, mechanical vibration, especially as applied to complex systems. The generalized coordinate concept is explained and put to extensive use. Numerical methods appropriate to vibration analysis are emphasized and explained in considerable detail.

I originally intended to make individual acknowledgement of former students who have been of assistance to me, but this has become impractical because of the numbers involved. Their criticisms and suggestions are appreciated. Special thanks are extended to Dr. C. R. Freberg for his suggestions and encouragement, to Dr. Harry Himelblau for his helpful and significant comments, and to Louise Maurer for assistance with the manuscript.

James B. Vernon

Contents

Recommended General References

The following short list of references is given for readers who would like additional explanation of topics related to those discussed in the text. The list is deliberately abbreviated to several books in each of the appropriate areas. Although many of these references are cited in the text, the list is intended primarily for general reference.

1. Vernon, James B., *Linear Vibration Theory: Generalized Properties and Numerical Methods*, John Wiley and Sons, Inc., New York, 1967.
2. Freberg, C. R., and E. N. Kemler, *Elements of Mechanical Vibration*, second edition, John Wiley and Sons, Inc., New York, 1949.
3. Tong, Kin N., *Theory of Mechanical Vibration*, John Wiley and Sons, Inc., New York, 1960.
4. Morrow, Charles T., *Shock and Vibration Engineering*, John Wiley and Sons, Inc., New York, 1963.
5. Church, Austin H., *Mechanical Vibrations*, second edition, John Wiley and Sons, Inc., New York, 1963.
6. Tse, Francis S., Ivan E. Morse, and Rolland T. Hinkle, *Mechanical Vibrations*, Allyn and Bacon, Inc., Boston, 1963.
7. Wylie, C. R., Jr., *Advanced Engineering Mathematics*, second edition, McGraw-Hill Book Company, Inc., New York, 1960.
8. Kreyszig, Erwin, *Advanced Engineering Mathematics*, John Wiley and Sons, Inc., New York, 1962,
9. Hildebrand, Francis B., *Methods of Applied Mathematics*, Prentice-Hall, Inc., Englewood Cliffs, 1952.
10. Churchill, Ruel V., *Complex Variables and Applications*, second edition, McGraw-Hill Book Company, Inc., New York, 1960.
11. Pipes, Louis A., *Matrix Methods for Engineering*, Prentice-Hall, Inc., Englewood Cliffs, 1963.
12. Pestel, Edward C., and Frederick A. Leckie, *Matrix Methods in Elastomechanics*, McGraw-Hill Book Company, Inc., New York, 1963.
13. Wilts, C. H., *Principles of Feedback Control*, Addison-Wesley Publishing Company, Inc., Reading, Massachusetts, 1960.
14. Raven, Francis H., *Automatic Control Engineering*, McGraw-Hill Book Company, Inc., New York, 1961.
15. Chestnut, Harold, and Robert W. Mayer, *Servomechanisms, and Regulating System Design*, second edition, John Wiley and Sons, Inc., New York, 1959.

16. Seifert, William W. and Carl W. Steeg, *Control Systems Engineering*, McGraw-Hill Book Company, Inc., New York, 1960.
17. Organick, Elliott I., *A Fortran Primer*, Addison-Wesley Publishing Company, Inc., Reading, Massachusetts, 1963.
18. Mc Cracken, Daniel D., *A Guide to Fortran Programming*, John Wiley and Sons, Inc., New York, 1961.
19. Jenness, Roger R., *Analog Computation and Simulation: Laboratory Approach*, Allyn and Bacon, Inc., Boston, 1965.
20. Jackson, Albert S., *Analog Computation*, McGraw-Hill Book Company, Inc., New York, 1960.

Linear Vibration and
Control System Theory

CHAPTER 1

Linear Vibration Theory

The purpose of this book is to relate useful topics in control system theory to the material usually associated with the study of mechanical vibration, and to explain the use of digital and analogue computers in the utilization of appropriate numerical methods in the analysis of vibration and control system problems.

This chapter is a summary of the portions of the companion volume (Ref. 1), *Linear Vibration Theory, Generalized Properties and Numerical Methods*, that are of major interest in relation to this book.

1.1 Simple Systems

Figure 1-1 shows an idealization of several simple linear systems excited by an external force. By convention, let a time-varying quantity be designated by a lower-case letter and the Laplace transform of this variable be designated by the corresponding capital letter. The transformed equations of motion for the systems of Fig. 1-1 are given in Equations 1-1, where x_0 and $\dot{x}_0$ are the initial displacement and velocity.

$$
\begin{aligned}
&\text{(a)} \quad X = \frac{1}{k} F \\[2mm]
&\text{(b)} \quad X = \frac{1}{cs} F + \frac{1}{s} x_0 \\[2mm]
&\text{(c)} \quad X = \frac{1}{ms^2} F + \frac{1}{s^2} \dot{x}_0 + \frac{1}{s} x_0 \\[2mm]
&\text{(d)} \quad X = \frac{1}{cs + k} F + \frac{c}{cs + k} x_0 \\[2mm]
&\text{(e)} \quad X = \frac{1}{ms^2 + cs} F + \frac{ms + c}{ms^2 + cs} x_0 + \frac{m}{ms^2 + cs} \dot{x}_0 \\[2mm]
&\text{(f)} \quad X = \frac{1}{ms^2 + k} F + \frac{ms}{ms^2 + k} x_0 + \frac{m}{ms^2 + k} \dot{x}_0 \\[2mm]
&\text{(g)} \quad X = \frac{1}{ms^2 + cs + k} F + \frac{ms + c}{ms^2 + cs + k} x_0 + \frac{m\dot{x}_0}{ms^2 + cs + k}
\end{aligned}
\tag{1-1}
$$

1

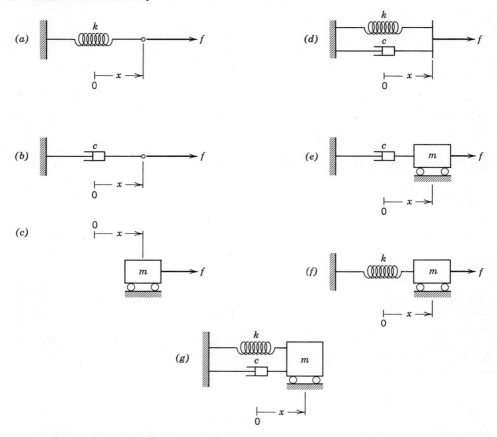

Fig. 1-1   Simple systems with force excitation.

The conventional single-degree-of-freedom vibration problem, damped and un-damped, is represented by g and f of Fig. 1-1 and Equations 1-1(g) and 1-1(f). It is clear from Equations 1-1 that the general solution can be formed by summing the results of an analysis of motion resulting from initial conditions and from the force considered separately. If the force is specified zero, the motion is that which occurs naturally or freely, that is, "natural vibration" or "free vibration." If the initial conditions are specified zero, and a force (function of time) is imposed, the forced motion resulting is usually composed of two parts, one that decays with time, designated as "transient," and one that remains after a long time, designated as "steady state." The steady-state motion resulting from a sinusoidal force input is often called "forced vibration."

Natural Vibration. A vibrating system is more easily understood in terms of its natural frequency and damping factor than in terms of its mass, spring, and damper components. Consequently, Equation 1-1(g) is more conveniently written as Equation 1-2.

$$X = \frac{1}{s^2 + 2\zeta\beta s + \beta^2}\frac{F}{m} + \frac{s + 2\zeta\beta s}{s^2 + 2\zeta\beta s + \beta^2}x_0 + \frac{1}{s^2 + 2\zeta\beta s + \beta^2}\dot{x}_0 \qquad (1\text{-}2)$$

where

$$\beta = \sqrt{\frac{k}{m}}$$

$$\zeta = \frac{c}{2\sqrt{mk}} = \frac{c}{c_{cr}} \tag{1-3}$$

$$c_{cr} = 2\sqrt{mk}$$

In Equations 1-3, β is the "undamped natural frequency," ζ the "damping factor," and c_{cr} the "critical damping constant."

The inverse Laplace transform of Equation 1-2, with $F = 0$, is Equation 1-4 if $-1 < \zeta < 1$, Equation 1-5 if $\zeta > 1$ or $\zeta < -1$, and Equation 1-6 if $\zeta = 1$ or $\zeta = -1$.

$$x = e^{-\zeta\beta t}\left[x_0 \cos(\beta\sqrt{1-\zeta^2}\,t) + \frac{\dot{x}_0 + \zeta\beta x_0}{\beta\sqrt{1-\zeta^2}}\sin(\beta\sqrt{1-\zeta^2}\,t)\right] \tag{1-4}$$

$$x = e^{-\zeta\beta t}\left[x_0 \cosh(\beta\sqrt{\zeta^2-1}\,t) + \frac{\dot{x}_0 + \zeta\beta x_0}{\beta\sqrt{\zeta^2-1}}\sinh(\beta\sqrt{\zeta^2-1}\,t)\right] \tag{1-5}$$

$$x = [(1 + \zeta\beta t)x_0 + \dot{x}_0 t]e^{-\zeta\beta t} \tag{1-6}$$

From these equations it is seen that $\zeta = 1$ or -1 is a boundary between oscillating or nonoscillating motion, and $\zeta = 0$ is a boundary between a stable and an unstable system ($\zeta < 0$ is not possible with dampers as implied in Fig. 1-1, however). For $\zeta = 0$ the motion is oscillatory at the undamped natural frequency, β. The natural frequency for a damped system is the "damped natural frequency," β_d, given by Equation 1-7.

$$\beta_d = \beta\sqrt{1-\zeta^2} \tag{1-7}$$

A graph of displacement for several damping ratios for motion starting from rest (zero initial velocity) is shown in Fig. 1-2. For $\zeta = 0$ the displacement periodically reaches a maximum. This maximum displacement is called the "amplitude" of the vibration. For $0 < \zeta < 1$ the amplitude decreases exponentially with time, and for $-1 < \zeta < 0$ the amplitude increases exponentially with time.

If a system is overdamped ($\zeta > 1$), the quadratic in the denominator of Equation 1-2 can be factored into two real factors,

$$\left(s + \frac{1}{T_1}\right)\left(s + \frac{1}{T_2}\right)$$

where

$$T_1 = \frac{1}{\zeta\beta\left(1 + \sqrt{1 - \frac{1}{\zeta^2}}\right)}$$

$$T_2 = \frac{1}{\zeta\beta\left(1 - \sqrt{1 - \frac{1}{\zeta^2}}\right)} \tag{1-8}$$

$$T_1 T_2 = \frac{1}{\beta^2}$$

The quantities T_1 and T_2 are "time constants," and are perhaps more easily understood by considering Fig. 1-1d and Equation 1-1(d).

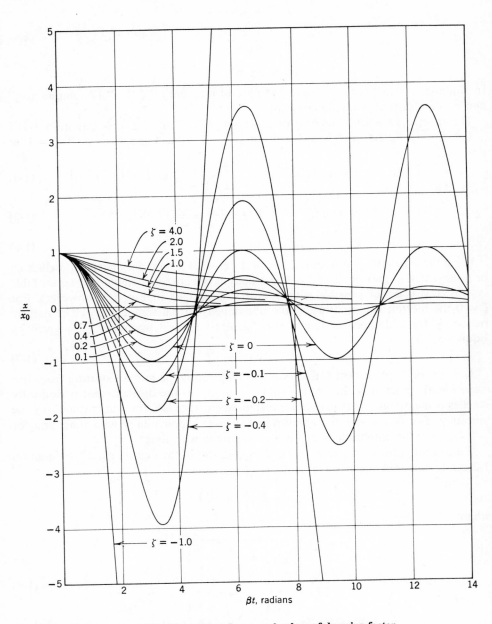

Fig. 1-2   Displacement as a function of time for several values of damping factor.

If the force is zero in Fig. 1-1d the inverse transform of Equation 1-1(d) is

where

$$\left. \begin{array}{c} \dfrac{x}{x_0} = e^{-t/T} \\[2mm] T = \dfrac{c}{k} \end{array} \right\}$$

(1-9)

A graph of x is shown in Fig. 1-3, where it is seen that the time constant, T, is the length of time required for the displacement to reach e^{-1} or 0.368 of its initial value, or alternatively the length of time for the displacement to reach zero if it continued at its initial rate.

For an overdamped system, the larger of the two time constants is the more important, and for $\zeta > 2$ the displacement curve is not very different for the second-order system of Fig. 1-1g and for the first-order system of Fig. 1-1d. This is to say that the inertia of the mass is not very important, and Fig. 1-2 can be used as an estimate of the displacement curve, using $T = c/k$ (which is approximately T_2 of Equation 1-8 for $\zeta > 2$).

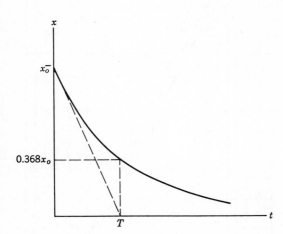

Fig. 1-3 Displacement as function of time for first-order system.

Forced Vibration. If the initial conditions are zero and the transient terms arising from the use of a sinusoidal forcing function are neglected, the remaining term describes the steady-state or forced vibration. If $f = f_0 \sin \omega t$ and the steady-state term of Equation 1-1(g) is computed using these assumptions, the result is

where

$$\left. \begin{array}{c} \dfrac{x}{\delta_{st}} = \dfrac{1}{\sqrt{\left[1 - \left(\dfrac{\omega}{\beta}\right)^2\right]^2 + \left(2\zeta\dfrac{\omega}{\beta}\right)^2}} \sin(\omega t + \phi_1) \\[4mm] \delta_{st} = \dfrac{f_0}{k} \\[4mm] \phi_1 = -\tan^{-1} \dfrac{2\zeta\dfrac{\omega}{\beta}}{1 - \left(\dfrac{\omega}{\beta}\right)^2} \end{array} \right\}$$

(1-10)

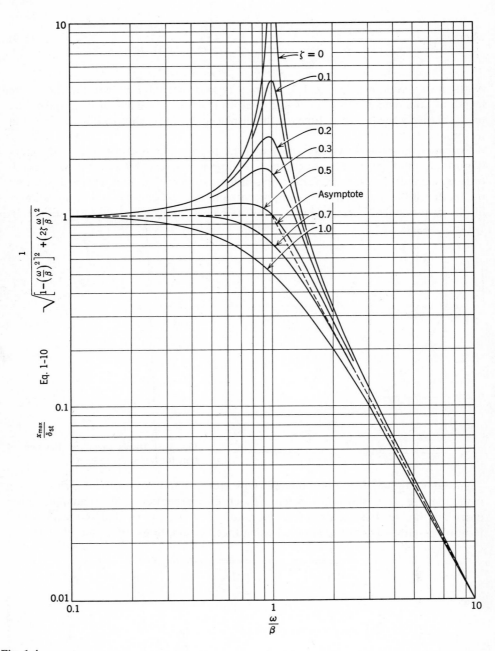

Fig. 1-4

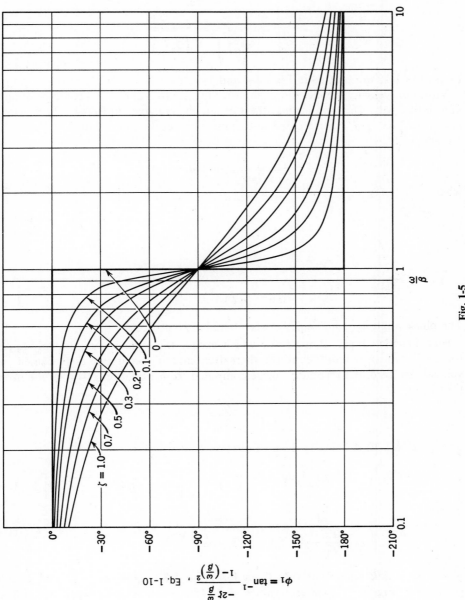

Fig. 1-5

$$\phi_1 = \tan^{-1} \frac{-2\zeta \frac{\omega}{\beta}}{1 - \left(\frac{\omega}{\beta}\right)^2} \;,\; \text{Eq. 1-10}$$

The angle ϕ_1 is the phase angle, a negative angle between 0 and -180 degrees. The "static deflection," δ_{st}, is the deflection which would exist if the force f_0 were a steady force instead of the amplitude of a sinusoidal force. From Equation 1-10 the ratio of amplitude of displacement to static deflection is seen to be

$$\frac{1}{\sqrt{\left[1 - \left(\frac{\omega}{\beta}\right)^2\right]^2 + \left(2\zeta\frac{\omega}{\beta}\right)^2}}$$

Equations 1-10 are plotted in Figs. 1-4 and 1-5.

Vibration velocity, acceleration, and force transmitted to the wall could be obtained in a similar way. These plots and others of interest are given in Ref 1. The first-order system of Fig. 1-1d, when treated in this manner, results in Equation 1-11 and Figs. 1-6 and 1-7.

where

$$\frac{x}{\delta_{st}} = \frac{1}{\sqrt{1 + (\omega T)^2}} \sin(\omega t + \phi_2)$$

$$T = \frac{c}{k}$$

$$\delta_{st} = \frac{f_0}{k}$$

$$\phi_2 = -\tan^{-1}(\omega T)$$

$$(1\text{-}11)$$

The phase angle ϕ_2 is an angle between 0 and -90 degrees.

Step Function Input. If the force which excites the system is a suddenly applied force, f_0, which remains constant thereafter, and if the initial displacement and velocity are zero, the response can be computed from Equation 1-1(g) as the inverse transform of

$$\frac{f_0}{ms(s^2 + 2\zeta\beta s + \beta^2)}$$

or Equation 1-12 if $0 \leq \zeta < 1$ and Equation 1-13 if $\zeta > 1$.

$$\frac{x}{\delta_{st}} = 1 - e^{-\zeta\beta t}\left[\cos(\beta\sqrt{1 - \zeta^2}\, t) + \frac{\zeta}{\sqrt{1 - \zeta^2}} \sin(\beta\sqrt{1 - \zeta^2}\, t)\right] \quad (1\text{-}12)$$

$$\frac{x}{\delta_{st}} = 1 + \frac{1}{\left(\frac{T_2}{T_1} - 1\right)} e^{-t/T_1} - \frac{1}{1 - \frac{T_1}{T_2}} e^{-t/T_2} \quad (1\text{-}13)$$

where $\delta_{st} = f_0/k$ and T_1 and T_2 from Equation 1-8. Equations 1-12 and 1-13 are graphed in Fig. 1-8 for several values of ζ. The relationship between Fig. 1-8 and Fig. 1-2 is obvious and interesting.

The response of a first-order system and an overdamped second-order system to a step-forcing input is plotted in Fig. 1-9. The dominant effect of the larger time constant for values of ζ exceeding about 2 is evident from this figure.

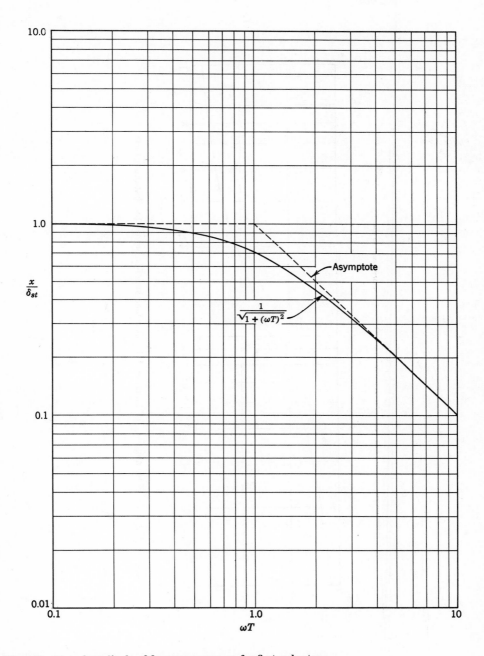

Fig. 1-6   Plot of amplitude of frequency response for first-order term.

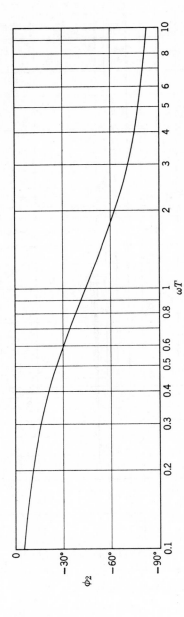

Fig. 1-7   Place angle ϕ_2, of Equation 1-11, as a function of frequency for first-order term.

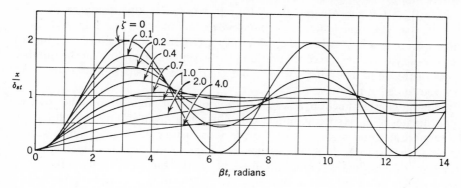

Fig. 1-8   Response of second-order system to step input.

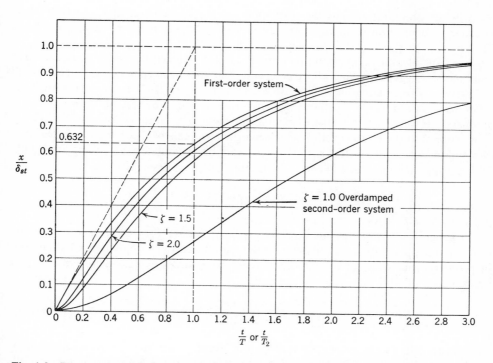

Fig. 1-9   Response of first-order system and second-order overdamped system to step input.

1.2 Lagrange Equation and Generalized Properties

Lagrange Equation. Equation 1-14 is the Lagrange equation for a multiple-degree-of-freedom system with energy dissipation and external forcing functions of time.

$$\frac{d}{dt}\left(\frac{\partial L}{\partial \dot{q}_i}\right) - \frac{\partial L}{\partial q_i} + \frac{\partial \mathcal{F}_d}{\partial \dot{q}_i} = Q_i \tag{1-14}$$

In Equation 1-14, L is the "Lagrangian," $T - V$, where T is kinetic energy and V is potential energy. The "generalized coordinates" are q_i (and their instantaneous rates of change with time are $\dot{q}_i$), where the subscript implies that one or more coordinates may be necessary to define the configuration of the system, depending on the number of degrees of freedom. The functions $\mathscr{F}_d$ and Q_i are the "dissipation function" and "generalized force" function.

The potential energy function, V, is a function of the configuration alone; that is, if the coordinates q_i have specific numerical values at a given instant, V will have a specific numerical value regardless of the previous history of the coordinate values or the instantaneous rates of change of the coordinates ($\dot{q}_i$), and the numerical value of V for a given coordinate configuration is always the same (not time dependent). This is equivalent to saying that a mathematical statement for V can be expressed in terms of the coordinates exclusively, or $V = V(q_1, q_2, \ldots)$.

The kinetic energy function, T, is dependent on the coordinates and on the rates of change of the coordinates; that is, it is (or may be) necessary to know both the coordinate configuration and the instantaneous rates of change of the coordinates in order to determine the kinetic energy of the system at a given instant, or $T = T(q_1, q_2, \ldots, \dot{q}_1, \dot{q}_2, \ldots)$.

Unfortunately, the dissipation function, $\mathscr{F}_d$, is not as general as the potential energy and kinetic energy functions, whose determination does not depend on the linearity of the system. The dissipation function for use in Equation 1-14 must be formulated differently depending on whether the energy dissipation is by viscous or nonviscous dampers. However, for viscous dampers, or where the damping force or torque is proportional to the relative velocity between the terminals of the damping device, the dissipation function for the entire system can be formulated by taking one half of the instantaneous rate of energy dissipation in the system. That is,

$$\mathscr{F}_d = \mathscr{F}_d(q_1, q_2, \ldots, \dot{q}_1, \dot{q}_2, \ldots) = \tfrac{1}{2}\dot{E}$$

if $\dot{E}$ is the *rate of dissipation* of energy in the system.

The generalized forces, Q_i, are functions of time; that is, $Q_i = Q_i(t)$. It is convenient to formulate the expressions for these forces using Equation 1-15, where W is the rate of production of work by all external forces, these forces expressed in terms of the coordinates, q_i, and their rates of change $\dot{q}_i$.

$$Q_i = \frac{\partial W}{\partial \dot{q}_i} \qquad (1\text{-}15)$$

This is equivalent to the statement that Q_i is a "force" such that the work represented by $Q_i\, dq_i$, accomplished in the time interval dt, is the same as the work done by all external forces in this same time interval as these forces displace through differential distances determined by dq_i. Example 1-1 of Section 1.4 clarifies this concept.

Principal Coordinates. Application of Equation 1-14, once for each coordinate, results in a set of simultaneous differential equations which govern the motion of the system. If the equations of this set are uncoupled (each equation contains only one coordinate), the coordinates selected to describe the system are "principal coordinates." The designation "generalized coordinate" is often used when principal coordinate is intended, so that the meaning may have to be determined from the context. The designation "normal coordinate" may also be used for principal co-ordinate.

Coordinates which suggest themselves from the nature of the physical system usually are not principal coordinates. Sometimes the coordinates used to describe a system are not principal coordinates for that system but may be principal coordinates for a subsystem (Example 1-2, Section 1.6 illustrates this use). It is usually a rather involved computation to determine a set of principal coordinates from a set of generalized coordinates.

For many systems the differential equations resulting from the application of Equation 1-14 are linear, or at least can be linearized for small displacements of the coordinates from an equilibrium configuration. Solution is then possible by application of one of several techniques. If the system is not forced ($Q_i = 0$), the solution results in the "normal modes" of vibration of the system, enabling the determination of principal coordinates to describe these normal modes. If the system is forced, it is often more convenient to determine the response using the principal coordinates than to determine the response from the ordinary coordinates or other coupled generalized coordinates.

Generalized Properties. If a set of coupled linear differential equations in ordinary coordinates is converted into a set of uncoupled equations in the principal coordinates by suitable transformation relationships between the coordinate systems, it is possible to treat each of the principal coordinates as if it were the coordinate of a single-degree-of-freedom system. Superposition of these results then gives the response of the complex system. For this purpose it is convenient to introduce the concepts of "generalized masses," "generalized springs," "generalized dampers," and "generalized forces." These are masses, springs, dampers, and forces for the equivalent single-degree systems which utilize the principal coordinates of the complex system.

If the kinetic energy, T in Equation 1-14, is a function of the coordinate velocities (and not of the coordinates), and if the differential equations resulting from Equation 1-14 are ordinary, linear differential equations with constant coefficients, then the kinetic energy can be expressed in the form $T = \frac{1}{2}M_1\dot{q}_1^2 + \frac{1}{2}M_2\dot{q}_2^2 + \cdots$, where the constants M_1, M_2, etc., may be considered generalized masses corresponding to the principal coordinates q_1, q_2, etc. Therefore, the generalized mass M_i corresponding to a principal coordinate q_i is the amount of mass traveling at the velocity $\dot{q}_i$ that has the same amount of kinetic energy as all of the masses in the system moving at their individual velocities as fixed by $\dot{q}_i$. The generalized masses may also be computed from Equation 1-16.

$$M_i = \frac{\partial^2 T}{\partial \dot{q}_i^2} \tag{1-16}$$

Similarly, the generalized spring constants may be computed from Equation 1-17. The same interpretation is available for the generalized spring; that is, the generalized spring corresponding to a principal coordinate q_i is the spring which, subjected to the displacement q_i, stores the same amount of potential energy as all the actual springs subjected to their actual deflections as defined by q_i.

$$K_i = \frac{\partial^2 V}{\partial q_i^2} \tag{1-17}$$

The generalized damping coefficient, C_i, accounts for all of the energy dissipation associated with the velocity, $\dot{q}_i$, when used in the expression $\frac{1}{2}C_i\dot{q}_i^2$ and may also be computed from Equation 1-18.

$$C_i = \frac{\partial^2 \mathcal{F}_d}{\partial \dot{q}_i^2} \qquad (1\text{-}18)$$

The generalized force corresponding to a generalized coordinate was discussed earlier. There is no difference if the generalized coordinate is also a principal coordinate. Equation 1-15 can be used to compute the generalized force.

Example 1-1, Section 1.4, illustrates some of these concepts relating to generalized properties.

1.3 Matrix Analysis of Multiple-Degree Systems

Matrix Formulation. Figure 1-10 represents a simple three-degree-of-freedom system suitable for illustration of matrix methods. Application of either Lagrange's or Newton's equation to this system yields Equations 1-19.

$$m_1\ddot{x}_1 + (c_1 + c_2)\dot{x}_1 + (k_1 + k_2)x_1 - c_2\dot{x}_2 - k_2x_2 = f_1(t)$$
$$-c_2\dot{x}_1 - k_2x_1 + m_2\ddot{x}_2 + (c_2 + c_3)\dot{x}_2 + (k_2 + k_3)x_2 - c_3\dot{x}_3 - k_3x_3 = f_2(t) \qquad (1\text{-}19)$$
$$-c_3\dot{x}_2 - k_3x_2 + m_3\ddot{x}_3 + c_3\dot{x}_3 + k_3x_3 = f_3(t)$$

Equations 1-19 can be expressed with the following matrix equation.

$$[M]\{\ddot{x}\} + [C]\{\dot{x}\} + [K]\{x\} = \{F\} \qquad (1\text{-}20)$$

Matrices $[M]$, $[C]$, and $[K]$ are square matrices, not necessarily diagonal or even symmetric in general, although in this illustration they are symmetric and $[M]$ is diagonal.

Matrix Iteration for Undamped Systems. To determine normal modes of an undamped system, let $[C] = [0]$ and $\{f\} = \{0\}$. If the system is initially disturbed from the equilibrium configuration, natural vibration occurs so that Equation 1-21 is satisfied for each normal mode.

$$\{x\} = \{A\} \cos \beta t \qquad (1\text{-}21)$$

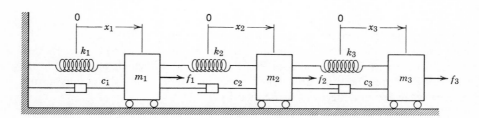

Fig. 1-10

where the absolute values of the elements of $\{A\}$ are the amplitudes of the elements of $\{x\}$ and the algebraic signs of $\{A\}$ indicate relative direction of the displacements of the variables. Differentiation of Equation 1-21 twice shows that $\{\ddot{x}\} = -\beta^2\{x\}$, and this, substituted in Equation 1-20 (with $[C] = [0]$, $\{f\} = \{0\}$), results in

or

$$[K]\{x\} = \beta^2[M]\{x\}$$
$$\left.\begin{array}{c} \\ \\ \end{array}\right\} \quad (1\text{-}22)$$
$$\{x\} = \beta^2[K]^{-1}[M]\{x\}$$

The matrix $[K]$ is often designated the "stiffness matrix," and its inverse the "flexibility matrix" or "matrix of influence coefficients." The matrix $[M]$ is usually called the "inertia matrix," and the combination $[K]^{-1}[M]$ may be termed the "dynamic matrix" or "dynamical matrix." Equations 1-22 and these definitions are incorporated in the following equations.

$$\{x\} = \beta^2[U]\{x\} \quad (1\text{-}23)$$

$$[U] = [K]^{-1}[M] = [\delta][M] \quad (1\text{-}24)$$

$$[K]^{-1} = [\delta] \quad (1\text{-}25)$$

Equation 1-23 does not imply that $\beta^2[U]$ is the unit matrix, but rather that there are combinations of the variables $\{x\}$ and β for which Equation 1-23 is satisfied. If $[U]$ were a diagonal matrix, the coordinates $\{x\}$ would be principal coordinates, since the individual equations represented by Equation 1-23 would be uncoupled. In this illustration $[U]$ would not be diagonal, and a transformation is desired which will result in a diagonal matrix. Let this transformation be defined by Equation 1-26.

$$\{x\} = [N]\{y\} \quad (1\text{-}26)$$

$$\{y\} = [N]^{-1}\{x\} \quad (1\text{-}27)$$

Substitution of Equation 1-26 in Equation 1-23 results in

$$\{y\} = \beta^2[N]^{-1}[U][N]\{y\} \quad (1\text{-}28)$$

or

$$\{y\} = \beta^2[V]\{y\} \quad (1\text{-}29)$$

where

$$[V] = [N]^{-1}[U][N] \quad (1\text{-}30)$$

The matrix $[V]$ is then a diagonal matrix and consequently $\beta^2[V]$ is the unit matrix, from which it is seen that the various values of β (natural frequencies) are the reciprocals of the square root of the diagonal elements of $[V]$.

The diagonalization transformation may be accomplished with a succession of transformations in an iterative manner by reducing two off-diagonal elements simultaneously to zero in each transformation. Successive transformations do not preserve the previous off-diagonal zeros, but if the transformations are continued iteratively, with progression around the matrix numerous times, all off-diagonal elements will approach zero relative to the diagonal elements. That is,

$$[V]_1 = [N]_1{}^{-1}[U][N]_1$$
$$[V]_2 = [N]_2{}^{-1}[V]_1[N]_2$$
$$\vdots \qquad \qquad \vdots$$
$$[V]_k = [N]_k{}^{-1}[V]_{k-1}[N]_k \qquad \qquad \text{(1-31)}$$
$$\vdots \qquad \qquad \vdots$$
$$[V]_n = [N]_n{}^{-1}[V]_{n-1}[N]_n = [V] \quad ([V] \text{ diagonal})$$
$$[N] = [N]_1[N]_2 \cdots [N]_k \cdots [N]_n$$
$$[V] = [N]^{-1}[U][N]$$

where the elements of the successive matrices can be computed from Equations 1-32. If the two off-diagonal elements which are supposed to become zero are $V_{k_{ij}}$ and $V_{k_{ji}}$, where the first subscript is the row number and the second subscript the column number, then the elements of $[N]_k$ necessary to cause this can be computed from the elements of $[V]_{(k-1)}$ using Equations 1-32. Use of these equations is demonstrated in Example 1-1 of Section 1.4.

$$a = \frac{V_{(k-1)_{jj}} - V_{(k-1)_{ii}}}{2V_{(k-1)_{ij}}} \qquad b = \frac{V_{(k-1)_{jj}} - V_{(k-1)_{ii}}}{2V_{(k-1)_{ji}}} \Bigg]$$

(If a and b are zero, select different elements and begin again.)

$$\left. \begin{aligned}
N_{k_{ii}} = N_{k_{jj}} &= \sqrt{\frac{1}{2}\frac{1}{1 + ab\left(1 + \sqrt{1 + \frac{1}{ab}}\right)}} \\[2mm]
N_{k_{ij}} &= -N_{k_{jj}}b\left(1 + \sqrt{1 + \frac{1}{ab}}\right) \\[2mm]
N_{k_{ji}} &= N_{k_{ii}}a\left(1 + \sqrt{1 + \frac{1}{ab}}\right) \\[2mm]
N_{k_{nn}} &= 1 \quad n \neq i \qquad \text{and} \quad n \neq j \\[2mm]
N_{k_{n,m}} &= 0 \quad n, m \neq i, j \qquad \text{and} \quad n, m \neq j, i
\end{aligned} \right\} \qquad \text{(1-32)}$$

The iterative procedure just described yields all the modes and frequencies simultaneously. We now describe another iterative procedure, the method of Duncan and Collar, which yields one mode and frequency at a time. Usually only a few of the low-frequency modes of a complex structure are calculated.

A column matrix for $\{x\}$ is assumed, which is used in the right side of Equation 1-23, resulting in a column matrix for the left side of Equation 1-23. If it should happen that the column matrix on the left is some constant times the assumed column matrix on the right, then the assumed column matrix is a description of a normal mode and the constant relating the two columns is the square of the frequency. If the column matrix on the left is not a simple constant times the assumed column matrix, then the left column matrix is "normalized" (divided by some convenient constant) and used on the right side as a new assumption. This procedure is repeated until eventually two successive columns are related by a constant to a sufficient degree of accuracy. The procedure converges on the lowest normal mode.

To determine the second mode and frequency, a restriction must be placed on the system, with the effect of preventing oscillation in the first mode. This can be accomplished by requiring that the first principal coordinate remain zero while the ordinary coordinates oscillate. This will be explained later. Equations 1-33 summarize the procedure for modifying the dynamic matrix $[U]$ to obtain a new dynamic matrix $[U]_1$ which is restricted as indicated above and whose iteration will lead to the second mode. The matrix $\{N\}_1$ defines Mode 1 corresponding to the principal coordinate y_1. The process is repeated for higher modes. Example 1-1 of Section 1.4 illustrates the procedure. This method, slightly modified, is programmed for digital computer solution and listed as Program A38NM in the Appendix.

$$\{N\}_1 = \begin{Bmatrix} \dfrac{\partial x_1}{\partial y_1} \\ \dfrac{\partial x_2}{\partial y_1} \\ \vdots \end{Bmatrix}$$

$$[B] = \{\tilde{N}\}_1[M]$$ \hfill (1-33)

$$[S]_1 = \begin{bmatrix} 0 & -\dfrac{B_2}{B_1} & -\dfrac{B_3}{B_1} & \cdots \\ 0 & 1 & 0 & \cdots \\ 0 & 0 & 1 & \cdots \\ \vdots & \vdots & \vdots & \vdots \end{bmatrix}$$

$$[U]_1 = [U][S]_1$$

Stiffness and Flexibility Matrices. The importance of the stiffness and flexibility matrices in the matrix formulation of vibration problems is obvious. It was seen that the stiffness matrix develops naturally from the application of the Lagrange equations to determine the equations of motion, and in fact an element K_{ij} of the stiffness matrix can be computed from Equation 1-34, as is easily verified by reference to the Lagrange formulation. In terms of Fig. 1-10, for the linear systems under consideration,

$$\frac{\partial V}{\partial x_i} = K_{i1}x_1 + K_{i2}x_2 + K_{i3}x_3$$

and

$$K_{ij} = \frac{\partial^2 V}{\partial x_i \, \partial x_j}$$ \hfill (1-34)

Similarly, for systems in which the kinetic energy is not a function of the coordinates, and for which linear differential equations result, the elements of the inertia matrix are

$$M_{ij} = \frac{\partial^2 T}{\partial \dot{x}_i \, \partial \dot{x}_j}$$ \hfill (1-35)

However, a different and useful concept applying to the stiffness and flexibility matrices is illustrated by the following discussion. The deflected configuration of a structure subject to static loads can be defined by displacements of suitable stations located on the structure. These are the coordinates $\{x\}$. Let loads in the positive directions of the x's be defined as $\{f\}$. That is, f_j is a load applied at Station j in the positive direction of x_j. Then an element δ_{ij} of the flexibility matrix may be determined from Equation 1-36.

$$\delta_{ij} = \frac{\partial x_i}{\partial f_j} \tag{1-36}$$

This is equivalent to the statement that if unit load is applied to Station j, *all other loads remaining zero*, then in general all stations will deflect and the deflection of Station i is δ_{ij}.

A similar statement for the effect of deflections on a structure is that if unit deflection of Station j occurs, *with all other deflections remaining zero*, then some combination of loads at all stations will be required to cause this, and the load at Station i is the element of the stiffness matrix K_{ij}. That is,

$$K_{ij} = \frac{\partial f_i}{\partial x_j} \tag{1-37}$$

Equations 1-36 and 1-37 also apply if the coordinates and forces are generalized coordinates and forces and if they are principal coordinates and the corresponding forces, although in this latter instance δ_{ij} and K_{ij} are zero if $i \neq j$.

Using these definitions for $[\delta]$ and $[K]$, it is not difficult to demonstrate that $[\delta]$ and $[K]$ are reciprocal matrices. Since $\{x\} = [\delta]\{f\}$ and $\{f\} = [K]\{x\}$, it is clear that $\{f\} = [K][\delta]\{f\}$. Although this last equation appears to require that $[K][\delta] = [1]$, this conclusion cannot be drawn immediately. ($\beta^2[U]$ is not $[1]$ in Equation 1-23, for instance). However, since $\{f\} = [K][\delta]\{f\}$ for *every possible* configuration of forces, not just certain configurations, it is possible to choose configurations which demonstrate that $[K]$ and $[\delta]$ must be reciprocal matrices. For instance, if $f_1 \neq 0$, but $f_2 = 0, f_3 = 0$, etc., then

$$x_1 = \delta_{11}f_1 + \delta_{12}0 + \delta_{13}0 + \cdots = \delta_{11}f_1$$
$$x_2 = \delta_{21}f_1 + \delta_{22}0 + \delta_{23}0 + \cdots = \delta_{21}f_1$$
$$x_3 = \delta_{31}f_1 + \delta_{32}0 + \delta_{33}0 + \cdots = \delta_{31}f_1$$
$$\text{etc.}$$

and when these values of $\{x\}$ are used to determine $\{f\}$, from $\{f\} = [K]\{\delta\}$,

$$f_1 = (K_{11}\delta_{11} + K_{12}\delta_{21} + K_{13}\delta_{31} + \cdots)f_1$$
$$f_2 = (K_{21}\delta_{11} + K_{22}\delta_{21} + K_{23}\delta_{31} + \cdots)f_1$$
$$\text{etc.}$$

Since $f_2 = 0, f_3 = 0$, etc., but $f_1 \neq 0$, it follows that the terms in the parentheses must be 1, 0, 0, etc., and these terms are the elements of the first column of the product $[K][\delta]$. Other load configurations can be used to establish the other elements of the product $[K][\delta]$ and show that $[K][\delta] = [1]$.

For some systems and definitions of coordinates it may happen that $[K]$ or $[\delta]$ is a singular matrix, and it would not be possible to compute one from the other. This happens, for instance, for a system whose masses are flexibly connected to each other although the entire system is free in space. Adequate interpretation is usually possible so that this complication does not adversely affect the analysis.

Matrix Formulation for Energy, Orthogonality, and Generalized Properties. For the linear systems under consideration, it is easily verified that the kinetic and potential energies can be expressed by the following matrix equations, in which $\{x\}$, $\{q\}$, $\{y\}$ are column matrices of coordinates, ordinary, generalized, and principal respectively, and $[M]$, $[M_q]$, $[M_p]$ and $[K]$, $[K_q]$, $[K_p]$ are inertia and stiffness matrices associated with these coordinates.

$$T = \frac{1}{2}\{\tilde{x}\}[M]\{\dot{x}\} = \frac{1}{2}\{\tilde{\dot{q}}\}[M_a]\{\dot{q}\} = \frac{1}{2}\{\tilde{\dot{y}}\}[M_p]\{\dot{y}\} \tag{1-38}$$

$$V = \frac{1}{2}\{\tilde{x}\}[K]\{x\} = \frac{1}{2}\{\tilde{q}\}[K_a]\{q\} = \frac{1}{2}\{\tilde{y}\}[K_p]\{y\} \tag{1-39}$$

The inertia and stiffness matrices, $[M_p]$ and $[K_p]$, are diagonal matrices.

If a set of ordinary coordinates, $\{x\}$, and a set of principal coordinates, $\{y\}$, are related by Equations 1-26 and 1-27, $\{x\} = [N]\{y\}$ and $\{y\} = [N]^{-1}\{x\}$, then each column of $[N]$ is a description of a normal mode. This is easily seen by letting all of the principal coordinates be zero except one, y_j, and noting that the column $\{x\}$ is then the corresponding column of $[N]$ multiplied by the factor y_j. Consideration of Equations 1-38 and 1-39 in relation to Equations 1-26 and 1-27, leads to Equations 1-40 and 1-41, the orthogonality relationships. These can also be verified by writing Equation 1-22 for two normal modes, thus:

$$[K]\{N\}_i = \beta_i{}^2[M]\{N\}_i, \quad \text{and} \quad \{\tilde{N}\}_j[K]\{N\}_i = \beta_i{}^2\{\tilde{N}\}_j[M]\{N\}_i$$

$$[K]\{N\}_j = \beta_j{}^2[M]\{N\}_j, \quad \text{and} \quad \{\tilde{N}\}_i[K]\{N\}_j = \beta_j{}^2\{\tilde{N}\}_i[M]\{N\}_j$$

Since the transpose of the product of three matrices is the product of the individual transposes in reverse order (reversal rule), the first of these equations could be transposed to give

$$\{\tilde{N}\}_i[\tilde{K}]\{N\}_j = \beta_i{}^2\{\tilde{N}\}_i[\tilde{M}]\{N\}_j$$

and since $[K]$ and $[M]$ may be considered to be symmetrical (or could have been made symmetrical by judicious manipulations of the equations), $[\tilde{K}] = [K]$ and $[\tilde{M}] = [M]$. This transposed equation and the second equation can then be combined to obtain

$$(\beta_i{}^2 - \beta_j{}^2)\{\tilde{N}\}_i[M]\{N\}_j = \{\tilde{N}\}_i[K]\{N\}_j(1 - 1) = 0$$

Since $\beta_i{}^2 \neq \beta_j{}^2$, Equation 1-40 results, and then since $\beta_j{}^2 \neq 0$, Equation 1-41 develops.

$$\{\tilde{N}\}_i[M]\{N\}_j = 0 \tag{1-40}$$

$$\{\tilde{N}\}_i[K]\{N\}_j = 0 \tag{1-41}$$

These are matrix orthogonality relationships stating that principal coordinates are not inertia-coupled or spring-coupled.

The generalized mass, spring constant, damping coefficient, and force for a principal coordinate y_i may be computed from matrix Equations 1-42 to 1-45. (The column $\{f\}$ is a column of forces applied in the positive direction of the coordinates $\{x\}$.)

$$M_{p_i} = \{\tilde{N}\}_i[M]\{N\}_i \tag{1-42}$$

$$K_{p_i} = \{\tilde{N}\}_i[K]\{N\}_i \tag{1-43}$$

$$C_{p_i} = \{\tilde{N}\}_i[C]\{N\}_i \tag{1-44}$$

$$Q_{p_i} = \{\tilde{N}\}_i\{f\} \tag{1-45}$$

The procedure for eliminating a mode using the Duncan and Collar iteration procedure (Equations 1-33) can be understood with the help of the orthogonality relationship, Equation 1-40. The deflected configuration of a system is determined by the values of all the coordinates. If all the principal coordinates are nonzero, then Equation 1-26 states that the values of the ordinary coordinates may be obtained from

$$\{x\} = \{N\}_1 y_1 + \{N\}_2 y_2 + \{N\}_3 y_3 + \cdots$$

The column $\{x\}$ is seen to be composed of various combinations of the modal columns, and it is clear that the multiplication $\{\tilde{N}\}_1[M]\{x\}$ would not be zero because part of $\{x\}$ is $\{\tilde{N}\}_1 y_1$ and $\{\tilde{N}\}_1[M]\{N\}_1 \neq 0$. However, principal coordinate y_1 can be arbitrarily set equal to zero by requiring that the multiplication $\{\tilde{N}\}_1[M]\{x\} = 0$, since this multiplication is then some combination of $\{\tilde{N}\}_1[M]\{N\}_2$, $\{\tilde{N}\}_1[M]\{N\}_3$, etc., and these are zero according to Equation 1-40. Therefore, if $\{\tilde{N}\}_1[M]\{x\} = 0$, the coordinates $\{x\}$ must be some combination of the other modal columns, $\{N\}_2$, $\{N\}_3$, etc. but containing none of column $\{N\}_1$. That is, the coordinates are constrained in such manner that the first mode is eliminated.

The first equation of $[S]_1$ of Equation 1-33 expresses this relationship. That is, if $[B] = \{\tilde{N}\}_1[M]$, then $[B]\{x\} = 0$ results in

$$B_1 x_1 + B_2 x_2 + \cdots = 0 \quad \text{or} \quad x_1 = -\frac{B_2}{B_1} x_2 - \frac{B_3}{B_1} x_3 - \cdots$$

If then $x_2 = x_2$, $x_3 = x_3$, etc., the relationship expresses the restriction that the first mode shall not be a component of $\{x\}$. When this column $\{x\}$ is used on the right side of Equation 1-23, that equation becomes $\{x\} = \beta^2[U][S]_1\{x\}$ and the new dynamic matrix is $[U]_1 = [U][S]_1$ as indicated in Equation 1-33.

1.4 Damped Systems and the Characteristic Equation

The Characteristic Equation. One method of estimating the effect of light damping in a system is to use the undamped modes to determine generalized damping coefficients, neglecting the coupling between modes. If the damping is significant, the coupling between the normal undamped modes cannot be neglected. The damped normal modes may differ appreciably from the undamped modes. A satisfactory way to determine the natural modes and frequencies for a heavily damped system (or for negatively damped systems) is to make use of the characteristic equation.

The transformed equations of motion can be written in the general form of Equation 1-46, where in a specific problem many of the coefficients would be zero.

$$(A_{11} + B_{11}s + C_{11}s^2)X_1 + (A_{12} + B_{12}s + C_{12}s^2)X_2 + \cdots$$
$$+ (A_{1m} + B_{1m}s + C_{1m}s^2)X_m = F_1(s)$$
$$(A_{21} + B_{21}s + C_{21}s^2)X_1 + (A_{22} + B_{22}s + C_{22}s^2)X_2 + \cdots$$
$$+ (A_{2m} + B_{2m}s + C_{2m}s^2)X_m = F_2(s) \quad (1\text{-}46)$$
$$\cdot \quad \cdot \quad \cdot \quad \cdot \quad \cdot \quad \cdot \quad \cdot \quad \cdot \quad \cdot \quad \cdot \quad \cdot \quad \cdot \quad \cdot \quad \cdot$$
$$(A_{m1} + B_{m1}s + C_{m1}s^2)X_1 + (A_{m2} + B_{m2}s + C_{m2}s^2)X_2 + \cdots$$
$$+ (A_{mm} + B_{mm}s + C_{mm}s^2)X_m = F_m(s)$$

The functions on the right in these equations would result from forcing functions or initial conditions or both. Any of the transforms $X_1, X_2, \ldots, X_m$, could be obtained from the ratio of two determinants, the denominator being the same for any of the variables. This denominator is a polynomial, the expansion of the following determinant.

$$\begin{vmatrix} (A_{11} + B_{11}s + C_{11}s^2)(A_{12} + B_{12}s + C_{12}s^2)\cdots(A_{1m} + B_{1m}s + C_{1m}s^2) \\ (A_{21} + B_{21}s + C_{21}s^2)(A_{22} + B_{22}s + C_{22}s^2)\cdots(A_{2m} + B_{2m}s + C_{2m}s^2) \\ \cdot \quad \cdot \quad \cdot \quad \cdot \quad \cdot \quad \cdot \quad \cdot \quad \cdot \quad \cdot \quad \cdot \quad \cdot \quad \cdot \\ (A_{m1} + B_{m1}s + C_{m1}s^2)(A_{m2} + B_{m2}s + C_{m2}s^2)\cdots(A_{mm} + B_{mm}s + C_{mm}s^2) \end{vmatrix} \quad (1\text{-}47)$$

In order to obtain the inverse transforms of $X_1, X_2, \ldots, X_m$, it is necessary for this polynomial to be in factored form. The polynomial set equal to zero is the characteristic equation, and the roots of the characteristic equation are the "eigenvalues" or characteristic values of s. The negatives of the roots are used to form the required factors of the polynomial.

The efficient expansion by digital computer of a high-order determinant of quadratics of the form shown in Equation 1-47 is an exercise in logic. A program for accomplishing this is given in the Appendix, Program A74PFD. It is worth noting that this can be useful in the solution of any set of simultaneous linear differential equations, even with higher-order elements than the quadratics of Equations 1-46, since additional variables can be introduced to reduce the order of the elements and increase the number of equations. For example, the two simultaneous differential equations represented by the transformed equations,

$$(s^4 + 2s^3 + s + 1)X + (s^3 + 3)Y = 0$$
$$(s^2 - 1)X + (s^4 + s + 1)Y = 0$$

could be changed by introducing two more variables,

$$u = \frac{d^2x}{dt^2} \quad \text{and} \quad v = \frac{d^2y}{dt^2}$$

to the transformed set of four second-order equations shown below.

$$(s + 1)X + 3Y + (s^2 + 2s)U + sV = 0$$
$$(s^2 - 1)X + (s + 1)Y + 0U + s^2V = 0$$
$$s^2X + 0Y - 1U + 0V = 0$$
$$0X + s^2Y + 0U - 1V = 0$$

For the vibration problem under study, however, the quadratic elements of Equations 1-46 and 1-47 are sufficient without modification. It is entirely possible that many of the coefficients of Equations 1-46 would be zero, but the degree of the polynomial would not exceed $2m$ in any event. When damping is present, the roots of the polynomial may be either real or complex numbers, so a trial-and-error method of solution is impractical. It is necessary to have a method for solving the general characteristic equation of order n, where $n \leq 2m$,

$$1 + C_1 s + C_2 s^2 + \cdots + C_{n-1} s^{n-1} + C_n s^n = 0 \qquad (1\text{-}48)$$

Factors of the Characteristic Equation. Regardless of whether the factors of the polynomial are real or complex, quadratic factors exist whose coefficients are real. Therefore, if a desired quadratic factor is $(1 + A_1 s + A_2 s^2)$, the original polynomial is the product of this quadratic and a new polynomial of lower degree,

$$(1 + A_1 s + A_2 s^2)(1 + B_1 s + \cdots + B_{n-3} s^{n-3} + B_{n-2} s^{n-2}) = 1 + C_1 s + \cdots + C_n s^n$$

If the left side of this equation is expanded and the coefficients of like powers are compared, Equations 1-49 result.

$$
\begin{aligned}
B_1 &= C_1 - A_1 \\
B_2 &= C_2 - A_2 - A_1 B_1 \\
B_3 &= C_3 - A_2 B_1 - A_1 B_2 \\
B_4 &= C_4 - A_2 B_2 - A_1 B_3 \\
& \cdot \quad \cdot \quad \cdot \quad \cdot \quad \cdot \quad \cdot \quad \cdot \quad \cdot \quad \cdot \\
B_k &= C_k - A_2 B_{k-2} - A_1 B_{k-1} \qquad \text{for} \quad 3 \leq k \leq n-1 \\
& \cdot \quad \cdot \quad \cdot \quad \cdot \quad \cdot \quad \cdot \quad \cdot \quad \cdot \quad \cdot \\
B_{n-1} &= f_1(A_1, A_2) = 0 \\
C_n - A_2 B_{n-2} &= f_2(A_1, A_2) = 0
\end{aligned}
\qquad (1\text{-}49)
$$

Both of the final two equations must be satisfied by a proper choice of A_1 and A_2. If an arbitrary choice of A_1 and A_2 is made, f_1 and f_2 would ordinarily not be zero. If it is assumed that a small change of A_1 and A_2 would reduce f_1 and f_2 to zero, and that Δf_1 and Δf_2 are the changes in f_1 and f_2 caused by small changes ΔA_1 and ΔA_2, then

$$f_1 + \Delta f_1 = 0 \quad \text{and} \quad f_2 + \Delta f_2 = 0$$

In order to satisfy these two equations, the procedure represented by Equations 1-50 can be used. New assumptions for A_1 and A_2 are computed from the old assumptions by this procedure, using Equation 1-49 as required. The procedure usually converges. Digital computer program A86FP of the Appendix utilizes this method.

$$\frac{\partial B_1}{\partial A_1} = -1 \qquad\qquad\qquad \frac{\partial B_1}{\partial A_2} = 0$$

$$\frac{\partial B_2}{\partial A_1} = -B_1 - A_1 \frac{\partial B_1}{\partial A_1} \qquad \frac{\partial B_2}{\partial A_2} = -1 \qquad (1\text{-}50)$$

$$\frac{\partial B_3}{\partial A_1} = -A_2 \frac{\partial B_1}{\partial A_1} - A_1 \frac{\partial B_2}{\partial A_1} - B_2 \qquad \frac{\partial B_3}{\partial A_2} = -A_2 \frac{\partial B_1}{\partial A_2} - A_1 \frac{\partial B_2}{\partial A_2} - B_1$$

$$\cdot \quad \cdot \quad \cdot \quad \cdot \quad \cdot \quad \cdot \quad \cdot \quad \cdot \qquad\qquad \cdot \quad \cdot \quad \cdot \quad \cdot \quad \cdot \quad \cdot \quad \cdot \quad \cdot \quad \cdot$$

(continued)

$$\frac{\partial B_k}{\partial A_1} = -A_2 \frac{\partial B_{k-2}}{\partial A_1} - A_1 \frac{\partial B_{k-1}}{\partial A_1} - B_{k-1} \qquad \frac{\partial B_k}{\partial A_2} = -A_2 \frac{\partial B_{k-2}}{\partial A_2} - A_1 \frac{\partial B_{k-1}}{\partial A_2} - B_{k-2}$$

$$\cdot \quad \cdot \quad \cdot \quad \cdot \quad \cdot \quad \cdot \quad \cdot \quad \cdot \quad \cdot \quad \cdot \quad \cdot \quad \cdot$$

$$\frac{\partial f_1}{\partial A_1} = \frac{\partial B_{n-1}}{\partial A_1} \qquad\qquad\qquad \frac{\partial f_1}{\partial A_2} = \frac{\partial B_{n-1}}{\partial A_2}$$

$$\frac{\partial f_2}{\partial A_1} = -A_2 \frac{\partial B_{n-2}}{\partial A_1} \qquad\qquad \frac{\partial f_2}{\partial A_2} = -B_{n-2} - A_2 \frac{\partial B_{n-2}}{\partial A_2}$$

$$\text{(1-50)}$$

$$\Delta A_1 = \frac{\begin{vmatrix} -f_1 & \dfrac{\partial f_1}{\partial A_2} \\[2mm] -f_2 & \dfrac{\partial f_2}{\partial A_2} \end{vmatrix}}{\begin{vmatrix} \dfrac{\partial f_1}{\partial A_1} & \dfrac{\partial f_1}{\partial A_2} \\[2mm] \dfrac{\partial f_2}{\partial A_1} & \dfrac{\partial f_2}{\partial A_2} \end{vmatrix}} \qquad\qquad \Delta A_2 = \frac{\begin{vmatrix} \dfrac{\partial f_1}{\partial A_1} & -f_1 \\[2mm] \dfrac{\partial f_2}{\partial A_1} & -f_2 \end{vmatrix}}{\begin{vmatrix} \dfrac{\partial f_1}{\partial A_1} & \dfrac{\partial f_1}{\partial A_2} \\[2mm] \dfrac{\partial f_2}{\partial A_1} & \dfrac{\partial f_2}{\partial A_2} \end{vmatrix}}$$

$$A_{1\text{new}} = A_1 + \Delta A_1 \qquad\qquad A_{2\text{new}} = A_2 + \Delta A_2$$

The extension of this procedure to the solution of a general set of nonlinear simultaneous algebraic equations is obvious. The result is summarized by Equations 1-50(a).

$$\{x\} = \begin{Bmatrix} x_1 \\ x_2 \\ \vdots \end{Bmatrix}, \qquad \text{an assumed solution}$$

$$\{f\} = \begin{Bmatrix} f_1(x_1, x_2, \ldots) \\ f_2(x_1, x_2, \ldots) \\ \cdot \quad \cdot \quad \cdot \quad \cdot \end{Bmatrix} = \{0\}$$

$$\text{(1-50a)}$$

$$[A] = \begin{bmatrix} \dfrac{\partial f_1}{\partial x_1} & \dfrac{\partial f_1}{\partial x_2} & \cdots \\[3mm] \dfrac{\partial f_2}{\partial x_1} & \dfrac{\partial f_2}{\partial x_2} & \cdots \\[3mm] \cdot & \cdot & \cdot \end{bmatrix}$$

$$\{x\}_{\substack{\text{new assumed} \\ \text{solution}}} = \{x\} - [A]^{-1}\{f\}$$

Normal Modes for Systems with Damping. After the quadratic factors have been determined in this manner, the factors that cannot be factored into linear factors represent modes of vibration. A description of these modes can be obtained by setting the $F(s)$ functions on the right side of Equations 1-46 to zero. Then normalize by dividing through each equation by one of the variables, for instance X_m, and solve any $m - 1$ of the equations simultaneously for the coordinate ratios X_1/X_m, X_2/X_m, etc., letting $s = -\zeta\beta + i\beta\sqrt{1 - \zeta^2}$, corresponding to the solution of $1 + A_1 s + A_2 s^2 = 0$. The ratios will be complex numbers if damping is present. This is summarized by Equations 1-51, where any $m - 1$ of the equations indicated must be solved simultaneously.

$$\left.\begin{aligned}
(f_{11} + ig_{11})\frac{X_1}{X_n} + (f_{12} + ig_{12})\frac{X_2}{X_n} + \cdots & \\
+ (f_{1(n-1)} + ig_{1(n-1)})\frac{X_{n-1}}{X_n} &= -f_{1n} - ig_{1n} \\
(f_{21} + ig_{21})\frac{X_1}{X_n} + (f_{22} + ig_{22})\frac{X_2}{X_n} + \cdots & \\
+ (f_{2(n-1)} + ig_{2(n-1)})\frac{X_{n-1}}{X_n} &= -f_{2n} - ig_{2n} \\
\vdots \qquad\qquad \vdots \qquad\qquad \vdots \qquad\qquad \vdots & \\
(f_{n1} + ig_{n1})\frac{X_1}{X_n} + (f_{n2} + ig_{n2})\frac{X_2}{X_n} + \cdots & \\
+ (f_{n(n-1)} + ig_{n(n-1)})\frac{X_{n-1}}{X_n} &= -f_{nn} - ig_{nn}
\end{aligned}\right\} \quad (1\text{-}51)$$

where

$$f_{jk} = \beta^2(2\zeta^2 - 1)C_{jk} - \zeta\beta B_{jk} + A_{jk}$$
$$g_{jk} = -2\zeta\beta^2\sqrt{1 - \zeta^2}\, C_{jk} + \beta\sqrt{1 - \zeta^2}\, B_{jk}$$
$$s = -\zeta\beta + i\beta\sqrt{1 - \zeta^2} \quad \text{from} \quad 1 + A_1 s + A_2 s^2 = 0$$

(A_{jk}, B_{jk}, and C_{jk} refer to Equations 1-46, but A_1 and A_2 refer to Equations 1-49.)

Example 1-1. This example will serve to illustrate the material in Sections 1.2, 1.3, and 1.4. Consider Fig. 1-10 without dampers and forces and let the spring constants each be one unit and the masses 1, 2, and 3 units respectively for m_1, m_2, and m_3. Reference to Equations 1-19, 1-20, 1-24, and 1-25 shows that

$$[M] = \begin{bmatrix} 1 & 0 & 0 \\ 0 & 2 & 0 \\ 0 & 0 & 3 \end{bmatrix} \quad [K] = \begin{bmatrix} 2 & -1 & 0 \\ -1 & 2 & -1 \\ 0 & -1 & 1 \end{bmatrix} \quad [\delta] = \begin{bmatrix} 1 & 1 & 1 \\ 1 & 2 & 2 \\ 1 & 2 & 3 \end{bmatrix} \quad [U] = \begin{bmatrix} 1 & 2 & 3 \\ 1 & 4 & 6 \\ 1 & 4 & 9 \end{bmatrix}$$

Both $[K]$ and $[\delta]$ are also easily computed directly from the physical model and Equations 1-36 and 1-37. For instance, a load applied at Station 3, f_3, would cause a displacement of Station 2 of

$$x_2 = \frac{f_3}{k_1} + \frac{f_3}{k_2}$$

so

$$\delta_{23} = \frac{\partial x_2}{\partial f_3} = 2$$

Similarly, a deflection of Station 3 (with other stations restrained from moving) would require a load on Station 2 of $f_2 = -k_3 x_3$, so $K_{23} = \partial f_2/\partial x_3 = -1$. Use of Equations 1-34 and 1-35 for computation of elements of $[K]$ or $[M]$ is also easily verified. For instance, since the kinetic energy is

$$T = \frac{1}{2}m_1\dot{x}_1^2 + \frac{1}{2}m_2\dot{x}_2^2 + \frac{1}{2}m_3\dot{x}_3^2, \qquad M_{33} = \frac{\partial^2 T}{\partial \dot{x}_3^2} = m_3 = 3$$

and since the potential energy is

$$V = \frac{1}{2} k_1 x_1{}^2 + \frac{1}{2} k_2 (x_2 - x_1)^2 + \frac{1}{2} k_3 (x_3 - x_2)^2$$

then

$$K_{23} = \frac{\partial^2 V}{\partial x_2\, \partial x_3} = k_3 \frac{\partial}{\partial x_2} (x_3 - x_2) = -k_3 = -1$$

Equation 1-23 therefore becomes

$$\{x\} = \beta^2 \begin{bmatrix} 1 & 2 & 3 \\ 1 & 4 & 6 \\ 1 & 4 & 9 \end{bmatrix} \{x\}$$

To illustrate the use of Equations 1-31 and 1-32, select U_{23} and U_{32} as the elements to be reduced to zero. In terms of Equations 1-32,

$$V_{0_{23}} = U_{23} = 6, \qquad V_{0_{32}} = U_{32} = 4, \qquad V_{0_{22}} = U_{22} = 4, \qquad V_{0_{33}} = U_{33} = 9$$

Then $a = 0.417$, $b = 0.625$. (If it had happened that a and b were zero, the rest of the computation would have been omitted and different elements selected for the next computation.)

$$N_{1_{22}} = N_{1_{33}} = 0.523, \qquad N_{1_{23}} = -1.047, \qquad N_{1_{32}} = 0.697$$

Thus

$$[N]_1 = \begin{bmatrix} 1 & 0 & 0 \\ 0 & 0.523 & -1.047 \\ 0 & 0.697 & 0.523 \end{bmatrix} \quad \text{and} \quad [N]_1{}^{-1} = \begin{bmatrix} 1 & 0 & 0 \\ 0 & 0.523 & 1.047 \\ 0 & -0.697 & 0.523 \end{bmatrix}$$

and when this matrix is used in Equations 1-31,

$$[V]_1 = [N]_1{}^{-1}[U][N]_1 = \begin{bmatrix} 1.000 & 3.13 & 0.520 \\ 1.570 & 12.03 & 0 \\ -0.173 & 0 & 0.977 \end{bmatrix}$$

For the next computation, select

$$V_{1_{12}} = 3.13, \qquad V_{1_{21}} = 1.57, \qquad V_{1_{11}} = 1.00, \qquad V_{1_{22}} = 12.03$$

and repeat the computation. The result is

$$[N]_2 = \begin{bmatrix} 0.190 & -1.390 & 0 \\ 0.695 & 0.190 & 0 \\ 0 & 0 & 1 \end{bmatrix} \qquad [V]_2 = \begin{bmatrix} 12.51 & 0 & -0.099 \\ 0 & 0.572 & 0.361 \\ -0.033 & 0.240 & 0.997 \end{bmatrix}$$

Note that the elements V_{23} and V_{32} are not zero now, but they are smaller relative to the diagonal elements than for the original matrix $[U]$. The computation continues in this way until all off-diagonal elements are sufficiently small relative to the diagonal elements that they can be considered zero.

To illustrate the Duncan and Collar iteration procedure, assume a coordinate vector for the right side of Equation 1-23. Any assumption is satisfactory, but since the third column of $[U]$ has the largest numbers, perhaps it will dominate the computation; therefore assume the coordinate vector proportional to the third column of $[U]$ but normalized on the third coordinate.

$$\{x\} = \beta^2 \begin{bmatrix} 1 & 2 & 3 \\ 1 & 4 & 6 \\ 1 & 4 & 9 \end{bmatrix} \begin{Bmatrix} 0.333 \\ 0.667 \\ 1.000 \end{Bmatrix} = \begin{Bmatrix} 4.667\beta^2 \\ 9.000\beta^2 \\ 12.000\beta^2 \end{Bmatrix}$$

If this column is normalized by dividing by $12\beta^2$ and the new column substituted on the right side of Equation 1-23,

$$\{x\} = \beta^2 \begin{bmatrix} 1 & 2 & 3 \\ 1 & 4 & 6 \\ 1 & 4 & 9 \end{bmatrix} \begin{Bmatrix} 0.389 \\ 0.750 \\ 1.000 \end{Bmatrix} = 12.389\beta^2 \begin{Bmatrix} 0.395 \\ 0.758 \\ 1.000 \end{Bmatrix}$$

It is seen that the normalized columns are more nearly equal after each iteration. When they are sufficiently close, the computation is stopped and the result is the normalized vector corresponding to the first (lowest-frequency) mode. In this example, this will be

$$\{N\}_1 = \begin{Bmatrix} 0.39522 \\ 0.75864 \\ 1.00000 \end{Bmatrix}$$

Substitution of this column in Equation 1-23 results in

$$\begin{Bmatrix} 0.39522 \\ 0.75864 \\ 1.00000 \end{Bmatrix} = \beta_1^2 \begin{bmatrix} 1 & 2 & 3 \\ 1 & 4 & 6 \\ 1 & 4 & 9 \end{bmatrix} \begin{Bmatrix} 0.39522 \\ 0.75864 \\ 1.00000 \end{Bmatrix} = 12.42978\beta_1^2 \begin{Bmatrix} 0.39522 \\ 0.75864 \\ 1.00000 \end{Bmatrix}$$

from which the first mode frequency is

$$\beta_1 = \sqrt{\frac{1}{12.42978}} = 0.284 \text{ rad/sec}$$

The matrix $[U]$ is modified to eliminate the first mode in order to compute the second mode frequency and vector by using Equations 1-33.

$$[B] = [0.39522 \quad 0.75864 \quad 1.00000] \begin{bmatrix} 1 & 0 & 0 \\ 0 & 2 & 0 \\ 0 & 0 & 3 \end{bmatrix} = [0.39522 \quad 1.51728 \quad 3.00000]$$

$$[S]_1 = \begin{bmatrix} 0 & -3.8391 & -7.5907 \\ 0 & 1 & 0 \\ 0 & 0 & 1 \end{bmatrix}$$

$$[U]_1 = [U][S]_1 = \begin{bmatrix} 0 & -1.8391 & -4.5907 \\ 0 & 0.1609 & -1.5907 \\ 0 & 0.1609 & 1.4093 \end{bmatrix}$$

Iteration of $\{x\} = \beta^2[U]_1\{x\}$ in the same way results in the second mode description and frequency.

$$\{N\}_2 = \begin{Bmatrix} -1.4210 \\ -1.6071 \\ 1.0000 \end{Bmatrix} \qquad \beta_2 = 0.933 \text{ rad/sec}$$

Then if $[U]_2$ is formed from $[U]_1$ using $\{N\}_2$, the third mode vector and frequency are determined.

$$\{N\}_3 = \begin{Bmatrix} 16.025 \\ -6.151 \\ 1.000 \end{Bmatrix} \qquad \beta_3 = 1.545 \text{ rad/sec}$$

Equations 1-42 and 1-43 can be used to obtain the generalized masses and spring constants for the three principal coordinates. For instance,

$$M_{p_1} = [0.39522 \quad 0.75864 \quad 1.00000] \begin{bmatrix} 1 & 0 & 0 \\ 0 & 2 & 0 \\ 0 & 0 & 3 \end{bmatrix} \begin{Bmatrix} 0.39422 \\ 0.75864 \\ 1.00000 \end{Bmatrix} = 4.31 \text{ units}$$

$$K_{p_1} = [0.39522 \quad 0.75864 \quad 1.00000] \begin{bmatrix} 2 & -1 & 0 \\ -1 & 2 & -1 \\ 0 & -1 & 1 \end{bmatrix} \begin{Bmatrix} 0.39522 \\ 0.75864 \\ 1.00000 \end{Bmatrix} = 0.347 \text{ units}$$

The first mode frequency is

$$\beta_1 = \sqrt{\frac{K_{p_1}}{M_{p_1}}} = 0.284 \text{ rad/sec}$$

confirming the direct computation of frequency.

A matrix relationship relating ordinary coordinates $\{x\}$ and principal coordinates $\{y\}$ is $\{x\} = [N]\{y\}$ where $[N]$ is formed from the modal columns. That is,

$$[N] = \begin{bmatrix} 0.39522 & -1.4210 & 16.025 \\ 0.75864 & -1.6071 & -6.151 \\ 1.00000 & 1.0000 & 1.000 \end{bmatrix}$$

If external forces at the three stations are not zero, a force matrix $\{f\}$ can be formed. The matrix of generalized forces $\{Q_p\}$ corresponding to the principal coordinates $\{y\}$ can be computed using Equation 1-45, which generalizes to $\{Q_p\} = [\tilde{N}]\{f\}$. A force of 1 unit magnitude applied to Station 2 in the positive direction of x_2 would therefore result in generalized forces of 0.75864, -1.6071, and -6.151 units for the principal coordinates corresponding to the three modes. The three principal coordinates can be treated separately as single-degree systems; thus, if this unit force is suddenly applied, coordinate y_1 for a single-degree system would respond according to

$$y_1 = \frac{Q_1}{K_{p_1}} (1 - \cos \beta_1 t) = 2.19(1 - \cos 0.284t)$$

Corresponding to this motion the three ordinary coordinates would displace according to $\{x\} = [N]\{y\}$.

$$x_1 = 0.395 \times 2.19(1 - \cos 0.284t)$$
$$x_2 = 0.758 \times 2.19(1 - \cos 0.284t)$$
$$x_3 = 1.000 \times 2.19(1 - \cos 0.284t)$$

Since the other generalized forces are not zero, there would be similar expressions involving $\cos 0.933t$ and $\cos 1.545t$, and the actual motion of each mass would be the sum of the three expressions for each coordinate.

The characteristic-equation method of analysis described in Section 1.4 can be illustrated with this example even though the damping is zero. The characteristic equation is

$$\begin{vmatrix} (s^2 + 2) & -1 & 0 \\ -1 & (2s^2 + 2) & -1 \\ 0 & -1 & (3s^2 + 1) \end{vmatrix} = 1 + 14s^2 + 20s^4 + 6s^6 = 0$$

The eigenvalues are $s^2 = -0.0805$, $s^2 = -0.869$, and $s^2 = -2.38$, determined by synthetic division since they are known to be real. The frequencies are $\sqrt{0.0805}$, $\sqrt{0.869}$, and $\sqrt{2.38}$, which are the same as previously determined. A modal column can be determined by substituting the eigenvalue in Equation 1-51. For example, use $s^2 = -0.869$ or $s = 0.933i$ in Equation 1-51. Then $f_{11} = 2.0 - 0.869 = 1.131$, $g_{11} = 0$, $f_{12} = -1.0$, etc., leading to the equations

$$1.131 \frac{X_1}{X_3} - 1.0 \frac{X_2}{X_3} = 0$$

$$-\frac{X_1}{X_3} + 0.262 \frac{X_2}{X_3} = 1.0$$

$$0 \frac{X_1}{X_3} - 1.0 \frac{X_2}{X_3} = 1.607$$

Any two of these equations solved simultaneously give the correct coordinate ratios for the second mode.

Although the quadratic factors for this characteristic equation were easily obtained by synthetic division, Equations 1-49 and 1-50 could have been used. In this example $n = 6$, $C_1 = C_3 = C_5 = 0$, $C_2 = 14$, $C_4 = 20$, $C_6 = 6$. Assume $A_1 = 1$, $A_2 = 1$. Then from Equations 1-49, $B_1 = -1$, $B_2 = 14$, $B_3 = -13$, $B_4 = 19$, $B_5 = f_1 = -6$, $f_2 = -13$. From Equations 1-50

$$\frac{\partial B_2}{\partial A_1} = 2, \qquad \frac{\partial B_3}{\partial A_1} = -15, \qquad \frac{\partial B_4}{\partial A_1} = 26,$$

$$\frac{\partial B_5}{\partial A_1} = \frac{\partial f_1}{\partial A_1} = -30, \qquad \frac{\partial f_2}{\partial A_1} = -26, \qquad \frac{\partial B_5}{\partial A_2} = 2,$$

$$\frac{\partial B_4}{\partial A_2} = -15, \qquad \frac{\partial B_5}{\partial A_2} = \frac{\partial f_1}{\partial A_2} = 26, \qquad \frac{\partial f_2}{\partial A_2} = -4,$$

$$\Delta A_1 = -0.455, \qquad \Delta A_2 = -0.168, \qquad A_{1\text{new}} = 0.545,$$

$$A_{2\text{new}} = 0.732.$$

These new values are now used for the assumed A_1 and A_2 and the computations repeated. Eventually A_1 will approach zero and A_2 one of the numbers

$$\frac{1}{0.0805}, \qquad \frac{1}{0.869}, \qquad \text{or} \qquad \frac{1}{2.38}$$

For small amounts of damping it is usually satisfactory to neglect the coupling between normal modes and consider that each of the normal modes is damped according to an equivalent generalized damping coefficient using Equation 1-44. For instance, if each damper had coefficient of 0.1, the damping coefficient matrix would have been

$$[C] = \begin{bmatrix} 0.2 & -0.1 & 0 \\ -0.1 & 0.2 & -0.1 \\ 0 & -0.1 & 0.1 \end{bmatrix}$$

and the first mode generalized damping coefficient would have been 0.0347, making the first mode damping factor $\zeta_1 = 0.0142$. This particular configuration of dampers would not result in coupling of the generalized coordinates, since relationships such as Equations 1-40 and 1-41 would also be zero using the damping coefficient matrix. Consequently, no error would result, even for large damping, under such circumstances. However, damping usually changes the normal mode description, and the assumption that the undamped normal modes are not coupled by the addition of damping is only an approximation, which could cause a significant error with large amounts of damping.

1.5 Lumped-Parameter Analysis of Continuous Systems

The analysis of continuous or distributed systems, such as beams or plates, by classical techniques leads to one or more partial differential equations. These equations can often be solved for simple systems, but many practical systems must be analyzed by numerical means. Usually this is accomplished by lumping the distributed elements in a judicious manner and applying the methods of the previous sections, or others which may be appropriate. The analysis then often hinges on the determination of a flexibility or stiffness matrix for the structure under consideration. The beam-flexibility-matrix equations which follow are programmed for digital computer use and appear as the A55 series in the appendix.

Flexibility Matrix for a Cantilever Beam. Methods appropriate for the analysis of beams, such as the method of virtual work, may be used to demonstrate Equations 1-52 and 1-53

$$y = \int_0^L \left(\frac{Mm}{EI} + \frac{VvQ}{GIb} \right) dx \tag{1-52}$$

$$\theta = \int_0^L \frac{Mm_r}{EI} dx \tag{1-53}$$

$y =$ linear deflection of a point in the beam under an external load
$\theta = dy/dx =$ angular deflection of a point in the beam under the load
$M =$ internal moment in the beam, caused by the loading
$m =$ internal moment in the beam caused by unit load applied in the positive direction of y and at the location where the deflection y is to be calculated
$m_r =$ internal moment in the beam caused by unit moment applied in the positive direction of θ and at the location where the angular deflection θ is to be calculated
$V =$ internal shear in the beam caused by the external loading
$v =$ internal shear load caused by the unit load (as for m)
$E =$ Young's modulus
$I =$ area moment of inertia
$G =$ shear modulus
$Q =$ first moment of area above the beam neutral axis
$b =$ width of beam cross section at the neutral axis

All of the variables in these integrands may be functions of x. If the beam is subdivided into several, or many, short segments, it is possible to consider each of these variables to remain constant for the short segment. Figure 1-11 illustrates the concept and defines distances used in Equations 1-54, 1-55, 1-56, and 1-57 applicable for a cantilever beam. These equations develop from the integrations defined in Equations 1-52 and 1-53 for the beam illustrated in Fig. 1-11, and may be used to construct the flexibility matrix for a cantilever beam. In these equations j is the station where the unit load or moment is applied, and i is the station where the linear or angular deflection is to be calculated. The stations are located at the midpoints of the segments. The flexibility-matrix elements, or influence coefficients, are defined as follows:

$y_{ij} =$ linear deflection at i caused by unit load at j
$\theta_{ij} =$ angular deflection at i caused by unit load at j

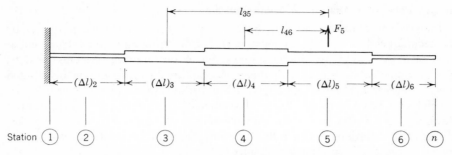

Fig. 1-11   Definition of distances for cantilever beam numerical analysis.

ϵ_{ij} = linear deflection at i caused by unit moment at j
ϕ_{ij} = angular deflection at i caused by unit moment at j

$$y_{ij} = \frac{(\varDelta l)_i^2}{8(EI)_i}\left[l_{ij} + \frac{1}{3}(\varDelta l)_i\right] + \frac{1}{2}\left(\frac{Q}{GIb}\right)_i(\varDelta l)_i$$

$$\left.\begin{array}{l} \\ + \sum_{k=2}^{k=(i-1)}\left[\dfrac{l_{ki}l_{kj} + \dfrac{1}{12}(\varDelta l)_k^2}{(EI_k)} + \left(\dfrac{Q}{GIb}\right)_k\right](\varDelta l)_k \\ \\ \hspace{6cm} j \geqq i \end{array}\right\} \text{(1-54)}$$

$y_{1j} = y_{i1} = 0$
$y_{pq} = y_{qp}$ (symmetrical)

$$\left.\begin{array}{l} \theta_{ij} = \dfrac{(\varDelta l)_i}{2(EI)_i}\left[l_{ij} + \dfrac{(\varDelta l)_i}{4}\right] + \sum_{k=2}^{k=(i-1)}\dfrac{l_{kj}}{(EI)_k}(\varDelta l)_k, \quad j \geqq i \\ \\ \theta_{ij} = \dfrac{(\varDelta l)_j^2}{8(EI)_j} + \sum_{k=2}^{k=(j-1)}\dfrac{l_{kj}(\varDelta l)_k}{(EI)_k}, \quad j < i \\ \\ \theta_{1j} = \theta_{i1} = 0 \end{array}\right\} \text{(1-55)}$$

$$\left.\begin{array}{l} \epsilon_{ij} = \dfrac{(\varDelta l)_i^2}{8(EI)_i} + \sum_{k=2}^{k=(i-1)}\dfrac{l_{ki}(\varDelta l)_k}{(EI)_k}, \quad j \geqq i \\ \\ \epsilon_{ij} = \dfrac{(\varDelta l)_j}{2(EI)_j}\left[l_{ij} + \dfrac{(\varDelta l)_j}{4}\right] + \sum_{k=2}^{k=(j-1)}\dfrac{l_{ki}(\varDelta l)_k}{(EI)_k}, \quad j \leqq i \\ \\ \epsilon_{1j} = \epsilon_{i1} = 0 \end{array}\right\} \text{(1-56)}$$

$$\left.\begin{array}{l} \phi_{ij} = \dfrac{(\varDelta l)_i}{2(EI)_i} + \sum_{k=2}^{k=(i-1)}\dfrac{(\varDelta l)_k}{(EI)_k}, \quad j \geqq i \\ \\ \phi_{1j} = \phi_{i1} = 0 \\ \\ \phi_{pq} = \phi_{qp} \text{ (symmetrical)} \end{array}\right\} \text{(1-57)}$$

In Equations 1-54 to 1-57 if $i = j$, then $l_{ij} = 0$. For y_{2j}, θ_{2j}, ϵ_{2j}, and ϕ_{2j} the summation is omitted, and if $i = j = n$ (last station), only the terms in the summation are used to compute y_{nn}, θ_{nn}, ϵ_{nn}, and ϕ_{nn} (omitting the other terms).

Equations 1-54 to 1-57 may be used to formulate a flexibility matrix for cantilever beams by combining submatrices as indicated in Equation 1-58.

$$[\delta] = \begin{bmatrix} [y][\epsilon] \\ [\theta][\phi] \end{bmatrix} \qquad (1\text{-}58)$$

Flexibility Matrix for a Beam with Redundant Flexible Supports. If a beam is supported flexibly at the various stations, or if a distributed flexible support can be approximated in this manner, the cantilever-beam flexibility matrix can be modified by considering the support loads as external loads, resulting in the flexibility matrix for beams with redundant flexible supports, Equations 1-59 to 1-61.

$$[\varDelta] = [\lambda]^{-1}[\mu] \qquad (1\text{-}59)$$

In Equation 1-59 the matrix $[\mu]$ is formed from the flexibility matrix for cantilever beams in the same way as $[\delta]$ (Equation 1-58), except that the elements of the first row of $[y]$ and $[\phi]$ (which are all zeros for the cantilever beam matrix) are replaced by unity, and the elements of the first row of $[\theta]$ are replaced by the lengths, l_{1j}.

The matrix $[\lambda]$, whose inverse is required, is formed from the spring constants for the flexible supports as indicated in Equation 1-60. In this equation the spring constants k and k_r are force per unit linear displacement and moment per unit angular displacement for the corresponding translational and rotational springs supporting the beam at the stations indicated by the subscripts.

$$[\lambda] = \begin{bmatrix}
k_1 & k_2 & k_3 & \cdots & k_n & 0 & 0 & 0 & \cdots & 0 \\
(k_1 y_{21}-1) & (k_2 y_{22}+1) & (k_3 y_{23}) & \cdots & (k_n y_{2n}) & (k_{r_1}\epsilon_{21}-l_{12}) & (k_{r_2}\epsilon_{22}) & (k_{r_3}\epsilon_{23}) & \cdots & (k_{r_n}\epsilon_{2n}) \\
(k_1 y_{31}-1) & (k_2 y_{32}) & (k_3 y_{33}+1) & \cdots & (k_n y_{3n}) & (k_{r_1}\epsilon_{31}-l_{13}) & (k_{r_2}\epsilon_{32}) & (k_{r_3}\epsilon_{33}) & \cdots & (k_{r_n}\epsilon_{3n}) \\
\cdot & \cdot & \cdot & & \cdot & \cdot & \cdot & \cdot & & \cdot \\
(k_1 y_{n1}-1) & (k_2 y_{n2}) & (k_3 y_{n3}) & \cdots & (k_n y_{nn}+1) & (k_{r_1}\epsilon_{n1}-l_{1n}) & (k_{r_2}\epsilon_{n2}) & (k_{r_3}\epsilon_{n3}) & \cdots & (k_{r_n}\epsilon_{nn}) \\
(k_1 l_{11}) & (k_2 l_{12}) & (k_3 l_{13}) & \cdots & (k_n l_{1n}) & k_{r_1} & k_{r_2} & k_{r_3} & \cdots & k_{r_n} \\
(k_1 \theta_{21}) & (k_2 \theta_{22}) & (k_3 \theta_{23}) & \cdots & (k_n \theta_{2n}) & (k_{r_1}\phi_{21}-1) & (k_{r_2}\phi_{22}+1) & (k_{r_3}\phi_{23}) & \cdots & (k_{r_n}\phi_{2n}) \\
(k_1 \theta_{31}) & (k_2 \theta_{32}) & (k_3 \theta_{33}) & \cdots & (k_n \theta_{3n}) & (k_{r_1}\phi_{31}-1) & (k_{r_2}\phi_{32}) & (k_{r_3}\phi_{33}+1) & \cdots & (k_{r_n}\phi_{3n}) \\
\cdot & \cdot & \cdot & & \cdot & \cdot & \cdot & \cdot & & \cdot \\
(k_1 \theta_{n1}) & (k_2 \theta_{n2}) & (k_3 \theta_{n3}) & \cdots & (k_n \theta_{nn}) & (k_{r_1}\phi_{n1}-1) & (k_{r_2}\phi_{n2}) & (k_{r_3}\phi_{n3}) & \cdots & (k_{r_n}\phi_{nn}+1)
\end{bmatrix}$$

$$(1\text{-}60)$$

The matrix $[\varDelta]$ is the flexibility matrix for the flexibly supported beam, and is defined by Equation 1-61.

$$[\varDelta] = \begin{bmatrix} [z][v] \\ [\alpha][\beta] \end{bmatrix} \qquad (1\text{-}61)$$

z_{ij} = linear deflection at i caused by unit load at j
v_{ij} = linear deflection at i caused by unit moment at j
α_{ij} = angular deflection at i caused by unit load at j
β_{ij} = angular deflection at i caused by unit moment at j

Flexibility Matrix for Beams with Inflexible Supports. If a support is so rigid that it can be considered inflexible, the previous analysis can be modified slightly to account for this. If the support is inflexible to translation at Station k, the kth column of $[\lambda]$ is changed to the following (the elements are obtained from $[\delta]$).

$$-1$$
$$-y_{2k}$$
$$-y_{3k}$$
$$\vdots$$
$$-y_{nk}$$
$$-l_{1k}$$
$$-\theta_{2k}$$
$$-\theta_{3k}$$
$$\vdots$$
$$-\theta_{nk}$$

If the support is inflexible to rotation at Station m, the $(m + n)$th column of $[\lambda]$ is changed to the following;

$$0$$
$$-\epsilon_{2,m+n}$$
$$-\epsilon_{3,m+n}$$
$$\vdots$$
$$-\epsilon_{n,m+n}$$
$$-1$$
$$-\phi_{2,m+n}$$
$$-\phi_{3,m+n}$$
$$\vdots$$
$$-\phi_{n,m+n}$$

Then if $[\varDelta]$ is computed from $[\lambda]^{-1}[\mu]$, the result is the influence-coefficient matrix for the beam with one or more rigid supports, except that the kth row of $[\varDelta]$ becomes the force reaction of the rigid (to translation) support at Station k for unit loads or moments applied at the various stations. Similarly, the $(m + n)$th row of $[\varDelta]$ becomes the moment reaction of the rigid (to rotation) support at Station $(m + n)$ for unit loads or moments applied at the various stations. In this form $[\varDelta]$ is useful in computing loads and moments in the beam, but if a true flexibility matrix is desired, the kth or $(m + n)$th rows should be altered to zero.

Flexibility Matrix for Free Beams. If the beam were free of all supports, the unit loads or moments would cause accelerations which would result in a distribution of reacting inertia loads and a corresponding deflection of the beam stations from the position they would occupy if the beam were completely rigid. The flexibility matrix for the free beam may be determined by making two sets of corrections to the cantilever beam matrix. The first set of corrections is given by Equations 1-62, and after these are added to the correponding elements of $[\delta]$, the second set of corrections is obtained from these new elements of $[\delta]$ using Equations 1-63, which are then added to the previously corrected elements to obtain the final flexibility matrix. A similar procedure may be used for beams having only one constraint, either flexible or rigid.

$$\Delta_1 y_{ij} = - \sum_{k=1}^{n} \left\{ \left[\frac{m_k}{M} + \frac{m_k(l_{1j} - l_{1c.g.})(l_{1k} - l_{1c.g.})}{I_M} \right] y_{ik} + \frac{m_k \rho_k^2}{I_M} (l_{1j} - l_{1c.g.}) \epsilon_{ik} \right\}$$

$$\Delta_1 \theta_{ij} = - \sum_{k=1}^{n} \left\{ \left[\frac{m_k}{M} + \frac{m_k(l_{1j} - l_{1c.g.})(l_{1k} - l_{1c.g.})}{I_M} \right] \theta_{ik} + \frac{m_k \rho_k^2}{I_M} (l_{1j} - l_{1c.g.}) \phi_{ik} \right\}$$

$$\Delta_1 \epsilon_{ij} = - \sum_{k=1}^{n} \left\{ \frac{m_k(l_{1k} - l_{1c.g.})}{I_M} y_{ik} + \frac{m_k \rho_k^2}{I_M} \epsilon_{ik} \right\} \qquad (1\text{-}62)$$

$$\Delta_1 \phi_{ij} = - \sum_{k=1}^{n} \left\{ \frac{m_k(l_{1k} - l_{1c.g.})}{I_M} \theta_{ik} + \frac{m_k \rho_k^2}{I_M} \phi_{ik} \right\}$$

$$\Delta_2 y_{ij} = - \frac{\sum_{k=1}^{n} m_k y_{kj}}{M} - \frac{(l_{1i} - l_{1c.g.})}{\sum_{k=1}^{n} m_k(l_{1k} - l_{1c.g.})^2} \sum_{k=1}^{n} m_k \left(y_{kj} - \frac{\sum_{k=1}^{n} m_k y_{kj}}{M} \right)(l_{1k} - l_{1c.g.})$$

$$\Delta_2 \theta_{ij} = - \frac{1}{\sum_{k=1}^{n} m_k(l_{1k} - l_{1c.g.})^2} \sum_{k=1}^{n} m_k \left(y_{kj} - \frac{\sum_{k=1}^{n} m_k y_{kj}}{M} \right)(l_{1k} - l_{1c.g.})$$

$$\Delta_2 \epsilon_{ij} = - \frac{\sum_{k=1}^{n} m_k \epsilon_{kj}}{M} - \frac{(l_{1i} - l_{1c.g.})}{\sum_{k=1}^{n} m_k(l_{1k} - l_{1c.g.})^2} \sum_{k=1}^{n} m_k \left(\epsilon_{kj} - \frac{\sum_{k=1}^{n} m_j \epsilon_{kj}}{M} \right)(l_{1k} - l_{1c.g.})$$

$$\Delta_2 \phi_{ij} = - \frac{1}{\sum_{k=1}^{n} m_k(l_{1k} - l_{1c.g.})^2} \sum_{k=1}^{n} m_k \left(\epsilon_{kj} - \frac{\sum_{k=1}^{n} m_k \epsilon_{kj}}{M} \right)(l_{1k} - l_{1c.g.})$$

$$(1\text{-}63)$$

In these equations m_k is a mass concentrated at Station k, ρ_k is the radius of gyration of this mass, M is the total mass, and I_M the total mass moment of inertia about the beam center of gravity.

Flexibility Matrix for Plates. A somewhat different procedure may be useful in determining the flexibility matrix for plates. It can be shown that the deflection of plates with variable thickness is governed by Equations 1-64 to 1-67, where x and y are independent rectilinear coordinates, z is the out-of-plane deflection at x, y; t is the plate thickness at x, y; p is the pressure against the plate at x, y; and E and μ are Young's modulus and Poisson's ratio.

$$u = \frac{\partial^2 z}{\partial x^2} \tag{1-64}$$

$$v = \frac{\partial^2 z}{\partial y^2} \tag{1-65}$$

$$w = \frac{\partial^2 z}{\partial x \, \partial y} \tag{1-66}$$

$$\frac{\partial^2}{\partial x^2} [t^3(u + \mu v)] + 2(1 - \mu) \frac{\partial^2}{\partial x \, \partial y} (t^3 w) + \frac{\partial^2}{\partial y^2} [t^3(\mu u + v)] = \frac{12(1 - \mu^2)}{E} p \tag{1-67}$$

Boundary-condition equations for fixed, hinged, and free edges are the appropriate combination of Equations 1-68 to 1-74.

$$z = 0 \tag{1-68}$$

$$\frac{\partial z}{\partial x} = 0 \quad (x = \text{constant}) \tag{1-69}$$

$$\frac{\partial z}{\partial y} = 0 \quad (y = \text{constant}) \tag{1-70}$$

$$u + \mu v = 0 \quad (x = \text{constant}) \tag{1-71}$$

$$\mu u + v = 0 \quad (y = \text{constant}) \tag{1-72}$$

$$\frac{\partial}{\partial x} [t^3(u + \mu v)] - 2(1 - \mu) \frac{\partial}{\partial y} (t^3 w) = 0 \quad (x = \text{constant}) \tag{1-73}$$

$$\frac{\partial}{\partial y} [t^3(\mu u + v)] - 2(1 - \mu) \frac{\partial}{\partial x} (t^2 w) = 0 \quad (y = \text{constant}) \tag{1-74}$$

For a fixed edge, Equations 1-68 and 1-69 or 1-70 would apply, depending on whether the boundary is for $x = $ constant or $y = $ constant. For a hinged edge, Equations 1-68 and 1-71 or 1-72 would apply. For a free edge, Equations 1-71 and 1-73 or 1-72 and 1-74 would apply. These equations must often be solved numerically. A simple method for doing this will now be described. It will be apparent that the method is applicable to other ordinary and partial differential equations.

If a function is approximated over a small interval in the x direction by a quadratic in x, that is, $f(x) = A_0 + A_1(x - x_n) + A_2(x - x_n)^2$, the coefficients could be obtained from the values of the function at three successive stations (not necessarily equally spaced), and then derivatives up to the second could be expressed in terms of these functional values. The result is shown as Equation 1-75, where the subscripts refer to stations defined in Fig. 1-12.

$$f_{el} = \frac{\epsilon \gamma (\epsilon - \gamma) f_{n-1} + (\beta + \gamma)(\epsilon + \beta)(\gamma - \epsilon) f_n + \epsilon \beta (\epsilon + \beta) f_{n+1}}{\beta \gamma (\beta + \gamma)}$$

$$\left(\frac{df}{dx}\right)_{el} = \frac{1}{l} \left[\frac{\gamma(2\epsilon - \gamma) f_{n-1} + (\beta + \gamma)(\gamma - \beta - 2\epsilon) f_n + \beta(2\epsilon + \beta) f_{n+1}}{\beta \gamma (\beta + \gamma)} \right] \tag{1-75}$$

$$\left(\frac{d^2 f}{dx^2}\right) = \frac{2}{l^2} \left[\frac{\gamma f_{n-1} - (\beta + \gamma) f_n + \beta f_{n+1}}{\beta \gamma (\beta + \gamma)} \right]$$

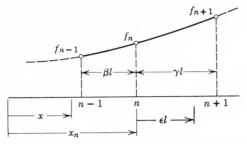

Fig. 1-12 $f(x)$ **over a portion of the x coordinate.**

In Equations 1-75, l is some incremental length and β and γ are positive factors (which may often be unity). The factor ϵ (note that $\epsilon = (x - x_n)/l$) may be positive or negative and greater or less in magnitude than β or γ, depending on whether the x-location is between stations $(n - 1)$ and $(n + 1)$ or outside this interval. If $\epsilon = -\beta$, 0, or $+\gamma$, the derivatives at the three stations are obtained in terms of the ordinates and Equations 1-75 become Equations 1-76.

$$\left(\frac{df}{dx}\right)_{n-1} = \frac{1}{l}\left[-\frac{\gamma + 2\beta}{\beta(\beta + \gamma)}f_{n-1} + \frac{\beta + \gamma}{\beta\gamma}f_n - \frac{\beta}{\gamma(\beta + \gamma)}f_{n+1}\right]$$

$$\left(\frac{df}{dx}\right)_{n} = \frac{1}{l}\left[-\frac{\gamma}{\beta(\beta + \gamma)}f_{n-1} + \frac{\gamma - \beta}{\beta\gamma}f_n + \frac{\beta}{\gamma(\beta + \gamma)}f_{n+1}\right]$$

$$\left(\frac{df}{dx}\right)_{n+1} = \frac{1}{l}\left[\frac{\gamma}{\beta(\beta + \gamma)}f_{n-1} - \frac{\beta + \gamma}{\beta\gamma}f_n + \frac{\beta + 2\gamma}{\gamma(\beta + \gamma)}f_{n+1}\right]$$ (1-76)

$$\left(\frac{d^2f}{dx^2}\right)_{n-1} = \left(\frac{d^2f}{dx^2}\right)_{n} = \left(\frac{d^2f}{dx^2}\right)_{n+1} = \frac{2}{l^2}\left[\frac{f_{n-1}}{\beta(\beta + \gamma)} - \frac{f_n}{\beta\gamma} + \frac{f_{n+1}}{\gamma(\beta + \gamma)}\right]$$

The strategy described in the discussion of Equation 1-47 may be employed in applying these equations to higher order derivatives than the second, or if greater accuracy and fewer simultaneous equations are desired, equations similar to Equations 1-75 and 1-76 can be derived for higher-order polynomials. Suppose that an mth order polynomial is used to fit the curve at $m + 1$ stations, or values of x, and the value of the function and its derivatives are required at some x not necessarily coinciding with one of these stations. An analysis similar to that leading to Equations 1-75 will result in the following matrix equations.

$$\{F\} = \begin{Bmatrix} f(x) \\ lf'(x) \\ l^2f''(x) \\ \cdots\cdots \\ l^mf^{(m)}(x) \end{Bmatrix} \qquad \{f\} = \begin{Bmatrix} f(x_1) \\ f(x_2) \\ f(x_3) \\ \cdots\cdots \\ f(x_{m+1}) \end{Bmatrix}$$

$$c_{ij} = \left(\frac{x_i - x_n}{l}\right)^{j-1}$$ (1-77)

$$e_{ij} = \frac{(j - 1)!}{(j - i)!}\left(\frac{x - x_n}{l}\right)^{j-1} \qquad j \geq i$$

$$e_{ij} = 0 \qquad j < i$$

$$\{F\} = [E][C]^{-1}\{f\}$$

$$\{F\} = [E][G]\{f\}$$

$$\{F\} = \begin{Bmatrix} f(\epsilon) \\ lf'(\epsilon) \\ \cdots \\ l^m f^{(m)}(\epsilon) \end{Bmatrix} \qquad \{f\} = \begin{Bmatrix} f_{n-2} \\ f_{n-1} \\ f_n \\ f_{n+1} \\ f_{n+2} \end{Bmatrix}$$

$$e_{ij} = \frac{(j-1)!}{(j-i)!}\,\epsilon^{j-i} \qquad j \geq i$$

$$e_{ij} = 0 \qquad j < i$$

$$d_{n-2} = \alpha(\alpha+\beta)(\alpha+\beta+\gamma)(\alpha+\beta+\gamma+\delta)$$
$$d_{n-1} = \alpha\beta(\beta+\gamma)(\beta+\gamma+\delta)$$
$$d_n = \beta\gamma(\alpha+\beta)(\gamma+\delta)$$
$$d_{n+1} = \gamma\delta(\beta+\gamma)(\alpha+\beta+\gamma)$$
$$d_{n+2} = \delta(\gamma+\delta)(\beta+\gamma+\delta)(\alpha+\beta+\gamma+\delta)$$

$$[G] = \begin{bmatrix}
0 & 0 & 1 & 0 & 0 \\[2mm]
\dfrac{\beta\gamma(\gamma+\delta)}{d_{n-2}} & \dfrac{-\gamma(\alpha+\beta)(\gamma+\delta)}{d_{n-1}} & \dfrac{\gamma(\gamma+\delta)(\alpha+2\beta)-\beta(\alpha+\beta)(2\gamma+\delta)}{d_n} & \dfrac{\beta(\alpha+\beta)(\gamma+\delta)}{d_{n+1}} & \dfrac{-\beta\gamma(\alpha+\beta)}{d_{n+2}} \\[4mm]
\dfrac{(\gamma-\beta)(\gamma+\delta)-\beta\gamma}{d_{n-2}} & \dfrac{(\alpha+\beta)(2\gamma+\delta)-\gamma(\gamma+\delta)}{d_{n-1}} & \dfrac{(\alpha+\beta)(\beta-2\gamma)-\alpha\delta-(\gamma+\delta)(2\beta-\gamma)}{d_n} & \dfrac{(\alpha+2\beta)(\gamma+\delta)-\beta(\alpha+\beta)}{d_{n+1}} & \dfrac{(\beta-\gamma)(\alpha+\beta)-\beta\gamma}{d_{n+2}} \\[4mm]
\dfrac{\beta-2\gamma-\delta}{d_{n-2}} & \dfrac{-\alpha-\beta+2\gamma+\delta}{d_{n-1}} & \dfrac{\alpha+2\beta-2\gamma-\delta}{d_n} & \dfrac{-\alpha-2\beta+\gamma+\delta}{d_{n+1}} & \dfrac{\alpha+2\beta-\gamma}{d_{n+2}} \\[4mm]
\dfrac{1}{d_{n-2}} & \dfrac{-1}{d_{n-1}} & \dfrac{1}{d_n} & \dfrac{-1}{d_{n+1}} & \dfrac{1}{d_{n+2}}
\end{bmatrix}$$

$$(1\text{-}78)$$

For the particular case, $m = 4$, requiring five stations, $n - 2$, $n - 1$, n, $n + 1$, $n + 2$, separated by the intervals αl, βl, γl, δl, in order left to right, the inverse for the general case can be taken and Equations 1-78 develop (see p. 36), where, as in Equations 1-75, $\epsilon = (x - x_n)/l$. Equations 1-78 can be used to find the function and derivatives at any point corresponding to ϵ. Derivatives at the left, center, and right stations are given in Appendix 2 of Ref. 1 in expanded form.

Suppose that the flexibility matrix for a plate is desired, where a typical element of the matrix is the deflection at one station caused by unit force at the same or a different station. For purposes of discussion, let the plate be rectangular with n equally spaced

y

$i+2$ $j-2$	$i+2$ $j=1$	$i+2$ j	$i+2$ $j+1$	$i+2$ $j+2$
$i+1$ $j-2$	$i+1$ $j-1$	$i+1$ j	$i+1$ $j+1$	$i+1$ $j+2$
i $j-2$	i $j-1$	i j	i $j+1$	i $j+2$
$i-1$ $j-2$	$i-1$ $j-1$	$i-1$ i	$i-1$ $j+1$	$i-1$ $j+2$
$i-2$ $j-2$	$i-2$ $j-1$	$i-2$ j	$i-2$ $j+1$	$i-2$ $j+2$

$\rightarrow x$

Fig. 1-13

stations in the x direction and m equally spaced stations in the y direction, for a total of $m \times n$ stations. If the unit load is applied at one of these stations, this can be simulated in Equation 1-67 by letting $p = 1/l^2$ at that station (zero elsewhere). The deflections will then be expressed in terms of this reference length l. Let stations on the plate be defined as in Fig. 1-13.

With the unit load applied at one station, there will be $m \times n$ stations where the deflection will be calculated. Since there are $m \times n$ stations where the load may be applied, the number of elements in the flexibility matrix will not exceed $(m \times n)^2$. It may be that not all of these elements will need to be computed.

Equation 1-67 is the fundamental differential equation governing the plate deflection. When Equation 1-76 is used with Equation 1-67 and applied at a general station i, j in the interior of the lattice of Fig. 1-13, values of u, v, and w at adjacent stations will appear. (Note that $\partial^2 f/\partial x\, \partial y$ may be interpreted as $\partial(\partial f/\partial y)/\partial x$ in determining cross derivatives.) The equation is

$$\mu(t^3u)_{i-1,j} + (t^3u)_{i,j-1} - 2(1+\mu)(t^3u)_{i,j} + (t^3u)_{i,j+1} + \mu(t^3u)_{i+1,j} + (t^3v)_{i-1,j}$$

$$+ \mu(t^3v)_{i,j-1} - 2(1+\mu)(t^3v)_{i,j} + \mu(t^3v)_{i,j+1} + (t^3v)_{i+1,j} + \frac{(1-\mu)}{2}(t^3w)_{i-1,j-1}$$

$$- \frac{(1-\mu)}{2}(t^3w)_{i-1,j+1} - \frac{(1-\mu)}{2}(t^3w)_{i+1,j-1} + \frac{(1-\mu)}{2}(t^3w)_{i+1,j+1}$$

$$= \frac{12(1-\mu^2)l^2p_{i,j}}{E}$$

When Equation 1-76 along with Equations 1-64, 1-65, and 1-66 are applied to this equation, values of z at points two stations removed from i, j also appear. Thus, Equation 1-67 becomes

$$(1-\mu)(t^3z)_{i-2,j-2} + 2(3+\mu)(t^3z)_{i-2,j} + (1-\mu)(t^3z)_{i-2,j+2} + 16\mu(t^3z)_{i-1,j-1}$$
$$- 32(1+\mu)(t^3z)_{i-1,j} + 16\mu(t^3z)_{i-1,j+1} + 2(3+\mu)(t^3z)_{i,j-2} - 32(1+\mu)(t^3z)_{i,j-1}$$
$$+ 20(5+3\mu)(t^3z)_{i,j} - 32(1+\mu)(t^3z)_{i,j+1} + 2(3+\mu)(t^3z)_{i,j+2} + 16\mu(t^3z)_{i+1,j-1}$$
$$- 32(1+\mu)(t^3z)_{i+1,j} + 16\mu(t^3z)_{i+1,j+1} + (1-\mu)(t^3z)_{i+2,j-2} + 2(3+\mu)(t^3z)_{i+2,j}$$
$$+ (1-\mu)(t^3z)_{i+2,j+2}$$

$$= \frac{96(1-\mu^2)}{E}l^4p_{i,j} \tag{1-79}$$

The right side of Equation 1-76 is zero if there is no pressure against the plate at Station i, j and is

$$\frac{96(1-\mu^2)}{E}l^2$$

if unit force is exerted against the plate at Station i, j.

Equation 1-79 applied to the interior stations ($j = 3$ to $n - 2$ and $i = 3$ to $m - 2$) provides $(n - 4)(m - 4)$ equations. The remaining equations necessary for simultaneous solution must develop from the appropriate boundary conditions. Reference to Equations 1-76 and Equations 1-68 to 1-74 will provide the necessary boundary-condition equations.

For illustration, consider a plate fixed on two opposite edges ($j = 1$ and $j = n$) and free on two opposite edges ($i = 1$, and $i = m$). On the $j = 1$ edge, $z_{i,1} = 0$, and from the first of Equations 1-76, $-3z_{i,1} + 4z_{i,2} - z_{i,3} = 0$, so that $4z_{i,2} - z_{i,3} = 0$ with i varying from 1 to m. Similarly, on the $j = n$ edge, $z_{i,n-2} - 4z_{i,n-1} = 0$, providing m equations.

When the values $z_{i,1} = 0$ and $z_{i,n} = 0$ are substituted in the equations resulting from Equation 1-79, the total number of variables in the set is reduced by $2m$, so that the total number of equations needed from the upper and lower boundary conditions is $nm - (n - 4)(m - 4) - 4m$, or $4n - 16$.

These are obtained by applying Equations 1-72 and 1-74 to Stations $1, j$ and m, j and letting j vary from 3 to $n - 2$. Typical equations on the lower edge are

$$\mu z_{1,j-1} + (1-2\mu)z_{1,j} + \mu z_{1,j+1} - 2z_{2,j} + 3z_{3,j} = 0$$

$$3(1-\mu)(t^3z)_{1,j-2} - 6\mu(t^3z)_{1,j-1} - 2(2-9\mu)(t^3z)_{1,j+1} - 6\mu(t^3z)_{1,j+1}$$
$$+ 3(1-\mu)(t^3z)_{1,j+2} - 4(1-\mu)(t^3z)_{2,j-2} + 8\mu(t^3z)_{2,j-1} + 2(1-12\mu)(t^3z)_{2,j+1}$$
$$+ 8\mu(t^3z)_{2,j+1} - 4(1-\mu)(t^3z)_{1,j+2} + (1-\mu)(t^3z)_{3,j-2} - 2\mu(t^3z)_{3,j-2}$$
$$+ 2(2+3\mu)(t^3z)_{3,j+1} - 2\mu(t^3z)_{3,j+1} + (1-\mu)(t^3z)_{3,j+2} - 2(t^3z)_{4,j}$$
$$= 0$$

For purposes of computation of the flexibility matrix for use in a vibration analysis, it is convenient if the outer two rows and columns are not included as stations where the unit load is applied, and if the other stations are located at points where masses are to be concentrated. Thus the size of the flexibility matrix would be $(n - 4)^2(m - 4)^2$, rather than n^2m^2, and the stations would probably not be uniformly spaced (especially near the edges). Also, better results can be obtained with the higher-order polynomials, Equations 1-78, than with the quadratics used in this discussion.

Since the stations where both loads and deflections are located are characterized by double subscripts, the flexibility matrix in this example would be characterized by four indices. As used in this text, the flexibility matrix has only two subscripts, one for the position of the unit load and one for the station where the deflection is desired. Therefore, it is convenient to have a systematic means of converting from double subscripts to single subscripts. Let k be a single index which is to designate the same location as a value of the double index i, j. As j varies from 1 to n and i varies from 1 to m, k will vary from 1 to $(n \times m)$. The value of k can be determined from i and j and Equation 1-80, and the value of i and j can be determined from k and Equation 1-81. In Equation 1-81 the division indicated is "fixed-point" division; that is, if the quotient is not an integer, it is truncated or rounded downward to the nearest integer.

$$k = (i - 1)n + j \tag{1-80}$$

$$\left. \begin{aligned} i &= \frac{k - 1}{n} + 1 \\ j &= k - (i - 1)n \end{aligned} \right\} \tag{1-81}$$

When this method is used with boundaries which are irregular or not parallel with the x or y axes, there is very little additional complication. For instance, suppose the slope in the direction perpendicular to an edge is supposed to be zero, but the edge is angled as indicated in Fig. 1-14. Assume that γ for the interval 7, 8, 9 is 0.7, that $\theta = 30°$, and that $\partial u / \partial q$ must be zero at Station 9.

$$\frac{\partial u}{\partial q} = \frac{\partial u}{\partial x} \frac{\partial x}{\partial q} + \frac{\partial u}{\partial y} \frac{\partial y}{\partial q} = \frac{\partial u}{\partial x} \cos \theta + \frac{\partial u}{\partial y} \sin \theta = 0$$

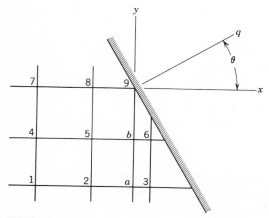

Fig. 1-14

Let $\beta = 1$, $\gamma = 0.7$ and $\epsilon = 0.7$ to determine $\partial u / \partial x$.

$$\left(\frac{\partial u}{\partial x}\right)_9 = \frac{0.49u_7 - 2.89u_8 + 2.40u_9}{1.19l}$$

Then let $\beta = 1$, $\gamma = 1$, $\epsilon = 0.7$ for the intervals 1 to 3 and 4 to 6 to find u_a and u_b, from which $(\partial u / \partial y)_9$ can be obtained using $\beta = \gamma = \epsilon = 1$. This results in

$$\left(\frac{\partial u}{\partial y}\right)_9 = \frac{u_a - 4u_b + 3u_9}{2l}$$

$$= \frac{-0.21u_1 + 1.02u_2 + 1.19u_3 + 0.84u_4 - 4.08u_5 - 5.10u_6 + 6u_9}{4l}$$

The equation $(\partial u / \partial q)_9 = 0$ therefore becomes

$$-0.011u_1 + 0.051u_2 + 0.060u_3 + 0.042u_4 - 0.204u_5$$
$$- 0.238u_6 + 0.143u_7 - 0.842u_8 + 1.000u_9 = 0$$

Gauss-Seidel Iteration. The analysis previously described often results in a set of equations which can be solved by an iteration scheme known as the Gauss-Seidel method. The principal advantage of this method is that it can be used where small differences between large numbers introduce errors in elimination methods of solution. In addition to the better precision afforded by this method (when applicable), it has an advantage for digital computer application when the system is characterized by a very large set of equations with only a few variables in each equation (sparse matrix). The advantage derives from greater speed and reduced memory capacity required of the computer with this method. It is easy to adapt the method to the inversion of a matrix.

In many physical problems the simultaneous algebraic equations exhibit the property that each equation is dominated by a different variable. If this is true, then it is possible to assume any arbitrary values for the unknowns and solve each equation for the dominant variable, progressing around and around the set of equations until the desired accuracy is obtained. For example, the set of equations

$$2x_1 + x_2 + x_3 = 3$$
$$x_1 + 2x_2 + x_3 = 4$$
$$x_1 + x_2 + 2x_3 = 1$$

could be written as

$$x_1 = \frac{1}{2}(3 - x_2 - x_3)$$

$$x_2 = \frac{1}{2}(4 - x_1 - x_3)$$

$$x_3 = \frac{1}{2}(1 - x_1 - x_2)$$

Then any assumed solution substituted into the first of these equations would result in a new value of x_1, to be used immediately in the second equation along with the other assumed values. The new value of x_2 is then used in the third equation, after which the calculation returns to the first equation. The newest values of all variables are used in each calculation. Convergence on the solution $x_1 = 1$, $x_2 = 2$, $x_3 = -1$ results.

The convergence of this procedure depends on the magnitude of the coefficient that multiplies the dominant variable. If the absolute value of the coefficient that multiplies the dominant variable in each equation is larger than the sum of the absolute values of the coefficients of all the other variables in the same equation, then the method will converge. This is not a necessary condition, however, and convergence will often occur for less stringent restrictions on the coefficients. For instance, the following set of equations does not satisfy the restrictions mentioned above, but nevertheless converges on the solution $x_1 = 1$, $x_2 = 2$, $x_3 = -1$, if the second equation is solved for x_2.

$$4x_1 + x_2 \qquad = 6$$
$$4x_1 + 3x_2 + 4x_3 = 6$$
$$x_2 + 4x_3 = -2$$

1.6 Generalized Properties in the Analysis of a Flexible Missile

The example which follows (taken from Ref. 1) illustrates the use of generalized properties in the analysis of a complex system. Reference to this example will be made in subsequent chapters.

Example 1-2. Investigate the stability of a missile having a flexible body and autopilot making whatever simplifying assumptions seem appropriate for the purposes of an illustrative example. The following discussion refers to Fig. 1-15.

Let it be supposed that a free beam with constant cross section can represent the missile body and that at a given instant during its flight its path is approximately vertically upward. An automatic pilot is supposed to maintain the missile attitude by producing transverse forces at the tail, f_c, either by the use of aerodynamic surfaces or by swiveling the thrust nozzle or auxiliary jets. Each portion of the missile body would experience aerodynamic loads, which for simplicity will be assumed to be limited to just one aerodynamic load, f_a, applied at Station 3, and which will be assumed to be proportional to the local angle of attack of Station 3, with no time delay in the load buildup (Fig. 1-15). The automatic pilot is supposed to provide stability by sensing (or sensing and calculating) the angle of the missile body in space, the angular velocity, and the angular acceleration, and

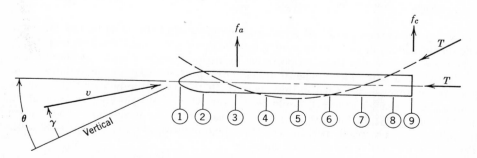

Fig. 1-15 Definitions for numerical analysis of a flexible missile with autopilot and aerodynamic coupling of generalized modes.

then requiring a corrective force, f_c, to be produced. However, the sensing element is located at Station 2, and so the information actually applies to that station rather than the missile as a whole. If the body did not bend, then the angle at Station 2 would of course be the same as at all stations, but because of the flexible body this cannot be assumed. Let it be assumed that the propulsion thrust does not alter the normal modes of the free beam, and that the transfer function between the corrective force, f_c, and the corrective force commanded by the autopilot, f_{cc}, is

$$\frac{F_c}{F_{cc}} = \frac{1}{1 + \dfrac{2\zeta}{\omega}s + \dfrac{s^2}{\omega^2}}$$

Assume that the first three bending modes are sufficient to represent body bending and that each mode is damped at 2% critical damping. Consider only motion in a plane (longitudinal stability). Assume that the main propulsion thrust is coincident with the local centerline at Station 9.

The equations are as follows. The rigid-body acceleration perpendicular to the flight path is $v\dot{\gamma}$ if γ is the flight path angle relative to the vertical direction in space, and v is the missile velocity. For rigid-body translation of the center of gravity perpendicular to the flight path, which is nearly vertical so that $\dot{\gamma}$ is a small angle,

$$mv\dot{\gamma} = f_a + f_c + mg\gamma + T[(\theta - \sigma_{91}q_1 - \sigma_{92}q_2 - \sigma_{93}q_3) - \gamma] \tag{1}$$

(For explanation of σ_{91}, σ_{92}, σ_{93} in this equation and Equations 2 to 5, see the discussion of f_a that follows). Rigid-body translation parallel to the flight path will be neglected in this example, assuming equilibrium of thrust and flight path acceleration. For rigid-body angular acceleration about the center of gravity.

$$I\ddot{\theta} = f_a(l_{c.g.} - l_3) + (l_9 - l_{c.g.})[-f_c + T(\sigma_{91}q_1 + \sigma_{92}q_2 + \sigma_{93}q_3)]$$
$$- T\left(\frac{\partial y_9}{\partial q_1}q_1 + \frac{\partial y_9}{\partial q_2}q_2 + \frac{\partial y_9}{\partial q_3}q_3\right) \tag{2}$$

In the three bending modes

$$M_1\ddot{q}_1 + C_1\dot{q}_1 + K_1q_1 = f_a\left(\frac{\partial y_3}{\partial q_1}\right) + \frac{\partial y_9}{\partial q_1}[f_c - T(\sigma_{91}q_1 + \sigma_{92}q_2 + \sigma_{93}q_3)] \tag{3}$$

$$M_2\ddot{q}_2 + C_2\dot{q}_2 + K_2q_2 = f_a\left(\frac{\partial y_3}{\partial q_2}\right) + \frac{\partial y_9}{\partial q_2}[f_c - T(\sigma_{91}q_1 + \sigma_{92}q_2 + \sigma_{93}q_3)] \tag{4}$$

$$M_3\ddot{q}_3 + C_3\dot{q}_3 + K_3q_3 = f_a\left(\frac{\partial y_3}{\partial q_3}\right) + \frac{\partial y_9}{\partial q_3}[f_c - T(\sigma_{91}q_1 + \sigma_{92}q_2 + \sigma_{93}q_3)] \tag{5}$$

In these equations the generalized forces on the right side of the equation are computed using the deflections in the various modes at the stations where the loads are applied.

The force f_a is assumed to be proportional to the local angle of attack at Station 3, so $f_a = k_a\alpha$ where α is the local angle of attack. (Any possible delay in the buildup of the aerodynamic forces is neglected in this example.) If the missile body were rigid and not rotating, the local angle of attack would be $(\theta - \gamma)$. Because of rigid-body rotation about the center of gravity, there is a velocity of the missile centerline at Station 3 in a direction perpendicular (or practically perpendicular) to the remote velocity, v, which would cause a decrease in the local angle of attack equal to

$$\frac{(\dot{\theta} - \dot{\gamma})(l_{c.g.} - l_3)}{v}$$

radians. There would be a similar decrease of local angle of attack caused by the velocity of Station 3 which results from the bending of the beam, or

$$\frac{\dot{q}_1\left(\frac{\partial y_3}{\partial q_1}\right) + \dot{q}_2\left(\frac{\partial y_3}{\partial q_2}\right) + \dot{q}_3\left(\frac{\partial y_3}{\partial q_3}\right)}{V}$$

radians. There would also be a change in local angle of attack caused by the fact that the local centerline is deflected in bending. This angle is simply the negative of the slope of the bending deflection curve in the various modes, or $-\sigma_{31}q_1 - \sigma_{32}q_2 - \sigma_{33}q_3$, where σ_{31} is the slope of the deflection curve in Mode 1 at Station 3 and similar definitions for the other coefficients. Therefore, substituting for α,

$$f_a = k_a\left[\theta - \gamma - \frac{(\dot{\theta} - \dot{\gamma})(l_{c.g.} - l_3)}{v} - \frac{\left(\frac{\partial y_3}{\partial q_1}\right)}{v}\dot{q}_1 - \frac{\left(\frac{\partial y_3}{\partial q_2}\right)}{v}\dot{q}_2 - \frac{\left(\frac{\partial y_3}{\partial q_3}\right)}{v}\dot{q}_3\right.$$

$$\left. - \sigma_{31}q_1 - \sigma_{32}q_2 - \sigma_{33}q_3\right] \qquad ⑥$$

Now consider the action of the autopilot. Let it be assumed for the purpose of this example that the job of the autopilot is to maintain a fixed attitude of the missile in space, nearly vertical, and that some guidance signal, of no present concern, would be required in order to set the correct attitude to produce a given flight path to accomplish a given mission. Let it be assumed that instruments are located at Station 2, which can detect or compute angular acceleration, velocity, or position without error. (Actually, any instrument would have a transfer function of some form which would relate the indicated quantity to the actual quantity, but in this example an ideal instrument is assumed.) If it is assumed that the force commanded by the autopilot is proportional to the angular position, velocity, or acceleration of the sensing instrument, and that the force commanded is in the direction to restore the rigid-body attitude to the desired value and to oppose angular velocity and acceleration, then

$$-f_{c_c} = k_\theta(\theta - \theta_g - \sigma_{21}q_1 - \sigma_{22}q_2 - \sigma_{23}q_3) + k_{\dot{\theta}}(\dot{\theta} - \sigma_{21}\dot{q}_1 - \sigma_{22}\dot{q}_2 - \sigma_{23}\dot{q}_3)$$

$$+ k_{\ddot{\theta}}(\ddot{\theta} - \sigma_{21}\ddot{q}_1 - \sigma_{22}\ddot{q}_2 - \sigma_{23}\ddot{q}_3) \qquad ⑦$$

where θ_g is the desired attitude for a particular instant as determined by guidance requirements. Finally, the relationship which relates the actual corrective force to the command force might be of the following form:

$$\frac{1}{\omega^2}\frac{d^2f_c}{dt^2} + \frac{2\zeta}{\omega}\frac{df_c}{dt} + f_c = f_{c_c} \qquad ⑧$$

If these eight equations are transformed, a matrix equation results (see p. 44). For purposes of this example let it be assumed that

$$v = 3000 \text{ fps}$$
$$m = 500 \text{ slugs}$$
$$T = 50,000 \text{ lbs}$$
$$L = 50 \text{ ft}$$
$$k_a = 50,000 \text{ lbs/rad}$$
$$\omega = 10 \text{ rad/sec}$$
$$\zeta = 0.7$$
$$(EI) = 1.0 \times 10^8 \text{ lb/ft}^2$$

$$
\begin{bmatrix}
mvs+(T-mg) & -T & T\sigma_{91} & T\sigma_{92} & T\sigma_{93} & -1 & -1 & 0 \\[4pt]
0 & Is^2 & -T\sigma_{91}(l_9-l_{c.g.})+T\dfrac{\partial y_9}{\partial q_1} & -T\sigma_{92}(l_9-l_{c.g.})+T\dfrac{\partial y_9}{\partial q_2} & -T\sigma_{93}(l_9-l_{c.g.})+T\dfrac{\partial y_9}{\partial q_3} & (l_3-l_{c.g.}) & (l_9-l_{c.g.}) & 0 \\[4pt]
0 & 0 & M_1s^2+K_1+\left(\dfrac{\partial y_9}{\partial q_1}\right)T\sigma_{91} & \left(\dfrac{\partial y_9}{\partial q_1}\right)T\sigma_{92} & \left(\dfrac{\partial y_9}{\partial q_1}\right)T\sigma_{93} & -\dfrac{\partial y_3}{\partial q_1} & -\dfrac{\partial y_9}{\partial q_1} & 0 \\[4pt]
0 & 0 & \left(\dfrac{\partial y_9}{\partial q_2}\right)T\sigma_{91} & M_3s^2+K_2+\left(\dfrac{\partial y_9}{\partial q_2}\right)T\sigma_{92} & \left(\dfrac{\partial y_9}{\partial q_2}\right)T\sigma_{93} & -\dfrac{\partial y_3}{\partial q_2} & -\dfrac{\partial y_9}{\partial q_2} & 0 \\[4pt]
0 & 0 & \left(\dfrac{\partial y_9}{\partial q_3}\right)T\sigma_{91} & \left(\dfrac{\partial y_9}{\partial q_3}\right)T\sigma_{92} & M_3s^2+K_3+\left(\dfrac{\partial y_9}{\partial q_3}\right)T\sigma_{93} & -\dfrac{\partial y_3}{\partial q_3} & -\dfrac{\partial y_9}{\partial q_3} & 0 \\[4pt]
-\dfrac{(l_{c.g.}-l_3)}{v}s+1 & \dfrac{(l_{c.g.}-l_3)}{v}s-1 & \left(\dfrac{\partial y_3}{\partial q_1}\right)\dfrac{s}{v}+\sigma_{31} & \left(\dfrac{\partial y_3}{\partial q_2}\right)\dfrac{s}{v}+\sigma_{32} & \left(\dfrac{\partial y_3}{\partial q_3}\right)\dfrac{s}{v}+\sigma_{33} & \dfrac{1}{k_a} & 0 & 0 \\[4pt]
0 & k_{\ddot\theta}s^2+k_{\dot\theta}s+k_\theta & -\sigma_{21}k_{\ddot\theta}s^2-\sigma_{21}k_{\dot\theta}s-\sigma_{21}k_\theta & -\sigma_{22}k_{\ddot\theta}s^2-\sigma_{22}k_{\dot\theta}s-\sigma_{22}k_\theta & -\sigma_{23}k_{\ddot\theta}s^2-\sigma_{23}k_{\dot\theta}s-\sigma_{23}k_\theta & 0 & 0 & -1 \\[4pt]
0 & 0 & 0 & 0 & 0 & 0 & \dfrac{s^2}{\omega^2}+\dfrac{2\zeta s}{\omega}+1 & -1
\end{bmatrix}
\begin{bmatrix}
\gamma \\ \theta \\ q_1 \\ q_2 \\ q_3 \\ F_a \\ F_c \\ F_{cc}
\end{bmatrix}
=
\begin{bmatrix}
0 \\ 0 \\ 0 \\ 0 \\ 0 \\ 0 \\ k_\theta\theta_g \\ 0
\end{bmatrix}
$$

For the assumed beam

$$I = m\frac{L^2}{12} = 104,200 \text{ slug/ft}^2$$

$$l_3 - l_{\text{c.g.}} = \frac{3}{14}L - \frac{L}{2} = -14.3 \text{ ft}$$

$$l_9 - l_{\text{c.g.}} = L - \frac{L}{2} = 25 \text{ ft}$$

From the normal modes for a free beam, calculated with the numerical methods of the previous sections and Programs A55 and A38NM of the Appendix,

$$\left(\frac{\partial y_3}{\partial q_1}\right) = 0.103 \qquad \left(\frac{\partial y_3}{\partial q_2}\right) = -0.900 \qquad \left(\frac{\partial y_3}{\partial q_3}\right) = 1.316$$

$$\left(\frac{\partial y_9}{\partial q_1}\right) = 2.068 \qquad \left(\frac{\partial y_9}{\partial q_2}\right) = -2.141 \qquad \left(\frac{\partial y_9}{\partial q_3}\right) = -2.173$$

$$\sigma_{21} = -0.188 \text{ rad/ft} \qquad \sigma_{31} = -0.167 \text{ rad/ft} \qquad \sigma_{91} = 0.188 \text{ rad/ft}$$
$$\sigma_{22} = -0.312 \text{ rad/ft} \qquad \sigma_{32} = -0.185 \text{ rad/ft} \qquad \sigma_{92} = -0.312 \text{ rad/ft}$$
$$\sigma_{23} = 0.405 \text{ rad/ft} \qquad \sigma_{33} = 0.060 \text{ rad/ft} \qquad \sigma_{93} = -0.405 \text{ rad/ft}$$

(Note that σ_{ij} can be computed from

$$\sigma_{ij} = \sum_{k=2}^{8} m_k \beta_j{}^2 \left(\frac{\partial y_k}{\partial q_j}\right)\theta_{ik}$$

where θ_{ik} is an element in the flexibility matrix)

$$M_1 = m = 500 \text{ slugs} \qquad K_1 = 534\frac{EI}{L^3} = 0.427 \times 10^6 \text{ lb/ft}$$

$$M_2 = m = 500 \text{ slugs} \qquad K_2 = 4240\frac{EI}{L^3} = 3.39 \times 10^6 \text{ lb/ft}$$

$$M_3 = m = 500 \text{ slugs} \qquad K_3 = 16,800\frac{EI}{L^3} = 13.45 \times 10^6 \text{ lb/ft}$$

Assume structural damping of 2% critical, so that

$$C_1 = 2(0.02)\sqrt{M_1 K_1} = 586 \text{ lb/(ft/sec)}$$
$$C_2 = 2(0.02)\sqrt{M_2 K_2} = 1655 \text{ lb/(ft/sec)}$$
$$C_3 = 2(0.02)\sqrt{M_3 K_3} = 3150 \text{ lb/(ft/sec)}$$

Assume control constants

$$k_\theta = 48,000 \text{ lb/rad} \qquad k_{\dot\theta} = 18,000 \text{ lb/(rad/sec)} \qquad k_{\ddot\theta} = 0$$

The characteristic equation for this system will result if the determinant of the matrix is set equal to zero. A digital computer program for determining the characteristic equation from a determinant having quadratic elements is given in the Appendix, Program A74PFD. For the constants chosen, the characteristic equation is approximately

$$1 + 4.85s + 3.63s^2 + 1.043s^3 + 0.1518s^4 + 1.306 \times 10^{-2}s^5 + 2.334 \times 10^{-4}s^6$$
$$+ 1.522 \times 10^{-5}s^7 + 4.61 \times 10^{-8}s^8 + 2.406 \times 10^{-9}s^9 + 1.714 + 10^{-12}s^{10}$$
$$+ 6.87 \times 10^{-14}s^{11}$$
$$= 0$$

This equation can be factored by a digital computer program given in the Appendix, Program A86FP. The roots are

$$s = -3.24 \pm 164.5i$$
$$s = -1.495 \pm 83.0i$$
$$s = -1.33 \pm 29.6i$$
$$s = -3.26 \pm 5.43i$$
$$s = -4.05$$
$$s = -2.52$$
$$s = -0.250$$

These roots all have negative real parts, and thus the missile is stable. This would not necessarily be true if the various constants had different values. For instance, if $k_{\dot{\theta}} = 0$, there would be roots at $s = 0.77 \pm 1.82i$, resulting in an oscillation with increasing amplitude. Also, if the stable system values of k_θ and $k_{\dot{\theta}}$ used in this example were either doubled or halved, a dynamically unstable system would result.

Systematic methods exist for adjusting system parameters for satisfactory performance. These methods are described in more detail in subsequent chapters.

1.7 Transient Response

Two methods for computing transient response are briefly described in this section, the convolution theorem and the Fourier transform.

Convolution Theorem. If two functions, $F(s)$ and $G(s)$, have inverse Laplace transforms, $f(t)$ and $g(t)$ respectively, the inverse transform of the product, $F(s)G(s)$ is given as

$$\mathscr{L}^{-1}[F(s)G(s)] = \int_{\lambda=0}^{\lambda=t} f(\lambda)g(t-\lambda)\,d\lambda \tag{1-82}$$

$$\mathscr{L}^{-1}[F(s)G(s)] = \int_{\lambda=0}^{\lambda=t} f(t-\lambda)g(\lambda)\,d\lambda \tag{1-82a}$$

Either of these forms is correct, and the choice of one or the other is strictly a matter of convenience in any given situation. The variable, λ, is merely a dummy variable in time. The character τ is often used instead of λ for this purpose.

If there is a transfer-function relationship between a force and displacement, say

$$\frac{X(s)}{F(s)} = G(s)$$

it is clear that the displacement in the time domain is

$$x(t) = \mathscr{L}^{-1}[F(s)G(s)]$$

and that Equation 1-82 is applicable. If the forcing function in the time domain is not an algebraic expression, $F(s)$ is not known as an algebraic expression, but it does not matter because $f(t)$, and therefore $f(\lambda)$ (or $f(t - \lambda)$), is known either as a table or as a graph of the function and can be utilized directly in Equation 1-82 if numerical integration is used. Of course $g(t - \lambda)$ (or else $g(\lambda)$) would have to be computed numerically in order to do this, but this is possible, since $G(s)$ is presumably a known function whose inverse may be taken and evaluated at the desired intervals. Even if $G(s)$ is not known, it may be that $g(t)$, and therefore $g(t - \lambda)$ (or else $g(\lambda)$), is known from experimental observation, and the response may be obtainable by numerical integration. This is explained in more detail as follows.

Although either Equation 1-82 or 1-82a is acceptable, let the first form be used hereafter, because the physical meaning of this form is more easily understood.

$$x(t) = \mathscr{L}^{-1}[F(s)G(s)] = \int_{\lambda=0}^{\lambda=t} f(\lambda)g(t-\lambda)\, d\lambda \qquad (1\text{-}83)$$

If $f(t)$ is the unit impulse function, its transform is unity and $x(t)$ becomes $g(t)$. Therefore, $g(t)$ is the response to unit impulse. The actual response $x(t)$ to an arbitrary forcing function $f(t)$ is then given by Equation 1-83, where $g(t)$ is the response to unit impulse. To compute the deflection x at a single instant t, the integration indicated by Equation 1-83 is performed, maintaining t constant. This integration must be repeated for any other instant. Numerical integration may be required if the forcing function $f(t)$ cannot be expressed as an algebraic equation.

Clearly, digital computer use is required for systems of moderate complexity. Program E11TRN of the Appendix provides the inverse transform of a very general transfer function, including multiple complex or real poles of any order, and the response to arbitrary forcing functions of systems having such transfer functions. The forcing function curves are approximated by straight line segments connecting discrete values of $f(t)$, but otherwise the calculations in this program are exact. Theory underlying the procedure used in this program is explained in Ref. 1.

Fourier Transform. In the previous discussion, the response of systems subject to transient forcing functions was described in terms of the response to unit impulse functions. The forcing function was considered to be composed of a series of small impulses and the responses to this series superimposed to determine the response to the actual forcing function. It is also possible to define a forcing function in terms of an infinite number of sine or cosine functions of infinitesimal amplitude. Then the response to these may be superimposed to determine the response to the actual forcing function. The description of the transient forcing function in terms of its harmonic components is accomplished by means of the Fourier Integral.

The function to be represented must be single-valued (except that it may have a finite number of finite discontinuities in a finite interval), it must not have infinite discontinuities ($\tan t$ is unacceptable, for instance), and it must approach zero as the independent variable approaches infinity in either the positive or negative direction (t^2 or e^t or e^{-t} are unacceptable, for instance, unless "cut off"). The function must also exhibit only a finite number of maximum or minimum points in a finite interval ($\sin(1/t)$ is unacceptable, for instance). For transient analyses nearly any forcing function of practical interest would obey these requirements and so be a possible subject for a Fourier analysis.

The Fourier Integral equation is shown in the complex exponential form in Equation 1-84, in which ω should be regarded as a parameter, rather than frequency, since it may assume negative values.

$$f(t) = \frac{1}{2\pi} \int_{\omega=-\infty}^{+\infty} e^{it\omega} \left[\int_{t=-\infty}^{+\infty} f(t)e^{-i\omega t}\, dt \right] d\omega \qquad (1\text{-}84)$$

The $f(t)$ inside the integral is the same function as that at the left side. However, the function inside the integral might be described by several different expressions, each valid for a different range of the variable t. After it is operated on as indicated by Equation 1-84, the left side describes the same function but with a single expression valid for all values of t. Equation 1-84 can be conveniently expressed as two equations, Equations 1-85.

$$g(\omega) = \int_{t=-\infty}^{+\infty} f(t)e^{-i\omega t} \, dt \equiv F[f(t)]$$

$$f(t) = \frac{1}{2\pi} \int_{\omega=-\infty}^{+\infty} g(\omega)e^{it\omega} \, d\omega \equiv F^{-1}[g(\omega)]$$

(1-85)

In Equation 1-85 $g(\omega)$ or $F[f(t)]$ is the Fourier transform of $f(t)$ and $f(t)$ or $F^{-1}[g(\omega)]$ is the inverse Fourier transform of $g(\omega)$. These definitions are not the only ones in use, and therefore whenever a table of Fourier transforms is consulted it is wise to ascertain the definitions used in the table. If $f(t)$ is an even function or an odd function, Equations 1-85 can be modified to Equations 1-86.

$$\left.\begin{aligned} g(\omega) &= \int_{t=0}^{\infty} f(t) \cos \omega t \, dt \\[2mm] f(t) &= \frac{2}{\pi} \int_{\omega=0}^{\infty} g(\omega) \cos t\omega \, d\omega \end{aligned}\right\} f(t) \text{ even}$$

$$\left.\begin{aligned} g(\omega) &= \int_{t=0}^{\infty} f(t) \sin \omega t \, dt \\[2mm] f(t) &= \frac{2}{\pi} \int_{\omega=0}^{\infty} g(\omega) \sin t\omega \, d\omega \end{aligned}\right\} f(t) \text{ odd}$$

(1-86)

Any real function can be considered as the sum of an even function and an odd function, where these functions may be determined as indicated in Equations 1-87.

$$f(t) = f_e(t) + f_o(t)$$

$$f_e(t) = \frac{f(t) + f(-t)}{2}$$

$$f_o(t) = \frac{f(t) - f(-t)}{2}$$

(1-87)

If these even and odd functions are used in Equation 1-85, the real and imaginary parts of the Fourier transform can be shown to be even and odd functions respectively (of ω), and therefore the integration involved in obtaining the inverse transform need only go from limits of 0 to infinity, as summarized in Equations 1-88. Of course, the imaginary part of this inverse is zero, since $f(t)$ in Equation 1-87 is a real function. (This is manifested as an integration from $-\infty$ to $+\infty$ of an odd function in the calculation of the inverse.)

$$\left.\begin{aligned} g(\omega) &= g_r(\omega) + ig_i(\omega) \\[2mm] g_r(\omega) &= 2 \int_{t=0}^{\infty} f_e(t) \cos \omega t \, dt \\[2mm] g_i(\omega) &= -2 \int_{t=0}^{\infty} f_o(t) \sin \omega t \, dt \\[2mm] g_r(\omega) &\text{ is an even function of } \omega \\[1mm] g_i(\omega) &\text{ is an odd function of } \omega \\[2mm] f(t) &= \frac{1}{\pi} \int_{\omega=0}^{\infty} [g_r(\omega) \cos t\omega - g_i(\omega) \sin t\omega] \, d\omega \end{aligned}\right\} \text{(1-88)}$$

In Equations 1-84 and 1-85, ω may have negative values and so must be considered a parameter rather than a frequency. However, in Equations 1-86 and 1-88 the use of negative values of ω is not required, and thus ω can properly be considered a frequency.

If it is known that the function $f(t)$ is identically zero for $t < 0$, then the last equation can be simplified somewhat, as follows.

$$f(-t) = 0 = \frac{1}{\pi} \int_{\omega=0}^{\infty} [g_r(\omega) \cos(-t\omega) - g_i(\omega) \sin(-t\omega)] \, d\omega$$

Since $\cos(-t\omega) = \cos(t\omega)$ and $\sin(-t\omega) = -\sin(t\omega)$,

$$\frac{1}{\pi} \int_{\omega=0}^{\infty} g_i(\omega) \sin(t\omega) \, d\omega = -\frac{1}{\pi} \int_{\omega=0}^{\infty} g_r(\omega) \cos(t\omega) \, d\omega$$

When this relation is used in the last of Equations 1-88,

$$f(t) = \frac{2}{\pi} \int_{\omega=0}^{\infty} g_r(\omega) \cos t\omega \, d\omega \qquad\qquad (1\text{-}89)$$

Equation 1-89 is valid only if $f(t) = 0$ for $t < 0$.

When the transient response to an arbitrary forcing function is computed using the Fourier transform, the system differential equations may be transformed as with the Laplace transform. In fact, the transfer function in terms of the Laplace transform variable s can be modified by replacing s with $i\omega$ (provided, of course, that the restrictions on the type of function which can have a Fourier transform are observed). Equation 1-90 represents the transfer function between deflection $x(t)$ and forcing function $f(t)$ in terms of the Fourier transforms $X(\omega)$ and $F(\omega)$.

$$\frac{X(\omega)}{F(\omega)} = T(\omega) \qquad\qquad (1\text{-}90)$$

If $f(t)$ is a transformable function, then $F(\omega)$ in Equation 1-90 can be computed, an expression for $X(\omega)$ or else numerical values of $X(\omega)$ at all values of ω are available. Then $x(t)$ can be computed using the second of Equations 1-85 or other appropriate equations. All of the transformed quantities, $F(\omega)$, $X(\omega)$, and $T(\omega)$ may have real and imaginary parts, but for a physical system subjected to a real forcing function $f(t)$, the response $x(t)$ which results from the calculation must be real with zero imaginary part.

The Fourier integral and transform method of analysis has no advantage over the Laplace transform method for the type of problems considered in this book. It is useful in the analysis of random vibration (a subject not included in this text) and also in any problem for which boundary conditions are specified at positive and negative infinity rather than at finite values of the independent variable, or where the forcing function falls off to zero gradually in the negative direction so that no zero value of the independent variable can be selected for which the effect of events at values more negative than this can be neglected. Since the Laplace transform has the effect of disregarding events which occur at values of the independent variable less than zero, it cannot be used unless some artifice is introduced so that effects of events occurring prior to zero are suitably simulated or approximated.

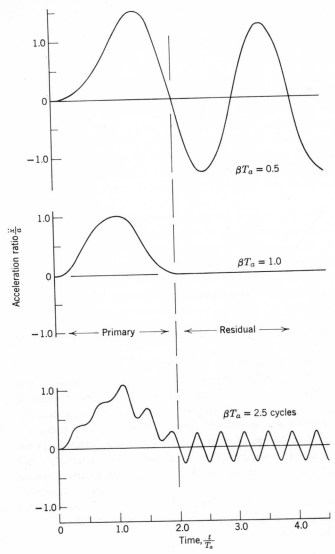

Fig. 1-17 Time history of acceleration response to input acceleration of Fig. 1-16 for three natural frequencies.

where $(s^2 Y)$ is the transform of the applied acceleration which forces the response.

The response acceleration can be computed from Equation 1-91 using the convolution theorem, Equation 1-83. The response acceleration during the time that the forcing acceleration exists is called "primary shock." The response acceleration which persists after the instant that the acceleration of the support point is restrained to zero is called the "residual shock." (A force is required to restrain the support point to zero acceleration, however, which may not be appropriate under some conditions.)

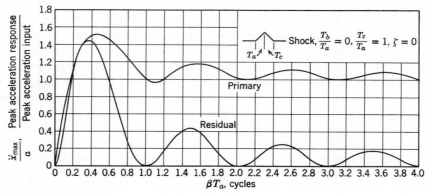

Fig. 1-18   Shock spectrum.

Although only the maximum value of the acceleration is used in a shock spectrum computation, there may be confusion between a response spectrum and a response history. A plot of Equation 1-91 is shown in Fig. 1-17 for three different values of natural frequency, $\beta = 0.5/T_a$, $\beta = 1.0/T_a$, and $\beta = 2.5/T_a$ cycles per second. For $t < 2T_a$, the forcing acceleration is still applied, and so the response during this interval is designated "primary" shock. For $t > 2T_a$, if the input acceleration is forced to be zero, there will be a residual oscillation, as indicated above, resulting in the accelerations shown. For this input and the specific natural frequency represented by $\beta = 1.0/T_a$, however, there is no residual oscillation. For $\beta = 0.5/T_a$ cycles per second, the maximum value of the primary response, at the time $t = 1.210T_a$, is used as one point on the shock spectrum of Fig. 1-18. The maximum value of the residual acceleration is also plotted as one point in Fig. 1-18. This peak value occurs at the times $t = 2.5T_a$, $3.5T_a$, etc. (Note that β is Equation 1-91 is in radians per second, but in Fig. 1-17 and 1-18 β is in cycles per second.) It is necessary to find the peak value of acceleration for other values of β in order to construct the shock spectrum of Fig. 1-18.

A digital computer program, A87SHK, is given in the Appendix for the computation of the shock spectrum for the system illustrated by Fig. 1-16. The result of the computation for the specialized shock of Fig. 1-16 with $T_b = 0$ and $T_a = T_c$ on a system without damping is shown in nondimensional form in Fig. 1-18. Several interesting facts may be noted in this plot. The maximum response occurs at values of βT_a less than 1.0, in this instance at 0.5 revolutions, and is about 1.5 times the peak input acceleration. (The theoretical upper limit for this ratio is 2.0 for shocks of the general form of Fig. 1-16, which is approached when T_b is large relative to T_a).

For $\beta T_a \geq 1.0$, the peak response is approximately the same as the peak input. Essentially no magnification or attenuation would incur for systems having natural frequencies greater than $1/T_a$ cycles per second.

If the purpose of a suspension system is to reduce the shock intensity, it will be necessary to provide values of βT_a less than about 0.2 cycles. That is, the maximum natural frequency should be less than $0.2/T_a$ cps, the smaller the better as far as shock attenuation is concerned, limited by practical considerations, of course.

The foregoing discussion applies to shocks whose description can be represented or at least approximated by Fig. 1-16. For shocks of this type the limiting peak response acceleration is twice the magnitude of the input acceleration (the value expected for shocks approaching a step function). Of course, it is possible that the input acceleration might not have a description of this simple form. For instance, it might have negative as well as positive values and might have more than just one pulse. For such "complex" shocks, the peak response could exceed the above limitation of twice the peak input acceleration for certain natural frequencies (similar to a resonance phenomenon), and the period of primary shock could contain negative as well as positive response accelerations.

Equations 1-92 and 1-93 are general equations for determining the response acceleration and rate of change of acceleration for complex shocks if they can be described, or at least approximated, by an acceleration history composed of straight-line segments. Note that t in these equations is the time after the beginning of one of these straight-line segments, not the time from the beginning of the shock.

$$a_x = a_{y_0} + \dot{a}_{y_0} t + e^{-\zeta \beta t}\left[(a_{x_0} - a_{y_0}) \cos \beta \sqrt{1 - \zeta^2}\, t \right.$$
$$\left. + \frac{\zeta \beta (a_{x_0} - a_{y_0}) + \dot{a}_{x_0} - \dot{a}_{y_0}}{\beta \sqrt{1 - \zeta^2}} \sin \beta \sqrt{1 - \zeta^2}\, t \right]$$

(1-92)

$$\dot{a}_x = \dot{a}_{y_0} + e^{-\zeta \beta t}\left[(\dot{a}_{x_0} - \dot{a}_{y_0}) \cos \beta \sqrt{1 - \zeta^2}\, t \right.$$
$$\left. - \frac{\beta(a_{x_0} - a_{y_0}) + \zeta(\dot{a}_{x_0} - \dot{a}_{y_0})}{\sqrt{1 - \zeta^2}} \sin \beta \sqrt{1 - \zeta^2}\, t \right]$$

(1-93)

where

$$a_x = \text{acceleration of the mass}$$
$$a_y = a_{y_0} + \dot{a}_{y_0} t = \text{acceleration of the platform}$$
$$a_{y_0} = \text{initial acceleration of the platform}$$
$$\dot{a}_{y_0} = \text{rate of change of platform acceleration, a constant}$$
$$a_{x_0} = \text{initial acceleration of the mass}$$
$$\dot{a}_{x_0} = \text{initial rate of change of mass acceleration}$$

The shock spectrum is not altered significantly by light damping, and Equations 1-92 and 1-93 can be simplified by letting $\zeta = 0$. If $\zeta = 0$, the maximum or minimum acceleration in the time interval $0 \leq t \leq T$ (the interval during which the shock is represented by the straight line $a_y = a_{y_0} + \dot{a}_{y_0} t$) occurs at either $t = 0$, $t = T$, or an instant between these for which $\dot{a}_x = 0$. This instant can be determined from Equation 1-94.

$$\tan(\beta t_m + \psi) = \pm \frac{\dot{a}_{y_0}}{\sqrt{(\dot{a}_{x_0} - \dot{a}_{y_0})^2 + \beta^2(a_{y_0} - a_{x_0}) - \dot{a}_{y_0}^2}}$$

$$\tan \psi = \frac{\dot{a}_{x_0} - \dot{a}_{y_0}}{\beta(a_{y_0} - a_{x_0})}$$

$$t_m = \text{time for } \dot{a}_x = 0$$

(1-94)

If the quantity under the square root is negative, there is no instant where $\dot{a}_x = 0$, and the maximum or minimum value of response acceleration is the value at either the beginning or the end of the time interval. This is also true if the time computed from Equation 1-94 does not fall within the interval for which the rate of change is the constant $\dot{a}_{y_0}$.

A digital computer program for the computation of the shock spectrum for a complex shock (zero damping) is provided in the Appendix.

CHAPTER 2

Control System Block Diagram Logic

2.1 General Comments

Increased understanding of factors affecting vibration of linear systems has resulted from the development during and since the Second World War of theory pertaining to feedback control systems. Much of this theory has been developed from an electrical engineering viewpoint and may be initially somewhat unfamiliar to those who have not been active in this field. The purpose of Chapters 2 to 7 is to introduce those parts of control-system theory which may contribute to a greater understanding of vibration of linear systems, and to do this primarily in terms of mechanical and mathematical concepts.

Perhaps the most distinguishing characteristic of a feedback control system is the existence of a "loop," whose function is to compare the value of some variable with the required value of that variable and if there is a difference, or error, to initiate action to reduce this error. Examples of such systems come readily to mind. The driver of a car detects the difference between his direction of motion and the direction of the road and turns the wheel accordingly. A thermostat governs the temperature of a water heater or a refrigerator by detecting the difference between the actual temperature and the desired temperature and turning on a heater or cooler to correct the error (although this may not be a linear system). Any system that can vibrate inherently possesses a loop in which a comparison and correction occur. For instance, the position of a mass supported by a spring is detected by the spring, and if it is different from the equilibrium position, a force is developed by the spring which will tend to return it to the equilibrium position. Not only position, but velocity and higher derivatives, and also integrals, enter the picture.

The tools of control-system theory which are most helpful in bringing order and understanding out of what is often merely a collection of differential equations are the following four subjects; block diagram logic, notation, and algebra; complex plane plots or Nyquist diagrams; frequency response or Bode plots for analysis and synthesis; and analysis and synthesis by use of the root locus, attributable mostly to Evans. These methods will be applied to some of the examples of Chapter 1 and Ref. 1 in order to keep the presentation on familiar grounds. It should be emphasized that these methods are more than convenient mechanisms for analysis, although they are also that. Their principal usefulness is in the added insight that they provide.

2.2 Block Diagrams for Simple Systems

A block diagram is used to display information in an orderly and graphic manner. Probably the most useful form is the functional block diagram, in which each block is labeled with its transfer function. Recall that a transfer function is the ratio of the Laplace transform of one variable divided by the transform of another variable, without accounting for any initial conditions. Normally, the numerator of this ratio is the transform of the output of some system, and the denominator the transform of the input to the system.

Consider once again the simple one-degree-of-freedom, mass-spring-damper system, with a force applied to the mass (Fig. 2-1). A block diagram can be constructed for this problem as follows. First, let the input to the system be the force f, a function of time, and let the output be the deflection x, also a function of time. Let the tension in the spring be f_k and in the damper attachment f_c. Then the net force available for accelerating the mass is $f - f_c - f_k$. Therefore,

$$m \frac{d^2x}{dt^2} = f - f_c - f_k$$

or

$$ms^2 X = F - F_c - F_k$$

(2-1)

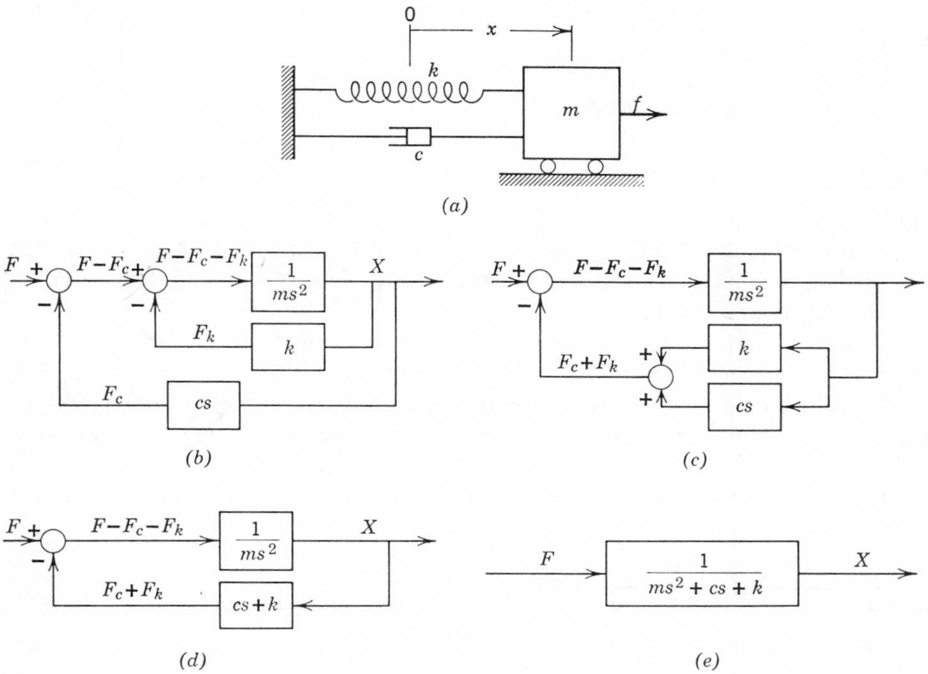

(a)

(b)

(c)

(d)

(e)

Fig. 2-1 Block diagram representation of mass-spring-damper system acted upon by a force.

where the capital letters indicate the Laplace transform of the corresponding lower-case variables and the initial-condition terms have been omitted. However, F_c and F_k also are functions of x. Since $f_c = c\,dx/dt$ and $f_k = kx$, then $F_c = csX$ and $F_k = kX$. Equation 2-1 and the foregoing facts are shown in block-diagram form in Fig. 2-1b, c, and d. Of course, Equation 2-1 could be solved to form

$$\frac{X}{F} = \frac{1}{ms^2 + cs + k}$$

and this is shown in block diagram form in Fig. 2-1e. The determination of transfer functions for typical control-systems elements is not included in this discussion, but the previous derivation shows how a transfer function is obtained from the differential equations governing the relationship between the input and output.

Several ideas are illustrated in Fig. 2-1. Each block is labeled with its transfer function. The input and output variables for each block are indicated, although sometimes not all intermediate variables are so shown. All connecting lines have arrowheads which designate the direction of the flow of information. At junction points signs are supplied which have the following significance: a plus sign means that at the summation point a variable does not have its sign changed, and if the sign is negative, the sign is changed in passing through the junction. A block diagram or section of a block diagram may be replaced with an equivalent diagram, as is evident from the various diagrams of Fig. 2-1.

Figure 2-2 represents a generalization of Fig. 2-1d. The functions G and H are both functions of s. G is a "forward transfer function" and H a "feedback transfer function." I is input and O output, actually the transforms of the input and output time-varying quantities. By inspection of Fig. 2-2 it is possible to write the following equation:

$$O = (I - HO)G$$

This is readily altered to Equation 2-2.

$$\frac{O}{I} = \frac{G}{1 + GH} \tag{2-2}$$

If Equation 2-2 is applied to Fig. 2-1d, the transfer function of Fig. 2-1e is obtained. Also, if Equation 2-2 is applied twice to Fig. 2-1b, once for the inner loop and then again for the outer loop, the transfer function of Fig. 2-1e is obtained. Equation 2-2 occurs frequently and should be remembered.

The phrases "open loop," "closed loop," "open-loop transfer function," and "closed-loop transfer function" are often encountered. With reference to Fig. 2-2, "open loop" means that the information from the feedback branch is interrupted, or opened, at the summation point, so that the system operates as if there were no feedback signal. "Closed loop" means that this feedback information *is* processed and used by elements of the system during operation. The "closed-loop transfer function"

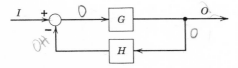

Fig. 2-2

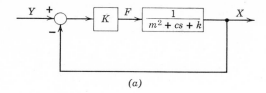

(a)

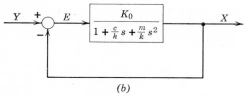

(b)

Fig. 2-3

is O/I of Fig. 2-2, or $G/(1 + GH)$. The "open-loop transfer function" is the transfer function around the loop, or GH. However, sometimes the phrase is used to describe the characteristics of the system if it operated open loop; that is, O/I for open loop, or simply G, the forward transfer function. The intended meaning must be determined from the context, if there is any question. If the feedback element H is unity, there is no difference in these two interpretations. Systems for which the feedback element is unity are designated as "unity-feedback" or "direct-feedback" systems, and usually the block for H is omitted, as in Fig. 2-3. If a block were used, it would be labeled with the transfer function 1.

It is usually the function of a control system to control the magnitude of some variable. For instance, suppose that in Fig. 2-1a the position of the mass is to be controlled, and the desired position, measured from the same zero as x, is designated y. Then let it be supposed that by some means not here specified the difference $(y - x)$ is sensed and a force proportional to this difference is generated. That is, $f = K(y - x)$ or $F = K(Y - X)$. This system could be represented by the block diagram of Fig. 2-3a or b. This is an example of a feedback control system utilizing direct feedback; that is, the feedback transfer function H is simply unity, and is therefore not shown in a separate block. The constant K_0 (equal to K/k) in the form shown in Fig. 2-3b is the "gain constant." (Any polynomials in s appearing in the transfer function are arranged so that the constant terms in the polynomials are unity.) The difference $(y - x)$ is the error e, or the transform $Y - X = E$, as labeled in Fig. 2-3b.

Figure 2-3b, therefore, represents a direct feedback control system in which the "controlled variable" is x, the "reference variable" is y, and the forward transfer function is

$$\frac{K_0}{1 + \dfrac{c}{k} s + \dfrac{m}{k} s^2}$$

or also

$$\frac{K_0}{1 + 2 \dfrac{\zeta}{\beta} s + \dfrac{s^2}{\beta^2}}$$

Application of Equation 2-2 to this system would yield

$$\frac{X}{Y} = \frac{\dfrac{K_0}{1 + K_0}}{1 + \dfrac{1}{1 + K_0}\dfrac{2\zeta}{\beta}s + \dfrac{1}{1 + K_0}\dfrac{s^2}{\beta^2}}$$

If $y(t)$ were the unit step function, for which $Y(s) = 1/s$, application of the final value theorem shows that x would be more nearly equal to the desired value y for large values of gain constant [$K_0/(1 + K_0)$ approaches unity]. However, increasing the gain constant also has an effect on the natural frequency of the system (increasing it) and on the damping factor (decreasing it), so that the transient response to an input is also affected by the gain constant.

2.3 Systems of Moderate Complexity

Figure 2-4 shows a standard form of a block diagram having more than one forward and feedback element and more than one input. The nomenclature used is conventional control system terminology wherein forward elements are designated by G, and feedback elements by H. The "controlled variable" is represented by C, and may be a position, velocity, temperature, or any other quantity whose value it is desired to regulate. The letter R is used to designate the "reference variable," which is often the desired value of the controlled variable. Another input, U, is an undesirable but unavoidable disturbance function. It is the function of the control system to provide good agreement between C and R, and also to suppress the effects of U. A desirable but unattainable goal would be to have $C/R = 1$ and $C/U = 0$. The quantities fed back are B_1 and B_2 in this diagram. In many systems H_1 may be unity so that B_1 is C. The variable E represents error, $R - B_1$ or $R - C$ if H_1 is unity, and the variable M represents an intermediate variable. While these are standard symbols, there is of course no need for us to be limited to these symbols, and symbols that are suggestive of the actual quantities involved in the control system may be used to improve the clarity of a specific block diagram.

A system may become more complicated and entangled than the system of Fig. 2-4. A slightly more complicated example is shown in Fig. 2-5a. It is usually necessary to modify the diagram before proceeding with the analysis. Although a set of rules

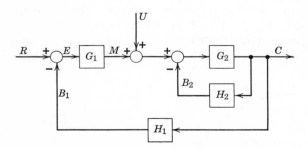

Fig. 2-4   Nomenclature for block diagrams.

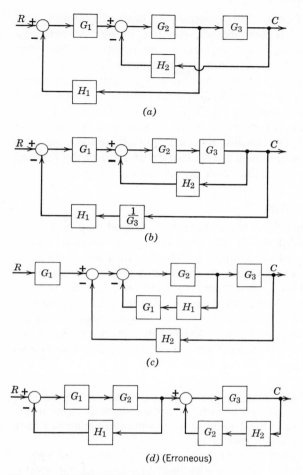

(a)

(b)

(c)

(d) (Erroneous)

Fig. 2-5   Simplification of block diagrams.

may be set up for different situations, it is probably better to make the modifications by application of logic rather than by rules, remembering that the block diagram is an organized presentation of information and that if a different but equivalent arrangement of elements is to be used, it must provide the same information as the original arrangement. Figure 2-5b shows one legitimate change in which the takeoff for the input to H_1 is moved "downstream" from G_3, resulting in an inner and outer loop, which is readily analyzed. In order to transfer the same input to G_1, however, another transfer function, $1/G_3$, had to be inserted in series with H_1. Figure 2-5c illustrates another legitimate modification—the modification being accomplished this time by moving a summing point. Here another transfer function, G_1, had to be inserted in series with H_1 in order to provide the same input to G_2 as the original diagram. Figure 2-5d shows an erroneous modification of Fig. 2-5a. Here the signal which is fed back through H_1 is not the same as for the original diagram.

One principle which may be of assistance in simplifying block diagrams is that takeoff points may be interchanged if they are not separated by blocks containing transfer functions (Fig. 2-5a to Fig. 2-5b), and summation points may be interchanged if they are not separated by blocks containing transfer functions (Fig. 2-5a to Fig. 2-5c), but a takeoff point and a summation point cannot be interchanged unless some other change is made to compensate for the different information in the takeoff branch. This was the source of the mistake in Fig. 2-5d. It is apparent from Fig. 2-5 that the designation of a function as a forward or feedback transfer function by the use of G or H does not require that the function be restricted to these uses. Manipulation of the block diagram may result in G in the feedback path or H in the forward path, and any function may appear more than once on the same diagram.

2.4 Block Diagram for Complex Systems

It often happens that the system whose block diagram is desired may be characterized by numerous simultaneous differential equations with a large amount of cross coupling between the variables. A block diagram or information flow diagram for such systems may be valuable for constructing an analogue computer simulation of the system, but may not be helpful for analysis purposes. Example 2-1, which follows, illustrates a means for obtaining a useful block diagram, with the necessary transfer functions, for the flexible missile of Example 1-2, a rather complex system with numerous cross-coupling effects. If the flexibility of the missile can be neglected, the diagram can be derived by means of logic as discussed in Section 2.3. This is also illustrated in the example.

Example 2-1. Construct a block diagram for the problem of Example 1-2. The guidance command signal, θ_g, is the reference variable. The attitude of the rigid-body centerline, θ, is the controlled variable. The purpose of the diagram is to present information in a form which is helpful in the selection of autopilot parameters.

It is possible to construct a block diagram from the equations of Example 1-2 without first modifying these equations. However, the resulting diagram is such an interlocking tangle of feedback and feedforward loops that simplification of the diagram by logic as described in Section 2.3 is extremely difficult, if not impossible, and a more systematic procedure is required. This will be described later in this example. If the missile were assumed to have a rigid body, the system could then be simplified by application of logic, and this will be done first. For this assumption the coordinates q_1, q_2, q_3 will not be used and the corresponding equations can be omitted. Then each of the other equations can be represented with subdiagrams (Fig. 2-6), after which they can be assembled to form an overall block diagram (Fig. 2-7). This diagram may then be simplified by the application of logic (Fig. 2-8). Once the system has been reduced to a block diagram of this sort, application of techniques to be described in subsequent chapters enables us to make a successful choice of parameters at our disposal (such as gain constants or sensing element location), or perhaps to introduce additional elements which will improve performance of the system. Accordingly, a simplified block diagram for the rigid missile is desired, from which the effect of choice of gain constants can be studied using techniques to be explained later. Development of this diagram follows.

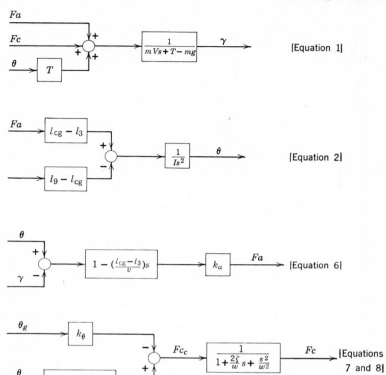

Fig. 2-6

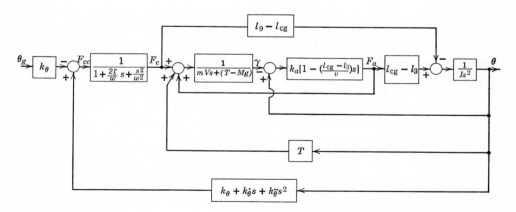

Fig. 2-7

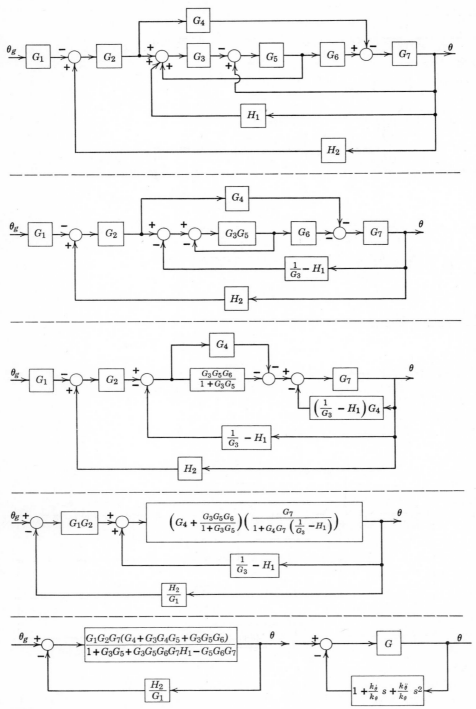

Fig. 2-8

$$G_1 = k_\theta$$

$$G_2 = \frac{1}{1 + \dfrac{2\zeta}{\omega}s + \dfrac{s^2}{\omega^2}} = \frac{1}{1 + 0.14s + 0.01s^2}$$

$$G_3 = \frac{1}{mVs + T - mg} = \frac{1}{1.5 \times 10^6 s + 33{,}900}$$

$$G_4 = l_9 - l_{\text{c.g.}} = 25$$

$$G_5 = k_a[1 - (l_{\text{c.g.}} - l_3)s] = 50{,}000(1 - 0.00475s)$$

$$G_6 = l_{\text{c.g.}} - l_3 = 14.3$$

$$G_7 = \frac{1}{Is^2} = \frac{1}{104{,}200s^2}$$

$$H_1 = 50{,}000$$

$$H_2 = k_\theta + k_{\dot\theta}s + k_{\ddot\theta}s^2$$

$$G = \frac{2.44 \times 10^{-4}k_\theta(1 + 13.33s)}{(1 + 0.14s + 0.01s^2)(1 + 0.374s)(1 - 0.389s)(1 - 93.0s)}$$

$$= \frac{0.0240k_\theta(s + 0.075)}{(s^2 + 14s + 100)(s + 2.67)(s - 2.57)(s - 0.0108)}$$

A method for simplifying the flexible body problem of Example 1-2 will now be described. We want to obtain a diagram somewhat similar to the final diagram just developed for the rigid-body problem, with the gain parameters segregated so that they may be selected later. The procedure will be illustrated with a smaller set of equations. Suppose that the following set of equations existed.

$$F_{11}(s)X_1 + F_{12}(s)X_2 + F_{13}(s)\theta = F_{14}(s)\theta_g$$

$$F_{21}(s)X_1 + F_{22}(s)X_2 + F_{23}(s)\theta = 0$$

$$F_{31}(s)X_1 + F_{32}(s)X_2 + F_{33}(s)\theta = 0$$

The first equation contains the various gain parameters which may be selected by the designer, analogous to Equation 7 of Example 1-2; the other two equations do not contain the gain parameters, analogous to the other equations of Example 1-2. Now the last two equations may be solved simultaneously to give X_1 and X_2 in terms of θ.

$$F_{21}X_1 + F_{22}X_2 = -F_{23}\theta$$

$$F_{31}X_1 + F_{32}X_2 = -F_{33}\theta$$

$$X_1 = \frac{\begin{vmatrix} -F_{23} & F_{22} \\ -F_{33} & F_{32} \end{vmatrix}}{\begin{vmatrix} F_{21} & F_{22} \\ F_{31} & F_{32} \end{vmatrix}}\theta \qquad X_2 = \frac{\begin{vmatrix} F_{21} & -F_{23} \\ F_{31} & -F_{33} \end{vmatrix}}{\begin{vmatrix} F_{21} & F_{22} \\ F_{31} & F_{32} \end{vmatrix}}\theta$$

If these were substituted in the first equation, the following equation would result.

$$F_{11}\begin{vmatrix} -F_{23} & F_{22} \\ -F_{33} & F_{32} \end{vmatrix}\theta + F_{12}\begin{vmatrix} F_{21} & -F_{23} \\ F_{31} & -F_{33} \end{vmatrix}\theta + F_{13}\begin{vmatrix} F_{21} & F_{22} \\ F_{31} & F_{32} \end{vmatrix}\theta = F_{14}\begin{vmatrix} F_{21} & F_{22} \\ F_{31} & F_{32} \end{vmatrix}\theta_g$$

The functions F_{11}, F_{12}, F_{13}, may contain the gain parameters, but at least one will not; for instance, in Equation 7 of Example 1-2 the function which multiplies f_{cc} does not contain k_θ, $k_{\dot\theta}$, or $k_{\ddot\theta}$. If all of the terms which contain the gain constants are moved to the right side of the equation, these terms can be considered the feedback elements in the block diagram. Suppose that F_{11} is a function not containing the gain constants. Then the previous equation could be written

$$\theta = \left\{(F_{14}\theta_g - F_{13}\theta)\begin{vmatrix} F_{21} & F_{22} \\ F_{31} & F_{32} \end{vmatrix} - F_{12}\begin{vmatrix} F_{21} & -F_{23} \\ F_{31} & -F_{33} \end{vmatrix}\theta\right\}\frac{1}{F_{11}\begin{vmatrix} -F_{23} & F_{22} \\ -F_{33} & F_{32} \end{vmatrix}}$$

The corresponding block diagram is illustrated by Fig. 2-9. In a more complicated problem, $|G_3|$ and $|H_2|$ could contain the sum of several determinants instead of just one.

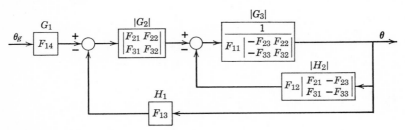

Fig. 2-9

In the original problem of Example 1-2 and this example, Row 7 contained the gain parameters, and Column 2 contained the functions which multiplied θ. Element 8 in Row 7 was the only nonzero element which did not contain the gain parameters. Therefore

$|G_2|$ = determinant formed from the original matrix if Column 2 and Row 7 are deleted.

$G_1 = k_\theta$

$$|G_3| = \frac{1}{-F_{78}|A|}$$

where $|A|$ is the determinant formed from the original matrix by first trading Columns 2 and 8 and then deleting Row 7 and Column 2

$F_{78} = -1$

$H_1 = k_\theta + k_{\dot\theta}s + k_{\ddot\theta}s^2$

$H_2 = (k_\theta + k_{\dot\theta}s + k_{\ddot\theta}s^2)(-F_{73}|B| - F_{74}|C| - F_{75}|D|)$

where $F_{73} = -\sigma_{21}$, $F_{74} = -\sigma_{22}$, $F_{75} = -\sigma_{23}$ from Example 1-2, and

$|B|$ is the determinant formed from the original matrix by trading Columns 2 and 3 and then deleting Row 7 and Column 2

$|C|$ is the determinant formed from the original matrix by trading Columns 2 and 4 and then deleting Row 7 and Column 2

$|D|$ is the determinant formed from the original matrix by trading Columns 2 and 5 and then deleting Row 7 and Column 2

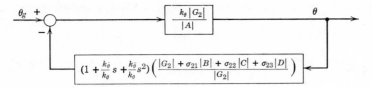

Fig. 2-10

The block diagram of Fig. 2-9 may be modified further to give that of Fig. 2-10. The determinants required may be obtained from $|G_2|$.

$$
|G_2| =
\begin{vmatrix}
mvs+T-mg & T\sigma_{91} & T\sigma_{92} & T\sigma_{93} & -1 & -1 & 0 \\[2ex]
0 & \begin{array}{c} -T\sigma_{91}(l_9-l_{c.g.}) \\ +T\dfrac{\partial y_9}{\partial q_1} \end{array} & \begin{array}{c} -T\sigma_{92}(l_9-l_{c.g.}) \\ +T\dfrac{\partial y_9}{\partial q_2} \end{array} & \begin{array}{c} -T\sigma_{93}(l_9-l_{c.g.}) \\ +T\dfrac{\partial y_9}{\partial q_3} \end{array} & (l_3-l_{c.g.}) & (l_9-l_{c.g.}) & 0 \\[3ex]
0 & \begin{array}{c} M_1s+C_1s \\ +K_1+\dfrac{\partial y_9}{\partial q_1}T\sigma_{91} \end{array} & \dfrac{\partial y_9}{\partial q_1}T\sigma_{92} & \dfrac{\partial y_9}{\partial q_1}T\sigma_{93} & -\dfrac{\partial y_3}{\partial q_1} & -\dfrac{\partial y_9}{\partial q_1} & 0 \\[3ex]
0 & \dfrac{\partial y_9}{\partial q_2}T\sigma_{91} & \begin{array}{c} M_2s+C_2s \\ +K_2+\dfrac{\partial y_9}{\partial q_2}T\sigma_{92} \end{array} & \dfrac{\partial y_9}{\partial q_2}T\sigma_{93} & -\dfrac{\partial y_3}{\partial q_2} & -\dfrac{\partial y_9}{\partial q_2} & 0 \\[3ex]
0 & \dfrac{\partial y_9}{\partial q_3}T\sigma_{91} & \dfrac{\partial y_9}{\partial q_3}T\sigma_{92} & \begin{array}{c} M_3s^2+C_3s \\ +K_3+\dfrac{\partial y_9}{\partial q_3}T\sigma_{93} \end{array} & -\dfrac{\partial y_3}{\partial q_3} & -\dfrac{\partial y_9}{\partial q_3} & 0 \\[3ex]
\begin{array}{c} -\dfrac{(l_{c.g.}-l_3)s}{v} \\ +1 \end{array} & \dfrac{\partial y_3}{\partial q_1}\dfrac{s}{v}+\sigma_{31} & \dfrac{\partial y_3}{\partial q_2}\dfrac{s}{v}+\sigma_{32} & \dfrac{\partial y_3}{\partial q_3}\dfrac{s}{v}+\sigma_{33} & \dfrac{1}{k_a} & 0 & 0 \\[3ex]
0 & 0 & 0 & 0 & 0 & \dfrac{s}{\omega}+\dfrac{2\zeta s}{\omega}+1 & -1
\end{vmatrix}
$$

$|A|$ is the same as $|G_2|$ except for Column 7 which should be replaced with the following column.

$$
\begin{matrix}
-T \\
Is^2 \\
0 \\
0 \\
0 \\
\left(\dfrac{l_{c.g.}-l_3}{V}s-1\right) \\
0
\end{matrix}
$$

$|B|$ is the same as $|G_2|$ except for Column 3, which should be replaced with the previous column.

$|C|$ is the same as $|G_2|$ except for Column 4, which should be replaced with the previous column.

$|D|$ is the same as $|G_2|$ except for Column 5, which should be replaced with the previous column.

When the numerical values of Example 1-2 are used for all values except the gain constants, using computer programs of the Appendix, the results shown in Fig. 2-11 are obtained.

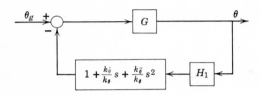

$$G = 2.27 \times 10^{-4}k_\theta \frac{\begin{array}{c}(1 + 13.16s)(1 + 0.234 \times 10^{-3}s + 0.372 \times 10^{-4}s^2)(1 + 0.495 \times 10^{-3}s \\ + 0.1466 \times 10^{-3}s^2)(1 + 0.1411 \times 10^{-2}s + 0.1201 \times 10^{-2}s^2)\end{array}}{\begin{array}{c}(1 + 0.374s)(1 - 0.386s)(1 - 93.6s)(1 + 0.236 \times 10^{-3}s + 0.370 \times 10^{-4}s^2) \\ \times (1 + 0.486 \times 10^{-3}s + 0.1457 + 10^{-3}s^2) \\ \times (1 + 0.1316 \times 10^{-2}s + 0.1122 \times 10^{-2}s^2)(1 + 0.14s + 0.01s^2)\end{array}}$$

$$H_1 = 0.997 \frac{\begin{array}{c}(1 + 13.44s)(1 - 0.0420s)(1 + 0.0435s)(1 - 0.1744 \times 10^{-1}s + 0.1190 \times 10^{-3}s^2) \\ \times (1 + 0.1784 \times 10^{-1}s + 0.1185 \times 10^{-3}s^2)\end{array}}{\begin{array}{c}(1 + 13.16s)(1 + 0.234 \times 10^{-3}s + 0.372 \times 10^{-4}s^2) \\ (1 + 0.495 \times 10^{-3}s + 0.1466 \times 10^{-3}s^2)(1 + 0.1411 \times 10^{-2}s + 0.1201 \times 10^{-2}s^2)\end{array}}$$

Fig. 2-11

CHAPTER 3

Complex Plane Plots and Nyquist Stability Criterion

3.1 Stability

A primary purpose of a control system is to maintain close correspondence between an output controlled variable and an input reference variable. This correspondence should be maintained not only in steady-state operation, but also during changes between steady-state conditions and changes caused by unavoidable disturbances. It is clear that this requirement cannot be satisfied unless the system is stable. Stability alone does not assure that the system will be satisfactory, but it will normally be unsatisfactory if the system is unstable. In terms of the closed-loop transfer function, this means that there must be no poles of C/R with positive real parts. For instance, if

$$\frac{C}{R} = \frac{6(s + 1)}{(s + 2)(s - 3)}$$

then there is a term in the inverse transform having the form e^{+3t}, which corresponds to the pole of C/R at $s = +3$. If

$$\frac{C}{R} = \frac{10(s + 1)}{(s + 3)(s^2 - 4s + 5)}$$

there is a term in the inverse transform having the form $e^{2t} \sin (t + \psi)$ corresponding to the two complex poles at $s = 2 + i$ and $s = 2 - i$ having the real part $+2$. Both of these transfer functions are unsatisfactory.

A transfer function,

$$\frac{C}{R} = \frac{2}{(s^2 + 1)(s + 2)}$$

possesses terms involving $\sin t$ and $\cos t$, corresponding to the poles on the imaginary axis. This is a borderline case, usually classified as unstable, but whether considered stable or unstable, it is unsatisfactory for a linear control system. (Nonlinear control systems may possess oscillatory terms and still be satisfactory if the amplitude of the oscillations is small.) A transfer function,

$$\frac{C}{R} = \frac{1}{s(1+s)}$$

possesses a pole at zero, also a borderline case, but whether this is satisfactory or not depends on the purpose of the control system. If the purpose is actually to control the rate of change of c, instead of c itself, this could represent a satisfactory system. Conceivably, even an unstable system could be satisfactory if the system is a subsystem of a more comprehensive system in which the instability of the subsystem is compensated.

Of course, if the denominator of C/R is known in factored form as in these examples, the question of stability can be settled by inspection. However, the factored form of C/R may not be easily obtained, or for other reasons it may be desirable to investigate the open-loop system to determine the stability of the closed-loop system. One way that this can be done is by application of the Nyquist criterion, which is most easily explained by use of a specific example.

3.2 The Nyquist Stability Criterion

Let it be required to investigate the stability of the system represented by Fig. 3-1 if

$$G = \frac{200}{s(1+10s)} \quad \text{and} \quad H = \frac{1}{1+2s}$$

It is recalled that the transfer function C/R is

$$\frac{C}{R} = \frac{G}{1+GH}$$

The system will be stable if the values of s for which $1 + GH = 0$ all have negative real parts (since the zeros of $(1 + GH)$ are also poles of C/R or the roots of the characteristic equation). Notice that it would be possible for this to be determined by substitution of G and H into this equation to obtain

$$\frac{C}{R} = \frac{1+2s}{1+0.005s+0.06s^2+0.1s^3}$$

and then solving the characteristic equation $1 + 0.005s + 0.06s^2 + 0.1s^3 = 0$ for its roots, which are $s = -2.37$, $s = 0.88 + 1.86i$, and $s = 0.88 - 1.86i$. These are the zeros of $(1 + GH)$ and also the roots of the characteristic equation, and it is seen that the complex roots have positive real parts. The denominator in factored form is $(1 + 0.422s)(1 - 0.417s + 0.236s^2)$. It is evident that the complex roots

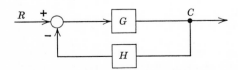

Fig. 3-1

represent a diverging oscillation for this system. However, it is desirable to determine whether this system is stable by consideration of only the open-loop transfer function,

$$GH = \frac{200}{s(1 + 2s)(1 + 10s)}$$

It is desired to determine if there is one or more zeros of $1 + GH$ in the right half of the complex plane for s. This can be done by letting s assume values which will enclose the right half plane and then observing what a plot of $(1 + GH)$ does for these values of s. This is essentially an application of the idea of conformal transformations, or mapping of a complex variable. In most applications the fact that there are unstable roots* of the characteristic equation would not be known in advance, but for purposes of explanation it is now assumed that there are two such zeros of $1 + GH$, at $s = 0.88 + 1.86i$ and $s = 0.88 - 1.86i$, as has already been shown. Therefore, if a path is chosen for the variation of s in $1 + GH$ so that the entire right half plane is enclosed, this path will encircle these two zeros.

Except for a slight complication at $s = 0$, which will be discussed shortly, a path for which s varies from $-i\infty$ to $+i\infty$ along the imaginary axis and then back to $-i\infty$ along a semicircle of infinite radius, as indicated in Fig. 3-2 would enclose the entire right half plane and any zeros located therein. A complex plane plot of $(1 + GH)$ for this variation of s is therefore required. However, the point $s = 0$ will have to be avoided, because at this point GH becomes infinite. This point may be avoided by circling around it to the right as indicated in Fig. 3-2b, or it could as well be avoided by going around to the left, with a slight change in the subsequent analysis, as will be described later.

Effect of Poles or Zeros on the Complex Plane Plot. Now an observation must be made establishing the effect of a pole or zero on the complex plane plot of GH. There is a

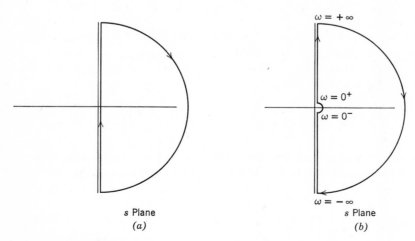

s Plane
(a)

$\omega = +\infty$

$\omega = 0^+$
$\omega = 0^-$

$\omega = -\infty$
s Plane
(b)

Fig. 3-2   Variation of s.

* Technically, it is the system which is unstable, not the roots. The term "unstable roots" is a convenient abbreviation.

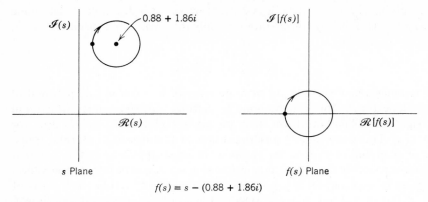

$$f(s) = s - (0.88 + 1.86i)$$

Fig. 3-3   Mapping between s and $f(s)$ for a simple function.

zero of $(1 + GH)$ at $0.88 + 1.86i$. If a plot of just the expression $s - (0.88 + 1.86i)$ were made for s varying so as to follow a path which describes a circle around $(0.88 + 1.86i)$ as a center, then it is apparent, or easily verified, that a plot of $s - (0.88 + 1.86i)$ would describe a circle about the origin as center (Fig. 3-3), the generation of this image circle proceeding in the same direction as s along its path. That is, if the path which s follows in circling around $(0.88 + 1.86i)$ is clockwise, then the quantity $s - (0.88 + 1.86i)$ will follow a clockwise path about the origin. However, if the function were

$$\frac{1}{s - (0.88 + 1.86i)}$$

instead of $s - (0.88 + 1.86i)$, the image circle would rotate in the opposite direction to the path of s. (The radius of the circle would also be different, but this is unimportant to the discussion.)

Now it is possible to appreciate that even if the path followed by s is not a circle, but a path of any shape that makes one rotation about this point, the plot of $s - (0.88 + 1.86i)$ also makes one rotation about the origin in the same direction (but not a circular plot), and the plot of

$$\frac{1}{s - (0.88 + 1.86i)}$$

makes one rotation in the opposite direction about the origin. Also, if the path for s does not encircle the point $(0.88 + 1.86i)$, the plots of $s - (0.88 + 1.86i)$ or

$$\frac{1}{s - (0.88 + 1.86i)}$$

do not encircle the origin. All of these conclusions follow without difficulty from the multiplication or division of complex numbers in their polar form.

The next extension of this idea is that the presence of other factors does not affect the number of rotations if only one zero or pole is enclosed by the path for s. That is, a plot of $[s - (0.88 + 1.86i)][s - (0.88 - 1.86i)]$ also rotates clockwise about the origin once if the path for s encloses only the one zero at $0.88 + 1.86i$. (A plot of

$$\frac{1}{[s + (0.88 + 1.86i)][s - (0.88 - 1.86i)]}$$

would rotate about the origin in the opposite direction.)

Finally, if more than one pole or zero were enclosed by the path describing the variation of s, the plot of the function would rotate about the origin once for each pole or zero, in the same direction for zeros and in the opposite direction for poles. Therefore, if Z is the number of zeros and P the number of poles of the function, $(1 + GH)$, enclosed by the path for s, then the number of rotations, R, of $(1 + GH)$ about the origin would be given by the equation

$$R = Z - P$$

or

$$Z = R + P$$

$$\left.\begin{array}{c} \\ \\ \\ \end{array}\right\} \quad (3\text{-}1)$$

Interpretation for Stability. In Equation 3-1, the path for s is shown in Fig. 3-2b; that is, clockwise about the right half plane, and R is the number of rotations of $(1 + GH)$ about the origin in the clockwise direction. Both Z and P are counted according to the order of the zero or pole. For instance, if

$$GH = \frac{(1 + s)}{(1 - 2s)^2(1 - 3s)(1 + 4s)}$$

P would be 3 rather than 2, even though there are only two poles in the right half plane.

If GH is in factored form, as is usual for this type of analysis, the P can be determined by inspection, since a pole of GH is also a pole of $1 + GH$. However, Z in Equation 3-1 (zeros of $1 + GH$) cannot be determined by inspection of the factored form of GH, but the number of zeros of $1 + GH$ which are located in the right half plane can be obtained from Equation 3-1. Since the zeros of $1 + GH$ are the poles of C/R, the system is stable only if there are no zeros of $1 + GH$ in the right half plane; that is, if $Z = 0$ from Equation 3-1.

It is customary to plot just GH rather than $1 + GH$. The plot of GH is displaced one unit to the left from the plot of $1 + GH$, so the only difference is that R in Equation 3-1 is also the number of rotations of a plot of GH about the -1 point in the clockwise direction.

Typical Complex Plane Plot. It is now possible to return to the investigation of the specific function which was being investigated,

$$GH = \frac{200}{s(1 + 2s)(1 + 10s)}$$

If $s = i\omega$ and ω varies from $-\infty$ to $+\infty$, except for the very small region around $s = 0$, then this would account for the left boundary of Fig. 3-2b. It is clear that as s varies along the circle of infinite radius, GH will be zero, so this portion of the plot of GH is not important. This will be true for any function for which the denominator of GH is of higher order than the numerator, which is true for many problems of practical

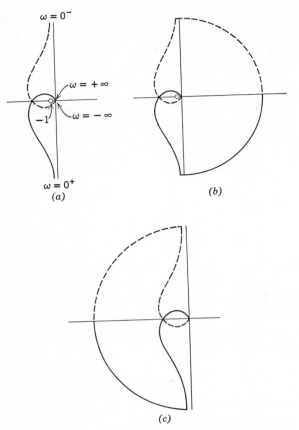

Fig. 3-4   Variation of GH as s varies according to Fig. 3-2.

interest. For this problem, then, only the small semicircle and the variation of s from $-i\infty$ to $+i\infty$ along the imaginary axis is of interest.

Let $s = i\omega$ and let ω start at 0^+ and increase to $+\infty$. Because of the s in the denominator, which has the dominant effect for ω near zero, the plot of GH for ω near 0^+ starts out at $-i\infty$. Then as ω increases, the terms $(1 + 10i\omega)$ and $(1 + 2i\omega)$ in the denominator deflect the plot of GH in the clockwise direction as the magnitude of GH decreases. A sketch of the portion of GH as ω varies from 0^+ to $+\infty$ would look like the solid portion of Fig. 3-4a.* The dotted portion of Fig. 3-4a corresponds to the variation of ω from $-\infty$ to 0^-, and is the reflection of the solid portion about the real axis. It only remains to determine how the plot of GH varies when s is in the neighborhood of zero. If reference is made to Fig. 3-4b, it is seen that the path for s is a semicircle of infinitesimal radius in the neighborhood of $s = 0$ in order to avoid the pole itself. The pole at $s = 0$ is thus excluded from the plot. As s varies around this semicircle, GH varies approximately as $200/s$, which is then a semicircle of infinite

---

* The sketch is not to scale and only indicates approximate characteristics. For instance, although the angle of GH approaches $-90°$ as ω approaches 0^+, the curve for GH does not reach the imaginary axis as an asymptote. (See Problem 3-3.)

radius; but since the s is in the denominator here, the plot of GH swings around clockwise on the infinite radius as the plot of s swings around counterclockwise on the infinitesimal radius. Therefore, the complete plot of GH is similar to that of Fig. 3-4b. Sometimes the dotted portions are omitted, since they are the reflection of the solid portions. It is seen that there are two clockwise rotations of the plot of GH about the -1 point, so $R = 2$ in Equation 3-1. Since the pole at $s = 0$ was not enclosed by the path chosen, and the other poles of GH are in the negative half plane, $P = 0$. From Equation 3-1, $Z = R + P = 2$, so there are two zeros of $1 + GH$ in the right half plane and the closed-loop system is unstable, as was already known for this function. If the path for s had gone to the left of the pole at $s = 0$ instead of to the right, the plot of GH would have looked like Fig. 3-4c, and there would have been only one clockwise encirclement of the -1 point (net), so that R would have been 1. However, for this case the pole at $s = 0$ would have been encircled by the path so that $P = 1$, and $Z = P + R = 2$, leading to the same conclusion.

3.3 Additional Remarks

We have completed the discussion of the Nyquist stability criterion, except to point out that the actual plot may not be necessary. The concept is often useful even if the plot itself is not constructed. Also, even if the system is stable, the proximity of the plot of GH to the -1 point is an indication of the dynamic characteristics of the system. It is often possible to improve a control system by modifying its transfer function so that the complex plane plot will be favorably affected. Discussion of such modifications may be found in subsequent chapters.

CHAPTER 4

Frequency Response

4.1 Preliminary Comments

The complex plane plot described in Chapter 3 is useful because it provides a means for understanding factors affecting the stability of the system and its performance when subjected to transient inputs. Often it is unnecessary to make these plots to scale, and a sketch of the approximate plot is usually sufficient for this general understanding, but other methods may be more useful for an actual analysis. The frequency-response method of analysis described in this chapter provides insight into factors which affect the system performance and in addition is convenient for numerical computations.

In the usual application, the system is a direct feedback system, the open-loop transfer function (which is also the forward transfer function) is available in its factored form, and there are no zeros or poles of this function in the right half plane. These are conditions which are often satisfied, but even when they are not, the frequency response plot may be of assistance when used in conjunction with a complex plane sketch. In addition, it is useful in the "describing function" method of analysis of nonlinear systems. Accordingly, an understanding of the frequency-response method of analysis is essential to an understanding of the performance of linear systems and factors affecting the vibration of linear systems.

4.2 System Type, Phase Margin, Gain Margin

System Type. For many direct feedback systems, there are no poles or zeros of G in the right half plane. That is, the forward transfer function is of the form

$$G = \frac{K(1 + T_a s)(1 + T_b s)\cdots\left[1 + \dfrac{2\zeta_a}{\beta_a}s + \dfrac{s^2}{\beta_a{}^2}\right]\left[1 + \dfrac{2\zeta_b}{\beta_b}s + \dfrac{s^2}{\beta_b{}^2}\right]\cdots}{s^n(1 + T_1 s)(1 + T_2 s)(1 + T_3 s)\cdots\left[1 + \dfrac{2\zeta_1}{\beta_1}s + \dfrac{s^2}{\beta_1{}^2}\right]\left[1 + \dfrac{2\zeta_2}{\beta_2}s + \dfrac{s^2}{\beta_2{}^2}\right]\cdots}$$

(4-1)

where all the time constants and damping factors are positive or zero. Then all poles and zeros of G would be located in the left half plane, on the imaginary axis, or at $s = 0$. The "type" of system is determined by the value of the integer n, which could be 0, 1, 2, or, possibly, other values. For functions having this form, P in the Nyquist criterion is zero (the path for s is selected to exclude poles located on the imaginary axis), so stability depends on whether there are clockwise encirclements of -1 when G is plotted as s varies along the imaginary axis. Accordingly, the angle of G for the condition $|G| = 1$ will tell whether the system is stable.

Phase Margin. Figure 4-1 shows a plot of a typical G for a Type 1 system. In this plot ϕ is the phase angle of G for a general point, and ϕ_0 is the phase angle at the point where the plot crosses the unit circle. If ϕ_0 is greater than 180 degrees, the closed-loop system is stable. If ϕ_0 is less than 180 degrees, the -1 point is encircled and the system is unstable. Consequently, the difference between ϕ and 180 degrees is of significance, and is called the "phase margin." The difference at the point where the plot crosses the unit circle is also called "Phase Margin," so confusion may exist, and the meaning of the term may have to be determined from the context. Thus Φ is the phase margin at a general point and Φ_0 is the Phase Margin. The Phase Margin, Φ_0, must be positive for a stable system and should be 45 degrees or more for a "good" system. The nearer the phase margin gets to zero, the more oscillatory is the system.

Gain Margin. Another criterion, "Gain Margin," is the factor by which the gain constant could be increased (multiplied) in order to cause the complex plane plot of G

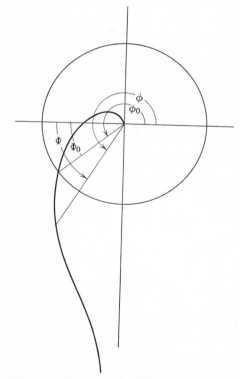

Fig. 4-1   Plot of G for typical Type 1 system.

to pass through -1. In a typical "good" control system this might be approximately 5, or more, but it could be as low as 2 for some systems.

4.3 Bode Plots

Bode showed that the phase angle of G could be related to the rate at which the magnitude of G decreases with increasing frequency. This leads to the method of analysis, called "frequency response," which is to be described in this section. In this method, the magnitude of G in decibels and the phase angle, or else phase margin, are plotted on semilog paper as functions of the frequency ω (plotted on the log scale) when $i\omega$ is substituted for s in G. The value of $|G|$ in decibels can be found from the numeric value of $|G|$ by the following equation.

$$|G|_{db} = 20 \log_{10} |G|_{numeric} \qquad (4\text{-}2)$$

For much preliminary work and for estimation of compensating networks (transfer functions to introduce into a system to insure stability or improve performance), it is often possible to omit the phase angle plot and to make use of an approximate attenuation plot (or plot of $|G|$). Exact plots should be used as a final check after selection of the proposed stabilizing transfer functions, however. The method of drawing the approximate attenuation plot will now be described.

Approximate Attenuation Plot. On the semilog plot of $|G|$ versus ω, if G were a constant as ω changed, the plot would simply be a horizontal line, as in Fig. 4-2, line a, for which $G = 20$, or 26 db. If G were a function such as $30/s$, it is easily verified that the plot of $|G|$ in decibels when $i\omega$ is substituted for s is a straight line on semilog paper, as indicated by line b. The magnitude of G changes at the rate of -20 decibels per decade for this function and for any function of the form K/s. The value of K merely shifts the curve vertically on the plot. Note that an easy way to determine a starting point for drawing such a line is to determine the value of ω for which $|G| = 1$, which is the same as zero decibels. For the function $30/s$ this would occur at $\omega = 30$, so the plot of $|30/s|$ would pass through the zero decibels line at $\omega = 30$. Similarly, the function $|16/s^2|$ would pass through the zero-decibels line at $\omega = 4$ with a slope of -40 db per decade, and other functions of the form Ks^n or K/s^n could easily be constructed by using a slope of $+20n$ for functions of the form Ks^n and $-20n$ for functions of the form K/s^n.*

It is now possible to see how the magnitude of G varies for functions having the form $K/(1 + Ts)$. For example, let

$$G = \frac{5}{1 + 0.2s}$$

or more conveniently,

$$G = \frac{5}{1 + \dfrac{s}{5}}$$

If $i\omega$ is substituted for s and the absolute value of the resulting complex number is taken, it is easily verified that as long as the ratio of $\omega/5$ is less than 1 the absolute

---

* The phrase -20 decibels per decade may be misleading. If a frequency ratio of 5 is considered to be a half-decade, this phrase implies a change of 10 decibels, but reference to a semilog plot will verify that such a conclusion is erroneous.

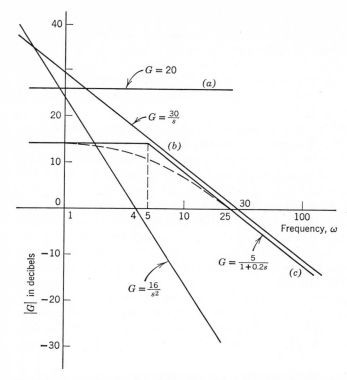

Fig. 4-2 Approximate attenuation plots for various transfer functions.

value of G is not much affected by ω, the number 1 being the dominant term in the denominator. Then when $\omega/5$ becomes greater than 1, it becomes the dominant term in the denominator. Therefore, the approximate straight-line attenuation plot of $G = 5/(1 + 0.2s)$ will be composed of the horizontal line at 14 db for $\omega < 5$, and for $\omega > 5$ the straight line corresponding to $G = 5/0.2s$, which crosses the zero-decibel line at $\omega = 25$ with -20 db per decade slope. This is line c on Fig. 4-2. The true magnitude curve differs slightly from this approximate curve in the frequency range near 5, approaching the straight-line asymptotes on either side of $\omega = 5$ as indicated by the dotted line on Fig. 4-2. More complicated functions of the form given by Equation 4-1 are easily plotted. At every ω for which $T\omega$ is unity, there is an upward or downward break of the approximate straight-line curve of 20 db per decade, depending upon whether the term is in the numerator or denominator. At every ω for which ω/β is unity in a quadratic factor, there is an upward or downward break of 40 db per decade, also depending on whether the term is in the numerator or denominator. A 40 db per decade change in slope also occurs at points where $T\omega = 1$ in factors of the form

$$(1 + Ts)^2 \qquad \text{or} \qquad \frac{1}{(1 + Ts)^2}$$

which are also equivalent to quadratic factors having $\zeta = 1$.

Exact Attenuation Plot. After the approximate straight-line diagram has been drawn, the exact curve can be formed, if desired, by correcting the approximate curve for each factor. These corrections are additive, of course, although in many instances the breaks are far enough apart so that the correction at a specific frequency is due primarily to only one of the factors, the one corresponding to the nearest break. The corrections can most easily be accomplished by overlaying the appropriate curves of Appendix II.

Phase Angle Plot. The phase angle or phase margin curve may also be constructed with the use of auxiliary curves, Appendix II. In order to use either the phase angle or attenuation curves of Appendix II, it is necessary to use graph paper having the same scales. Then the corrections for each of the factors can be determined by successively aligning the break points with the $\omega/\omega_0 = 1$ point of the appropriate correction curve. When the process has been completed, a good picture of the variation of G throughout the frequency range is provided, including the important region near zero decibels on the attenuation plot, from which the question of stability may be settled by reference to the phase angle curve. After the open-loop frequency response curves of G have been determined, it is possible to obtain the closed-loop frequency response, $G/(1 + G)$, by means to be described later.

However, the principal advantage of the frequency response method of analysis is that it makes it possible to determine easily what must be done to improve the dynamic characteristics of the system. This will be illustrated with an example later, but first the significance of the gain constant and of the slope of the approximate attenuation curve should be appreciated.

Significance of the Gain Constant. Usually the forward transfer function, G, is determined by elements in the system over which the designer has only partial control. He may not be able to choose an ideal function. However, for purposes of discussion let it be assumed that any desired function could be used for the forward transfer function in a direct feedback system. Consider the function, $G = K/s$. For this function the attenuation curve has a slope of -20 db per decade and crosses zero decibels at $\omega = K$. From

$$\frac{C}{R} = \frac{G}{1 + G} = \frac{1}{1 + \dfrac{s}{K}}$$

$$C = R\left(\frac{1}{1 + \dfrac{s}{K}}\right)$$

Now if $r = \sin \omega t$ or $R = \dfrac{\omega}{s^2 + \omega^2}$

$$C = \frac{\omega}{s^2 + \omega^2}\left(\frac{1}{1 + \dfrac{s}{K}}\right)$$

If the inverse transform of this function were taken, there would be one term which would damp out corresponding to the $[1 + (s/K)]$ term in the denominator, and another term corresponding to the quadratic factor $(s^2 + \omega^2)$, which would not damp out. It is clear that the frequency response plots which have been described (either closed-loop or open-loop) are just the steady-state phase and magnitude of the output if the input is varied sinusoidally. Hence, the name "frequency response" implies the response of a system to a sinusoidal input of various frequencies. For

$$G = \frac{K}{s} \quad \text{and} \quad \frac{C}{R} = \frac{1}{1 + \dfrac{s}{K}}$$

it is clear that the magnitude of c would be nearly equal to the magnitude of r for $\omega < k$, but for higher frequencies the system could not follow the input. The frequency at which the plot of G crosses zero decibels is thus the frequency at which the system begins to fail to function properly. This frequency is higher for larger values of gain constant, K, which means that if such systems were required to follow accurately a rapidly changing input, they should have a large value of gain constant.

Another way of seeing this is to consider the transient response if the input or reference value is suddenly changed by one unit. That is, let $r = u(t)$ (the unit function), for which $R = 1/s$. Then the inverse transform is

$$c = \mathscr{L}^{-1}\left[\frac{1}{s\left(1 + \dfrac{s}{K}\right)}\right] = 1 - e^{-Kt}$$

This shows that the value of the controlled variable, or output, approaches the value of the input reference asymptotically without overshoot, and the time required to reach some arbitrary percentage of the final value is less for higher gain constants, which again implies that for rapidly changing inputs, high gain constants are required. However, high gain constants often lead to stability problems, although this is not true of the transfer functions under discussion at present. It is noted that the phase angle for the frequency response plot of K/s is -90 degrees for all values of ω, including the value for which the attenuation curve crosses zero decibels. Therefore, the Phase Margin is $+90$ degrees.

Significance of Attenuation Curve Slope. Next, suppose that the forward transfer function, G, were of the form K/s^2, for which the attenuation curve decreases at the rate of 40 db per decade. For this function

$$\frac{C}{R} = \frac{G}{1 + G} = \frac{1}{1 + \dfrac{s^2}{K}}$$

The frequency response plot of this function goes to infinity at $\omega^2 = K$. Also, the phase angle of G is 180 degrees for all frequencies, including that for which the curve of $|G|$ crosses zero decibels, so that the Phase Margin is zero.

If R is $1/s$, corresponding to the unit step function, the transient response of the closed-loop system becomes $C = 1 - \cos \sqrt{K}\,t$, which oscillates without damping between the limits of 0 and 2. It is apparent that this type of function, having -40 db per decade slope at zero decibels, is the borderline case of instability. If the forward transfer function were $G = K/s^3$, with a slope of -60 db/decade, the Phase Margin would be -90 degrees, and the closed-loop system would be dynamically unstable, as is evident from

$$\frac{C}{R} = \frac{G}{1+G} = \frac{K}{s^3 + K} = \frac{K}{(s + K^{1/3})(s^2 - K^{1/3}s + K^{2/3})}$$

It appears that as a general rule the approximate attenuation plot should cross the zero-decibel line with a slope of -20 db per decade in order for satisfactory dynamic characteristics to exist. In general, if this slope is maintained for the interval from $+12$ to -12 db, the system characteristics will be satisfactory, although if extremely large negative slopes (over 80 db/decade) exist just outside this region, or for other unusual exceptions, stability difficulty might be encountered. This criterion greatly facilitates the determination of the necessary stabilizing transfer functions.

Nichols Chart. After the exact attenuation plot and the phase angle plot for G have been determined, it is possible to obtain the closed-loop frequency response plots (phase and magnitude) by use of the Nichols chart, Appendix II. Its use is illustrated in Example 4-1.

4.4 Internal Feedback

Although the method of analysis described is directly applicable only to unity feedback systems, it is also useful in systems having frequency dependent feedback transfer functions and systems with internal feedback loops. For such systems it is possible to consider the transfer function of a closed-loop portion as

$$\frac{G}{1+GH} \quad \text{or} \quad \frac{O}{I} = \frac{1}{H}\frac{GH}{1+GH} \tag{4-3}$$

In this equation O/I could be C/R if H is the outer feedback function, or it could be an interior transfer function. Note that $GH/(1 + GH)$ is like a direct feedback system $G/(1 + G)$ where the GH replaces G. Therefore, the Nichols chart may be used to evaluate this quantity. Also, note that if $|GH| \gg 1$, O/I is practically $1/H$, and if $|GH| \ll 1$, O/I is practically G. It is often useful to extend these approximations to the boundary and say that if $|GH| > 1$, $O/I = 1/H$, and if $|GH| < 1$, $O/I = G$. For these approximations, the absolute value of O/I at any particular frequency would be the lesser of the two quantities $|G|$ or $|1/H|$. This concept makes it possible to determine quickly a satisfactory internal feedback transfer function for improving the performance of a direct feedback system. However, the approximation is not valid for $|GH|$ near unity and is also misleading if the function $GH/(1 + GH)$ describes an unstable or nearly unstable system as demonstrated in the example which follows. This example also illustrates the material in the earlier sections of this chapter as well as the use of internal feedback.

Example 4-1. In a direct feedback system the forward transfer function is

$$G = \frac{100(1 + 0.5s)}{s(1 + 2s)(1 + 0.04s + 0.01s^2)}$$

Use this transfer function to illustrate the frequency response method of analysis and suggest ways to improve the system. Most of the analysis will refer to the use of internal feedback as indicated in Fig. 4-3, although the discussion will begin with "series" or "cascade"

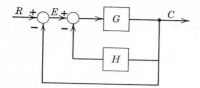

Fig. 4-3

methods of compensation; that is, elements inserted into the forward circuit in order to favorably affect G.

First, construct an approximate straight-line attenuation plot for G (Fig. 4-4). For values of frequency less than 0.5 this plot is the same as for $100/s$, which would intersect the zero decibel line at $\omega = 100$. However, the factor $1/(1 + 2s)$ becomes effective for values of ω greater than 0.5, so that the slope from 0.5 to 2 is -40 db per decade. Then for ω between 2 and 10, the slope returns to -20 db per decade, and above 10 the slope is -60 db per decade because of the term $0.01s^2$ in the quadratic factor. Only the portions of this plot between $+30$ and -30 db are needed, although the frequencies of the break points out of range of the graph paper should be noted for later construction of exact curves.

It is noted that this approximate attenuation plot has a slope of -60 db per decade in the region of zero decibels (Fig. 4-4), so it would be expected that the system would be unstable. Several ways of remedying this suggest themselves immediately. The gain constant could be reduced from 100 to about 10, which would have the effect of translating the entire curve downward about 20 db, causing zero crossover to occur in a region for which the slope is -20 db per decade. As will be seen later, this would result in a Phase Margin at zero crossover of about 60 degrees, which is satisfactory. However, the Gain Margin would be only about 3 db, indicating trouble since this should not be less than 6 db (numeric factor of 2), so the gain should probably be reduced a little more than 20 db.

Even if this 20 db reduction in gain would provide satisfactory dynamic characteristics, it might be that the loss of steady-state accuracy resulting from the reduced gain would be undesirable. One way to reduce the gain in the high-frequency region without changing the gain constant would be the insertion of a "lag network" in the forward circuit. That is, a transfer function such as $(1 + 2s)/(1 + 20s)$ in series with G would produce a 20 db downward displacement of the approximate curve for frequencies greater than $\omega = 0.5$ without changing the gain constant. However, for frequencies between 0.05 and 0.5, the curve would be steeper than at present, which would probably mean that this correction would produce a system dynamically somewhat worse than the straight gain change of 20 db. A check of this (not shown here) reveals that the Phase Margin at zero crossover would be about 49 degrees, still apparently satisfactory although the Gain Margin is still too low, and a check on the Nichols plot indicates that the time constants of the lag network should be altered to provide about 22 db gain reduction instead of 20 db.

The above lag network could be made into a "lag-lead network" by using the function

$$\frac{1 + 2s}{1 + 20s} \quad \frac{1 + 0.1s}{1 + 0.01s}$$

which would reduce the steepness of the slope for ω between 10 and 100 and probably help considerably in correcting the dynamic characteristics, although a gain increase might be necessary. Other functions could be used in series with G, the principal objective being to achieve -20 db per decade for the region between approximately $+12$ and -12 db.

The significance of the words "lag" or "lead" is in the effect on the phase angle of G. A lag network causes $\underline{/G}$ to become more negative while a lead network increases the

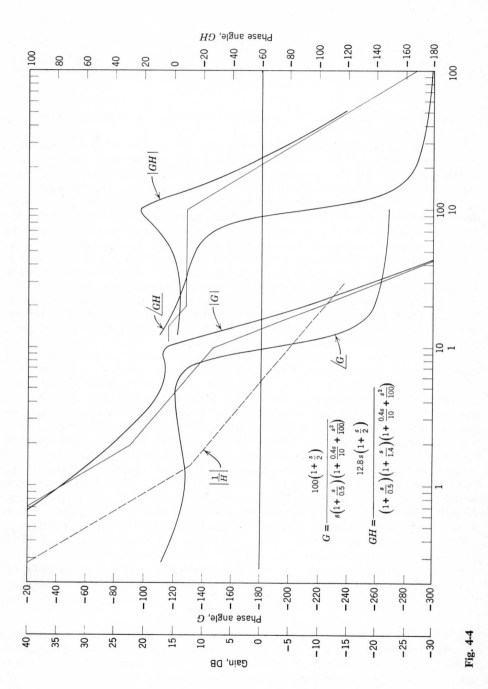

$$G = \frac{100\left(1 + \frac{s}{2}\right)}{s\left(1 + \frac{s}{0.5}\right)\left(1 + \frac{0.4s}{10} + \frac{s^2}{100}\right)}$$

$$GH = \frac{12.8s\left(1 + \frac{s}{2}\right)}{\left(1 + \frac{s}{0.5}\right)\left(1 + \frac{s}{1.4}\right)\left(1 + \frac{0.4s}{10} + \frac{s^2}{100}\right)}$$

Fig. 4-4

84

angle. Numerator factors in a transfer function have a leading effect and denominator factors a lagging effect.

However, in order to illustrate a different point, the method of stabilization chosen for further investigation is that of internal feedback. That is, the forward transfer function will be modified by an internal feedback loop (Fig. 4-3). This can be done by drawing a satisfactory straight-line attenuation plot and obtaining an expression for H from this plot. In this case, a plot of $1/H$ which intersects the plot of G at approximately -12 db and has a slope of -20 db/decade between $+12$ and -12 db would suggest the following function for H (shown dashed in Fig. 4-4 as $1/H$).

$$H = \frac{0.128s^2}{1 + 0.715s}$$

Of course these constants could be rounded off with little effect, but they will be retained as shown at least until the end of the analysis.

One possible way to proceed with the analysis would be to determine a new forward transfer function which would produce the lower of the approximate curves for $1/H$ or G at all frequencies. Such a transfer function would be

$$G_{\text{approx.}} = \frac{100(1 + 0.715s)}{s(1 + 12.5s)(1 + 0.046s)^2}$$

which yields the straight line approximations of $1/H$ for frequencies between 0.08 and 22 rad/sec, and G outside this range. The Phase Margin for such a function could be shown to be 47 degrees at zero crossover, indicating satisfactory dynamic characteristics. However, this is only approximately correct, and a final check using exact methods would normally be required. This final check is now described.

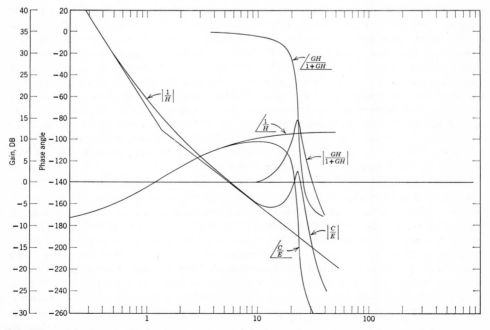

Fig. 4-5

First the exact attenuation diagram and the exact phase angle curve for *GH* and 1/*H* must be drawn (Figs. 4-4 and 4-5). Although not really needed, an exact plot of magnitude and angle for *G* is drawn in order to check the performance of the system with no stabilizing measures (Fig. 4-4). These curves may be obtained rapidly with the aid of the charts in Appendix II. These charts are drawn to the scale of 10 db to the inch for the linear scale and 2.5 in. per cycle for the log scale. If graph paper of the same scale is used, these charts can be used as overlays, shortening the labor involved. By turning the charts over or inverting them, or both, it should be possible to find a function which would match the asymptotes for each break point for linear or quadratic factors in the numerator or denominator. Also, a correction curve is provided, by which the approximate straight-line diagram could be corrected if this is more convenient. To use these curves it is necessary to overlay the appropriate figure with the sheet on which the frequency response is being plotted, aligning a break point with the center line of the figure. A correction must be made at all frequencies for each factor in the function, using the corresponding break points one after another. However, usually only one, or perhaps two, of the factors will contribute a significant correction to the magnitude plot at any particular frequency. The correction to the phase angle is more noticeable at frequencies remote from the break-point frequency, so that this plot often requires the superposition of several corrections at any particular frequency. Although a plot over the entire frequency spectrum is often desirable in order to obtain a complete picture, the important portion of the plot is in the range of frequencies near zero decibels for whichever of the functions, *G* or 1/*H*, has the lower value of magnitude at crossover. In this example the frequency range from perhaps 1 to 40 would be of most interest. The plots of angle and magnitude for *G* and *GH* are shown on one graph in Fig. 4-4 for this range of frequencies (with displaced abscissa to reduce confusion). The corrections for the quadratic factor were obtained from the curve for $\zeta = 0.2$ for this specific function.

For this value of ζ it is noted that the exact attenuation plot for *G* lies above the approximate plot for the region of interest and that the Phase Margin at zero crossover (of the exact plot) is -72 degrees, indicating instability as expected. A gain reduction of 20 db for the entire curve would cause the exact attenuation plot to cross zero decibels at a point where the Phase Margin is about 60 degrees. (A change in gain constant would not affect the phase angle curve, of course.) It is interesting to note that if the approximate curve were used as a criterion here, a gain reduction of about 15 db would place the zero crossover for the approximate curve about midway between the steeper slopes on each side of the 20 db/decade portion of the curve, but that because the exact attenuation plot lies considerably above the approximate plot, a gain change of 15 db would still leave the zero crossover for the exact curve in a region of negative phase margin and therefore instability. This is a consequence of the value of ζ in this particular problem. If ζ had been 1, probably 15 db gain change would be about right.

The exact curves for $|GH|$ and $\underline{/GH}$ are shown (Figs. 4-4 and 4-6). These are to be used with the Nichols chart (Appendix II) to determine the magnitude and angle of the function $GH/(1 + GH)$. In order to use the Nichols chart conveniently, it is necessary to use graph paper of the same scale (10 or 20 divisions to the inch) and also use the same scale for the variables, namely, 10 db per inch for the ordinate and 40 degrees per inch for the abscissa. Then the graph (Fig. 4-6) may be superimposed on the Nichols chart, providing easier reading and also making it possible to determine the effect of changes in the gain constant by simply sliding the graph up or down on the Nichols chart. At a specific frequency the value of $|GH|$ and $\underline{/GH}$ determine a point on the Nichols chart from which the values of $|GH/(1 + GH)|$ and $\underline{/GH/(1 + GH)}$ may be determined and replotted on the frequency response plot (Fig. 4-5). (It is noted in passing that for $|GH|$ greater than about 12 db the

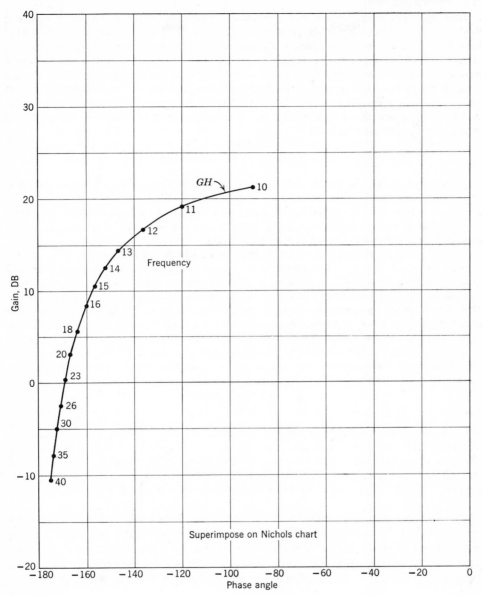

Fig. 4-6

function $GH/(1 + GH)$ is approximately unity and for $|GH|$ less than about -12 db the function $GH/(1 + GH)$ is approximately GH.

After the exact values of magnitude and angle for the function $GH/(1 + GH)$ have been determined, these are added to the magnitude and angle of $1/H$ to determine the frequency response for the equivalent forward transfer function, C/E (Fig. 4-5). From this plot, it is seen that the Phase Margin for the overall system is -10 degrees, indicating unsatisfactory dynamic characteristics.

This result illustrates the necessity of making a final exact check of a design which was fixed with an approximate straight-line attenuation plot. However, the result could have been foreseen and a more satisfactory feedback function selected. Superposition of the plot of GH (Fig. 4-6) on the Nichols chart reveals that the trouble arises because the curve passes too close to the origin. Since the transfer function for C/E (the equivalent forward transfer function including the interior feedback) is composed of $1/H$ and $GH/(1 + GH)$ in series, if the system described by $GH/(1 + GH)$ is unstable or nearly unstable, the effect of $1/H$ may not be able to counteract the unfavorable effect of $GH/(1 + GH)$. For the specific form of H assumed here,

$$\frac{K_h s^2}{1 + T_h s}$$

it might appear that a favorable effect would result if both K_h and T_h were increased in order to try to make $1/H$ intersect G at a lower gain and still maintain the desired slope of $1/H$ at zero decibels. This would result in a slower control system since $1/H$ would cross zero decibels at a lower frequency. Also, increasing K_h and T_h would cause the plot of GH to pass even closer to the origin of the Nichols chart, and probably counteract the effect of $1/H$. A better feedback function could be selected which would cause the curve of GH to pass the origin of the Nichols chart (or the point, -1, on the complex plane plot) at a greater distance. This could be achieved in this example by making sure that the straight-line attenuation line for GH should cross zero decibels with a slope of -20 db per decade. This curve crosses zero decibels where the straight-line plots of G and $1/H$ intersect; and thus another guide for determining a satisfactory feedback transfer function is that the straight-line attenuation plot of GH should have -20 db/decade slope at the frequency where G and $1/H$ intersect, especially if a lightly damped quadratic factor is involved as in this instance. In this example, this would occur if another factor were inserted in the numerator of H, so that

$$H = \frac{0.128s^2(1 + 0.06s)}{(1 + 0.715s)}$$

The addition of such a factor would have the effect of deflecting the curve of GH on the Nichols chart away from the origin. If the numerator factor could not be added without also adding another denominator factor, reference to the straight-line plot of $|GH|$ shows that the time constant for the denominator factor should be small, say about 0.01, in order to cause the effect of this factor to be unimportant in the vicinity of $|GH| = 0$ db.

This example has been included to illustrate the frequency response method of analysis. It has also demonstrated how this method leads to improved understanding of a system and the factors which may be important in the system. Actual computations may be facilitated by the use of Program D52FR of the Appendix, which uses the digital computer to calculate the frequency response if G and H are specified.

4.5 Transient Response from the Frequency Response

If the frequency response curve, C/R, is known, it is possible to obtain the transient response using the Fourier inverse transform. It may be that transfer functions for elements of the system are not known, but frequency response curves for these elements are available or can be obtained by experiment. If so, the frequency response curves for C/R can be obtained in numerical form. The stability of the system can also be ascertained in the process as described in previous sections. If the system is stable, the Fourier inverse transform provides a direct method for numerically computing the time response, $c(t)$, for a known input, $r(t)$. Let

$$\frac{C}{R} = h_r(\omega) + ih_i(\omega)$$

Then

$$C(i\omega) = R(i\omega)[h_r(\omega) + ih_i(\omega)]$$

where $C(i\omega)$ is the Fourier transform of $c(t)$, and $R(i\omega)$ is the Fourier transform of $r(t)$. If $r(t)$ is known only as a tabular or graphical relationship, the Fourier transform may still be taken numerically if it is transformable (Ref. 1), so that a numerical relationship is available for $C(i\omega)$. Let this be described by $C(i\omega) = g_r(\omega) + ig_i(\omega)$. [Obviously, this is not to be confused with $G(i\omega)$, the forward function.] It is usually assumed in the computation of a transient response that the system is quiescent prior to time $t = 0$. Therefore, Equation 1-89 may be used to determine $c(t)$.

$$c(t) = \frac{2}{\pi} \int_{\omega=0}^{\infty} g_r(\omega) \cos t\omega \, d\omega \qquad (4\text{-}4)$$

The numerical evaluation of this integral at different values of t presents no problem.

The time response to unit step input is often used to evaluate the performance of a system. This application requires a slight modification, since $r(t) = u(t)$ is not a transformable function. As described in Ref. 1, the inverse Fourier transform can still be taken, however. The transform of $u(t)$ for this application may be considered the limit of the transform of $e^{-\alpha t}u(t)$ where $\alpha \to 0$, resulting in $R(i\omega) = 1/i\omega$. In these circumstances

$$C(i\omega) = \frac{1}{i\omega} [h_r(\omega) + ih_i(\omega)]$$

but the line integral of Equation 4-4 must be taken along the contour indicated in Fig. 4-7, thereby avoiding the pole at $\omega = 0$. Then

$$c(t) = \frac{2}{\pi} \int_{\omega=\epsilon}^{\infty} \frac{h_i(\omega)}{\omega} \cos t\omega \, d\omega + \frac{2}{\pi} \int_{\text{arc}} \mathscr{R}\left[\frac{he^{i\omega t}}{i\omega} d\omega\right]$$

The contour in the vicinity of the origin is the arc of a circle of infinitesimal radius ϵ. Along this arc $h(i\omega)$ may be approximated by a real constant, K ($K = 1$ for a direct feedback Type 1 or 2 system), so that the second integral along the path $\omega = \epsilon e^{i\theta}$ becomes

$$\frac{2}{\pi} \int_{\theta=-\pi/2}^{0} K \, d\theta = K$$

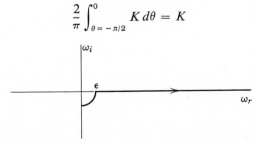

Fig. 4-7

Thus, for unit step input,

$$c(t) = K + \frac{2}{\pi} \int_{\omega = \epsilon \to 0}^{\infty} \frac{h_i(\omega)}{\omega} \cos t\omega \ d\omega \qquad (4\text{-}5)$$

This is illustrated for a simple system in Example 4-2. The integral of Equation 4-5 may be evaluated numerically if necessary provided that the system is known to be stable. Further modification can be made if the location of unstable roots is known, but this application is of limited interest.

Example 4-2. If $C/R = 1/(1 + s)$ and $r(t) = u(t)$ or $R(s) = 1/s$, determine $c(t)$ using the Fourier inverse transform, assuming the system is quiescent prior to $t = 0$.

The Fourier transform may be written directly from the Laplace transform

$$h_r + ih_i = \frac{1}{1 + i\omega} = \frac{1 - i\omega}{1 + \omega^2}$$

Along the infinitesimal circular arc of Fig. 4-7, $h \to 1$, so $K = 1$.

$$c(t) = 1 + \frac{2}{\pi} \int_{\omega = \epsilon \to 0}^{\infty} \frac{1}{\omega} \frac{-\omega}{1 + \omega^2} \cos t\omega \ d\omega$$

$$= 1 - \frac{2}{\pi} \int_{0}^{\infty} \frac{\cos t\omega}{1 + \omega^2} \ d\omega$$

This integral can be evaluated by residue theory (Ref. 1), resulting in

$$c(t) = 1 - e^{-t}$$

as expected.

This simple example did not require numerical integration, but it is clear that if C/R were given as a graphical or tabular function of ω, as $|C/R|$ and $\underline{/C/R}$, the only difference in the analysis would be that the constant K of Equation 4-5 would be $|C/R|$ at $\omega \to 0$, and $h_i(\omega)$ would be obtained from $|C/R|$ sin $\underline{/C/R}$ for each ω. The integral of Equation 4-5 would be evaluated numerically instead of analytically at the desired time intervals.

CHAPTER 5

Root Locus

5.1 Preliminary Comments

An important tool for analysis and synthesis of linear systems, attributable princi-pally to Evans, is known as the "Root Locus" method. As with the complex plane and frequency response methods, its importance derives from the fact that it helps provide insight into the significant aspects of any particular system. It is not restricted to direct feedback systems nor to systems with open loop poles and zeros in the left half plane.

It is recalled that for any closed-loop system with "degenerative feedback" (the quantity being fed back is subtracted rather than added to the reference value), the closed-loop transfer function is

$$\frac{C}{R} = \frac{G}{1 + GH}$$

The closed-loop response will be determined by the roots of the denominator of this equation. They must all be in the left half plane in order that the system be stable. Also, the more negative they are, the more rapid the response. This can be seen by considering a simple function such as

$$\frac{C}{R} = \frac{a_1 a_2}{(s + a_1)(s + a_2)}$$

and letting R be the transform of the unit step function, $1/s$, so that

$$c = \mathscr{L}^{-1} \frac{a_1 a_2}{s(s + a_1)(s + a_2)} = 1 - \frac{a_2}{a_2 - a_1} e^{-a_1 t} - \frac{a_1}{a_1 - a_2} e^{-a_2 t}$$

It is evident that the larger a_1 and a_2, the more rapidly the value of c approaches its final value of unity. Also, the position of the roots on the complex plane is related to important quantities such as the natural frequency and damping factor. Accordingly, a knowledge of how the roots of $1 + GH$ vary when the gain constant of GH (or some other parameter of interest) varies should be of considerable assistance in understanding the system.

5.2 Construction of the Locus

Requirements. It is more convenient for the root locus method of analysis if the functions G and H are expressed so that the coefficients of s in linear factors and of s^2 in quadratic factors are unity. This is different from the complex plane and frequency response methods, where it is more convenient if the constant term is unity, but there is no problem involved in shifting from one form to the other, provided that the gain constant is modified accordingly. Let it be assumed, therefore, that it is required to find the values of s for which $GH = -1$ (or $1 + GH = 0$) in a function having the form

$$GH = \frac{K(s + A_a)(s + A_b)\cdots(s + B_a + iC_a)(s + B_a - iC_a)\cdots}{s^n(s + A_1)(s + A_2)\cdots(s + B_1 + iC_1)(s + B_1 - iC_1)\cdots} \tag{5-1}$$

In this form the quadratic factors have been converted to their equivalent complex linear factors, which occur in conjugate pairs.

In order that $GH = -1$, it is necessary that the angle of the complex number, GH, be 180 degrees and the magnitude of GH be unity. Thus, the complex number, s, must be selected so that the angle of the complex number, GH, is 180 degrees. When such a complex number for s is determined, a value of K could then be found which would make the magnitude of GH unity, although this value of K might not necessarily be the same as the value specified in the transfer function. However, after a locus of values of s for which $GH = 180$ degrees has been found, somewhere along this locus will be found a number for which $|GH| = 1$ for the specified value of K.

The procedure for determining the root locus is to determine the locus of points for which $GH = 180$ degrees. This is easily done with the use of a "spirule." However, the instrument will not be described here, for lack of space. The locus can also be determined by use of a digital computer, as illustrated by Program D91RTL (Appendix). However, there are certain portions of the root locus that can be deduced by logic, and it is these which lead to increased understanding. The rest of this discussion will be devoted to the rules which govern these portions of the root locus.

Rules for Existence of the Locus.

Rule 1. Roots can exist on the real axis only in regions for which there is an odd number of poles and/or zeros of GH on the real axis to the right. This is evident when it is realized that the angle of GH is composed of the addition of the angles from a proposed value of s to the various zeros of GH and the subtraction of the angles to the various poles of GH. For instance, suppose that

$$GH = \frac{K(s + 2)}{(s + 1)(s + 3)}$$

Then a pole of GH is located at -1 and -3, and a zero at -2, as indicated in Fig. 5-1. If s is a real number between -1 and -2, the angle to the complex number, $s - (-1)$, is 180 degrees, and the angles to the complex numbers, $s - (-2)$, and $s - (-3)$, are zero, so that one part of the locus can lie between -1 and -2. Similarly, one part of the locus can exist on the real axis for values of s less than -3, but not between -2 and -3, because there the angle of GH would have to be zero instead of 180 degrees. For regenerative feedback, for which $1 - GH = 0$ instead of $1 + GH = 0$ and $\underline{/GH} = 0$ degrees instead of 180 degrees, the locus could exist only in regions for

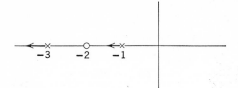

Fig. 5-1 $GH = \dfrac{K(s + 2)}{(s + 1)(s + 3)}.$

which there is an even number of poles and/or zeros of GH on the real axis to the right.

Rule 2. A branch of the root locus starts at each open-loop pole, with $K = 0$, and ends at each open-loop zero, or at infinity, with K becoming infinite. This is a consequence of the fact that the magnitude of GH must be unity. If s takes a value near an open-loop pole, the magnitude of GH would become very large (because of the near-zero denominator) unless K becomes very small. On the other hand, if s takes a value near an open-loop zero, K would have to be very large to counteract the near-zero term in the numerator. However, if the denominator of GH is a higher-order polynomial in s than the numerator, then s can go to infinity somewhere in the complex plane in such a way that $|GH| = 1$ for K approaching infinity. For the un-usual case where the polynomial in the numerator of GH is of higher order than the denominator, there is an excess of zeros over poles, and one or more branches which end at the zeros must start, for $K = 0$, at infinity instead of at an open-loop pole. Thus, there are as many branches of the root locus as the number of poles or zeros of GH, whichever is larger (usually poles). Figure 5-1 shows an example of a locus starting at an open-loop pole, -1, and ending at an open-loop zero, -2, and another branch starting at the open-loop pole, -3, and ending at infinity.

Rule 3. The locus will approach asymptotes as K becomes infinite (provided that the order of the denominator of GH exceeds the numerator; if the numerator has the higher order, then the locus approaches the asymptotes for K approaching zero instead of infinity, and if the order of numerator and denominator are equal, there are no asymptotes, all loci starting at poles and ending at zeros). The number of asymptotes is equal to the number by which the order of the denominator of GH exceeds that of the numerator (or vice versa in the unlikely event that the numerator has the higher order), and the configuration of the asymptotes can be determined with simple equations which are now deduced. Suppose that the denominator of GH is of higher order than the numerator. Then the asymptotes are approached for large values of K and s. If GH is of the form indicated by Equation 5-1, it is possible to show that for s large, the value of GH may be approximated by the following func-tion, where only the first two terms are retained, and where D is the order of the denominator polynomial and N the order of the numerator polynomial. (D is assumed to be larger than N.)

$$GH = \frac{K}{s^{(D-N)} + (A_1 + A_2 + \cdots + 2B_1 + 2B_2 + \cdots \atop \qquad\qquad - A_a - A_b - \cdots - 2B_a - 2B_b - \cdots)s^{(D-N-1)}}$$

A function which would give the same results for $|s| \to \infty$ is

$$GH = \frac{K}{(s + E)^{D-N}} = \frac{K}{s^{(D-N)} + (D - N)E^{(D-N+1)} + \cdots}$$

By comparison,

$$E = \frac{A_1 + A_2 + \cdots + 2B_1 + 2B_2 + \cdots - A_a - A_b - \cdots - 2B_a - 2B_b - \cdots}{(D - N)} \quad (5\text{-}2)$$

A plot for which

$$GH = \frac{K}{(s + E)^{D-N}} = -1$$

is composed of straight lines intersecting at $s = -E$ and making angles of

$$\frac{180(1 + 2k)}{(D - N)}$$

degrees with the positive real axis, where k is 0, 1, 2, etc. to $(D - N - 1)$. Note that if regenerative feedback were used, for which $GH = +1$, the only difference in the asymptotes is that the angles to the straight lines are determined by

$$\frac{360(1 + 2k)}{(D - N)}$$

Rule 4. For some configurations of open-loop poles and zeros, there will be points along the real axis at which the root locus will break away from the real axis. These breakaway points can be determined by assuming a value of s just off the real axis and applying the criterion that $GH = 180$ degrees (for degenerative feedback). To illustrate this with a simple function, for example,

$$GH = \frac{K(s + 3)}{(s + 1)(s + 2)}$$

which is shown in Fig. 5-2, it is immediately evident from Rule 1 that a locus can exist on the real axis between -1 and -2 and less than -3. Also, from Rule 3 it is clear that there is only one asymptote and the angle to it is 180 degrees so this is the negative real axis. Since there can be no locus on the real axis between -2 and -3, but a root must approach the zero at -3 for high values of K, it must approach from the negative side. Also, since the two roots which depart from the poles at -1 and -2 must eventually reach infinity or a zero, it is evident that there must be a point between -1 and -2 where the locus breaks away from the real axis, and another point on the real axis less than -3 where the locus returns to the real axis. Whenever one root exists off the real axis, its complex conjugate also exists, so that all loci have conjugate branches and the entire figure is symmetrical with respect to the real axis. At the breakaway (or return) points, then, one root would break away above and the other below the axis. The return point need not be designated differently, so it is customary to refer to either the breakaway or return point as a breakaway point. At a breakaway point, let a point on the root locus just barely off the real axis be selected (Fig. 5-2b) so that angles θ_2 and θ_3 are near zero and θ_1 is near 180 degrees. In order that the point be on the root locus, it is necessary that $\theta_3 - \theta_1 - \theta_2 = -180$ degrees, or $\theta_1 + \theta_2 - \theta_3 = 180$ degrees. This is true because if s has the complex value indicated, then θ_1, θ_2, and θ_3 are the angles of the factors, $s - (-1)$, $s - (-2)$, and $s - (-3)$,

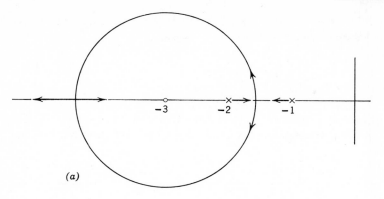

(a)

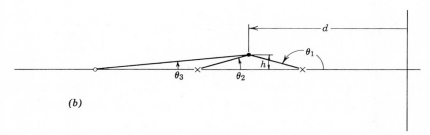

(b)

Fig. 5-2 $GH = \dfrac{K(s + 3)}{(s + 1)(s + 2)}.$

or $s + 1$, $s + 2$, and $s + 3$ respectively. Since these angles are near 0 degrees or near 180 degrees, it is possible to represent the angles (in radians) as

$$\theta_1 = \pi - \frac{h}{-1 - d}, \qquad \theta_2 = \frac{h}{d - (-2)}, \qquad \theta_3 = \frac{h}{d - (-3)}$$

(Note that the definition of $+d$ is to the right of zero, so that when a number is substituted for d in this example it will have a negative value.)

Now if the criterion that $\theta_1 + \theta_2 - \theta_3 = 180$ degrees is applied, the following equation results

$$\pi + \frac{h}{d + 1} + \frac{h}{d + 2} - \frac{h}{d + 3} = \pi$$

which can be simplified to

$$\frac{1}{d + 1} + \frac{1}{d + 2} - \frac{1}{d + 3} = 0$$

This is satisfied where $d = -1.59$ or -4.42, the breakaway points in Fig. 5-2a. The general form, if the open-loop poles and zeros are real, is then

$$\frac{n}{d} + \frac{1}{d + A_1} + \frac{1}{d + A_2} + \cdots = \frac{1}{d + A_a} + \frac{1}{d + A_b} + \cdots$$

Where n, A_1, A_2, A_a, A_b, etc. are defined by Equation 5-1. It is possible to show that if some of the open-loop poles or zeros are complex, the term corresponding to the conjugate pair of poles or roots is of the form

$$\frac{2}{d + B} \frac{1}{1 + \left(\dfrac{C}{d + B}\right)^2}$$

where B and C are defined by Equation 5-1. (If it should happen that $d + B = 0$, then the contribution from the corresponding term vanishes.) The rule can then be summarized as

$$\frac{n}{d} + \frac{1}{d + A_1} + \frac{1}{d + A_2} + \cdots + \frac{2}{d + B_1} \frac{1}{1 + \left(\dfrac{C_1}{d + B_1}\right)^2} + \frac{2}{d + B_2} \frac{1}{1 + \left(\dfrac{C_2}{d + B_2}\right)^2} + \cdots$$

$$= \frac{1}{d + A_a} + \frac{1}{d + A_b} + \cdots + \frac{2}{d + B_a} \frac{1}{1 + \left(\dfrac{C_a}{d + B_a}\right)^2} + \frac{2}{d + B_b} \frac{1}{1 + \left(\dfrac{C_b}{d + B_b}\right)^2} + \cdots$$

$$(5\text{-}3)$$

Rule 5. The root locus leaves a pole or enters a zero at an angle which can be determined in the following manner. The method is illustrated by the specific function,

$$GH = \frac{K(s + 1)}{s(s + 8)(s + 2 + 3i)(s + 2 - 3i)}$$

Of course, the direction in which the locus enters or leaves poles or zeros on the real axis is already known for this function, and it is here required to determine in what direction the locus leaves the complex open-loop pole at $s = -2 + 3i$. If s is a value on the locus, but very close to the open-loop pole, the angle formed by the factors $(s - 0)$, $[s - (-1)]$, $[s - (-8)]$, and $[s - (-2 - 3i)]$ are practically the same as the angles formed by drawing lines from the various poles and zeros to the pole in

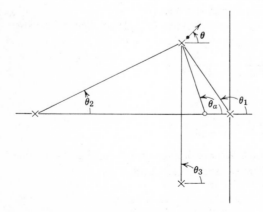

Fig. 5-3   Root locus leaving a complex pole $GH = \dfrac{K(s + 1)}{s(s + 8)(s^2 + 4s + 13)}$.

question, as indicated by the angles, θ_1, θ_2, θ_3, θ_a, (Fig. 5-3). Then the angle θ must be such that $\theta + \theta_1 + \theta_2 + \theta_3 - \theta_a = 180$ degrees or $\theta = 90° - \theta_1 - \theta_2 + \theta_a$ since θ_3 is 90 degrees. For this example, $\theta = 90 - 123.7 - 26.6 + 108.4 = 48.1$ degrees. A similar analysis applies to the locus near open-loop zeros, and if in this example the complex factors had been in the numerator instead of in the denominator, the result would have been $-(180 + 108.4 + 90 - 123.7 - 26.6) = -131.9$ degrees for the angle between the horizontal and the locus at the zero.

The general rule can therefore be written as follows. At a first-order pole or zero of the open-loop transfer function, the root locus of the closed-loop transfer function will form an angle as defined in Fig. 5-3 so that

$$\theta_p = 180° + \theta_a + \theta_b + \cdots - \theta_1 - \theta_2 - \theta_3 - \theta_4 - \cdots$$
$$\theta_z = -(180° + \theta_a + \theta_b + \cdots - \theta_1 - \theta_2 - \theta_3 - \theta_4 - \cdots)$$
$$(5\text{-}4)$$

At higher order poles or zeros, more than one branch will leave or enter the pole or zero. The angles which these branches make are easily deduced in the same way. For example, in Fig. 5-3 if the pole were a double pole or second order pole,

$$\theta = \frac{1}{2}(180° + \theta_a - \theta_1 - \theta_2 - 2\theta_3) = \frac{1}{2}(\theta_a - \theta_1 - \theta_2)$$

for one branch, and this value plus 180 degrees for the other branch leaving that pole. For double poles or zeros on the real axis, it is easily deduced that the loci are perpendicular to the real axis at these points.

For regenerative feedback instead of degenerative feedback, the angles add up to zero instead of 180 degrees, so the 180° term in Equation 5-4 is missing.

5.3 Effects of Changes in the Transfer Function

An understanding of the effects on the root locus plot of possible changes in the forward or feedback transfer functions enables the designer to make an intelligent selection of transfer functions to be inserted in order to improve the performance of the system. This understanding is probably best gained by experience, but there are certain general effects of interest, which are briefly discussed below.

Effect of Open Loop Pole or Zero. A zero has a tendency to attract the locus, and so the addition of an open-loop zero in the left half plane tends to increase stability of roots which may be unstable, or nearly unstable. An example is shown in Fig. 5-4. The reason for the effect in Fig. 5-4 is easily recognized as the change in the angle of the asymptotes from 60 to 90 degrees. (Of course, it must be remembered that the addition of the zero will also have an effect on how far along the locus a closed-loop root is located for a given value of gain constant.) The effect of removing a zero is obviously the reverse of the effect of adding the zero. The effect of adding an open-loop pole is also the reverse of adding an open-loop zero, the poles repelling the locus and decreasing the angle of the asymptotes.

Effect of Phase-Lag Transfer Function. The addition of a pole and zero in close proximity to each other would have very little effect on the root locus some distance away from the pole and zero, but might enable a favorable change of gain constant

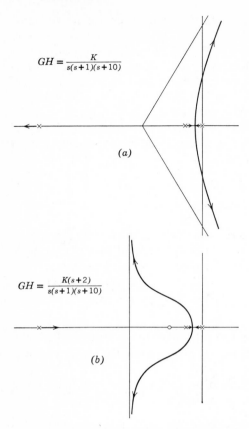

$$GH = \frac{K}{s(s+1)(s+10)}$$

(a)

$$GH = \frac{K(s+2)}{s(s+1)(s+10)}$$

(b)

Fig. 5-4   Effect on root locus of addition of open-loop zero.

to be made. This is the effect of the "phase-lag network" mentioned in Chapter 4. That is, a function such as $(1 + T_a s)/(1 + T_1 s)$, where $T_1 > T_a$, is the same as

$$\frac{T_a}{T_1}\left(\frac{s + \dfrac{1}{T_a}}{s + \dfrac{1}{T_1}} \right)$$

and so the gain constant could be increased by approximately T_1/T_a without noticeable adverse effect on the position of the closed-loop roots along the locus for points remote from $1/T_a$ and $1/T_1$. This is illustrated in Fig. 5-5, where it is seen that at the crossing of the imaginary axis the gain constant K' is increased by a factor of four by the addition of the phase-lag network. (It is the constant K' rather than K which should be as large as possible for good steady-state accuracy and rapid response.)

Effect of Phase-Lead Transfer Function. The effect of a "phase-lead network" is illustrated in Fig. 5-6. A phase-lead network is one having a transfer function

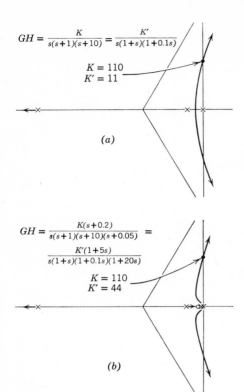

$$GH = \frac{K}{s(s+1)(s+10)} = \frac{K'}{s(1+s)(1+0.1s)}$$

$$K = 110$$
$$K' = 11$$

(a)

$$GH = \frac{K(s+0.2)}{s(s+1)(s+10)(s+0.05)} = $$

$$\frac{K'(1+5s)}{s(1+s)(1+0.1s)(1+20s)}$$

$$K = 110$$
$$K' = 44$$

(b)

Fig. 5-5 Effect of lag function on gain constant.

$(1 + T_a s)/(1 + T_1 s)$, where $T_a > T_1$. If the values of the open-loop poles and zeros in Fig. 5-5 were merely reversed, the effect on gain constant would be unfavorable. In order for the lead network to have a favorable effect, it is necessary that the open-loop pole and zero should not be in close proximity to each other (relative to the other poles and zeros). Figure 5-6 shows the effect of adding a phase-lead network so that the open-loop pole at -1 is effectively moved to -10. The crossing of the imaginary axis then occurs at a higher value of K' than for the system without phase lead. It also crosses at a higher frequency, indicating a faster system.

The effects of phase lag and phase lead could be combined to obtain a "lag-lead network," which could combine the useful effects of each type of network if the time constants were properly chosen.

Electrical Circuits for Phase-Lag and Phase-Lead Transfer Functions. Physical elements for obtaining phase-lag, phase-lead, or lag-lead transfer functions or other transfer functions are not discussed in detail in this text. However, for electrical systems these functions can be achieved by use of resistors and capacitors in circuits such as those of Fig. 5-7. Other functions are discussed in Chapter 9 in connection with analogue computers. Schematic mechanical systems for achieving various transfer functions are suggested by Problem 2.3.

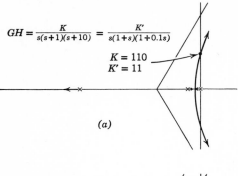

$$GH = \frac{K}{s(s+1)(s+10)} = \frac{K'}{s(1+s)(1+0.1s)}$$

$$K = 110$$
$$K' = 11$$

(a)

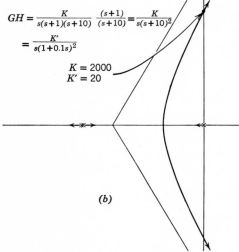

$$GH = \frac{K}{s(s+1)(s+10)} \frac{(s+1)}{(s+10)} = \frac{K}{s(s+10)^2}$$

$$= \frac{K'}{s(1+0.1s)^2}$$

$$K = 2000$$
$$K' = 20$$

(b)

Fig. 5-6   Effect of lead function on root locus.

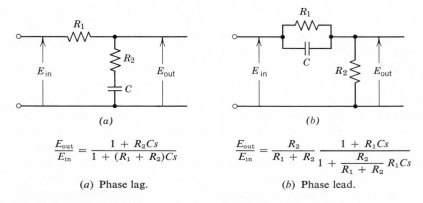

(a)   (b)

$$\frac{E_{out}}{E_{in}} = \frac{1 + R_2Cs}{1 + (R_1 + R_2)Cs}$$ $$\frac{E_{out}}{E_{in}} = \frac{R_2}{R_1 + R_2} \frac{1 + R_1Cs}{1 + \frac{R_2}{R_1 + R_2}R_1Cs}$$

(a) Phase lag.   (b) Phase lead.

Fig. 5-7   Electrical circuits for phase-lag or phase-lead transfer functions.

CHAPTER 6

Steady-State Performance

6.1 System Type

Chapters 3, 4, and 5 have dealt with the general performance of a control system. Although this is perhaps of greatest importance from the viewpoint of dynamics and vibration, the steady-state performance is also of interest and will be briefly discussed in this chapter. Consider first a direct feedback system with a forward transfer function of the form of Equation 4-1, or

$$G = \frac{K_n}{s^n} \phi(s)$$

where the $\phi(s)$ is composed of numerator and denominator factors each having a constant term of unity, such as

$$(1 + Ts) \quad \text{or} \quad \left(1 + \frac{2\zeta}{\beta} s + \frac{s^2}{\beta^2}\right)$$

As mentioned in Section 4.2, the value of n determines the type of system. It also has a bearing on the steady-state characteristics.

Type 0 System. If $n = 0$, the closed-loop transfer function becomes

$$\frac{C}{R} = \frac{K_0\phi(s)}{1 + K_0\phi(s)}$$

and if $R = \Delta/s$ (for a step function), then

$$C(s) = \frac{\Delta}{s} \frac{K_0\phi(s)}{1 + K_0\phi(s)}$$

and

$$R - C = \frac{\Delta}{s} \frac{1}{1 + K_0\phi(s)}$$

Application of the final value theorem to this expression shows that the steady-state error, $r - c$, for large values of time is

$$r - c = \frac{\varDelta}{1 + K_0}$$

It is clear that the Type 0 system cannot maintain exact correspondence between the reference and controlled variables and that the steady-state error is reduced for large values of K_0. The fact that the steady-state controlled variable is not exactly equal to the reference variable may not necessarily be a disadvantage if the reference value can be modified in order to provide the desired value of the controlled variable (by calibration of a control knob, for instance).

Type 1 System. If it is required that the steady-state controlled variable and reference variable be exactly equal, then it is necessary to use a Type 1 or Type 2 system (or an even higher type). For a Type 1 system, where

$$n = 1$$

$$\frac{C}{R} = \frac{\frac{K_1}{s}\phi(s)}{1 + \frac{K_1}{s}\phi(s)} = \frac{K_1\phi(s)}{s + K_1\phi(s)}$$

and if $R = \varDelta/s$, then

$$R - C = \frac{\varDelta}{s + K_1\phi(s)}$$

and application of the final value theorem shows that the steady-state error, $r - c$, is zero. That is, a constant value of reference input, $\varDelta$, will be reproduced without error by a Type 1 system. Therefore, the Type 1 system would be equivalent to a Type 0 system with an infinite gain constant as far as steady-state performance is concerned.

If the reference value changed at constant velocity, indefinitely (instead of a step function), then $r(t) = vt$, $R(s) = v/s^2$, and

$$C(s) = \frac{vK_1\phi(s)}{s^2[s + K_1\phi(s)]}$$

or

$$R - C = \frac{v}{s}\left[\frac{1}{s + K_1\phi(s)}\right]$$

Application of the final value theorem to this expression shows that the steady-state difference between the reference variable and controlled variable (or error) is a constant, $r - c = v/K_1$. This equation shows that a Type 1 system could not follow exactly an input having a constant rate of change, and also that the higher the gain constant K_1, the less the steady-state error for these constant velocity inputs. (Of course, there is no error for constant inputs, as was seen previously.)

Type 2 System. A similar analysis for Type 2 systems would show that for either the constant input or input with constant rate of change the steady-state error would be zero, but for an input having a constant acceleration, $r = at^2$, the steady-state error would be

$$r - c = \frac{a}{K_2}$$

Again, the favorable effect of high gain constant on steady-state error is noted.

The gain constant, K_0, is dimensionless, whereas the constants, K_1 and K_2, have the dimensions of $1/t$ and $1/t^2$ respectively. Although the steady-state performance of Type 1 or Type 2 systems is better than the Type 0 system, these systems may be more subject to stability difficulties.

Effect of Internal Feedback on System Type. The effect of an internal feedback loop may be to reduce the system type. If the feedback transfer function is of the form

$$K_H \frac{(1 + T_a s)(1 + T_b s) \cdots}{(1 + T_1 s)(1 + T_2 s) \cdots}$$

the system type will be reduced to Type 0, as far as steady-state performance is concerned, and the equivalent Type 0 gain constant is $1/K_H$. If the internal feedback function is of the form

$$K_H \frac{s^m (1 + T_a s)(1 + T_b s) \cdots}{(1 + T_1 s)(1 + T_2 s) \cdots}$$

then the equivalent system will be Type m, if $m < n$, and the equivalent Type m gain constant will be $1/K_H$. However, it is not possible to increase from lower type to higher type systems by choice of an internal feedback function of this form (unless K_H is negative). If a reduction in type of system is to be avoided, the value of m must not be less than n. These conclusions all stem from the discussion of the effect of internal feedback contained in Section 4.4.

Conversion to Direct Feedback System. The foregoing discussion was related to systems having an outer direct feedback loop. If the feedback function is not unity, the system may be converted to an equivalent direct feedback system by the device of letting $H = 1 + (H - 1)$ and considering $(H - 1)$ as an internal feedback loop.

6.2 Response to a Disturbance

The discussion in Section 6.1 showed that steady-state agreement between controlled variable and reference variable is improved for higher system types and for larger gain constants. A similar analysis would show that these factors also decrease the steady-state error caused by an unwanted disturbance. An undesirable disturbance which remains constant would result in a permanent change in the controlled variable for a Type 0 system, but for Type 1 or Type 2 systems the final change in the controlled variable would be zero unless the unwanted disturbance increased at constant velocity or acceleration respectively. Of course, even for a Type 0 system, the final error could be decreased by resetting the reference value to account for the inherent error. In addition, for all types the transient errors could be reduced by feeding a signal from the unwanted variable through a portion of the forward path. This is illustrated in the example which follows. Although higher type systems and higher gains improve steady-state accuracy, it has been noted earlier that these factors also tend to decrease system stability and may lead to transient errors from the more

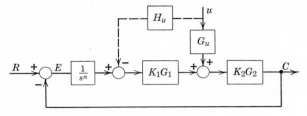

Fig. 6-1

oscillatory response of these systems. Thus there is a limit to the improvement which can be made by these means.

Example 6-1. Discuss the system in Fig. 6-1 from the point of view of response of the controlled variable to an undesirable disturbance.

This diagram is redrawn (Fig. 6-2) to enable the transfer function, C/U, to be easily expressed.

$$\frac{C}{U} = (G_u - H_u K_1 G_1) \frac{s^n K_2 G_2}{s^n + K_1 K_2 G_1 G_2}$$

It is assumed, of course, that the original transfer functions have been manipulated so that G_1 and G_2 contain only factors of the form $(1 + Ts)$ or

$$\left(1 + \frac{2\zeta}{\beta} s + \frac{s^2}{\beta^2}\right)$$

It is clear from the final value theorem that s^n in the numerator of this transfer function insures that no steady-state error would exist for $n = 1$ or 2 and U a step function. If $n = 0$, a steady-state error proportional to $K_2/(1 + K_1 K_2)$ would result from a step disturbance. This error would be decreased for small values of K_2 and large values of K_1. Even if Type 1 or Type 2 systems were used so that the final error would be zero, the transient errors resulting from the disturbance could be reduced by feeding a function of the disturbance signal through a portion of the forward path as indicated by the dotted line. If it is assumed that G_u and $K_2 G_2$ are functions which are inherent in the system and beyond the control of the designer, it may still be possible to select H_u in such a way as to affect favorably the function $(G_u - H_u K_1 G_1)$ in order to minimize transient errors. Of course, it would be a mistake to feed this function into the forward path upstream from the $1/s^n$ block, because the $1/s^n$ function would then insure the existence of a steady-state error rather than a lack of it.

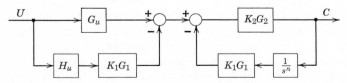

Fig. 6-2

Physical Interpretation. The way a function such as $1/s$ causes the final steady-state error to be zero from a physical point of view may be visualized as follows. Suppose first that there were no such function present. Then a disturbance would cause a change in C, with a corresponding error. This error would be used to activate elements which would tend to decrease the error, but the error could not be reduced to zero since the signal to the correcting elements would exist only if an error existed. Therefore, such a system could only oppose and limit the error, at best. However, if the error were integrated with respect to time (which is what the function $1/s$ implies), a constant error would result in a signal to the correcting elements, which would continue to grow. Therefore the error itself could become smaller and smaller, since it is the integral of the error which activates the corrective elements rather than the error itself.

Designations for Controllers. A controller which utilizes an integration element, resulting therefore in a Type 1 system, is often referred to as an "integral controller," the controller for a Type 0 system, for which the signal to the corrective elements is proportional to the error, is often referred to as a "proportional controller." If the signal to the corrective elements is proportional to the derivative of the error, this mode of control may be referred to as "rate" or "derivative" control. This mode would not be used by itself, but in combination with the other forms. An integral controller may also be referred to as an "automatic reset" controller.

If the signal to the corrective elements is proportional to both the error and the integral of the error, the combination may be referred to as "proportional plus automatic reset," and if the signal is also proportional to the rate of change of the error, the combination would be "proportional plus reset plus derivative." The reasons for these combinations are as follows. Although an integral controller will assure that the final error will be zero, the fact that it responds to the integral of error means that load changes or operating-point changes may cause relatively large transient inaccuracy. If the corrective action were initiated by the error or derivative of the error, the transient inaccuracy should be less since corrective measures are effective earlier.

Effect of Controllers on Forward Transfer Function. Combinations like this are really only methods of inserting lead functions into the forward transfer function of a

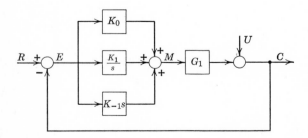

Fig. 6-3

Type 1 system. Suppose the error signal is operated on as indicated in Fig. 6-3. The three forward elements may be combined to give

$$\frac{M}{E} = \frac{K_1}{s} + K_0 + K_{-1}s = \frac{K_1 + K_0 s + K_{-1}s^2}{s}$$

$$\frac{M}{E} = \frac{K_1}{s}\left(1 + \frac{K_0}{K_1}s + \frac{K_{-1}}{K_1}s^2\right)$$

The quantity in parentheses may be a quadratic factor or it may be factorable into two linear factors, with the corresponding zeros occurring at points determined by the ratios of the gain constants. It is clear, therefore, that these combinations may be analyzed by the methods previously discussed.

CHAPTER 7

Missile Application

7.1 Open-Loop Transfer Functions for Missile

The theory developed in Chapters 3 to 6 will now be applied to the problem of selecting the proper gain constants for the autopilot in the flexible missile problem of Example 1-2. The block diagrams for the missile (both rigid body and flexible body) were determined in Example 2-1. In terms of the general diagram of Fig. 7-1, the values of G and H_1 are as follows.

Rigid Body

$$G = 0.024k_\theta \frac{(s + 0.075)}{(s + 2.67)(s - 2.57)(s - 0.0108)(s^2 + 14s + 100)}$$

$$= 2.44 \times 10^{-4}k_\theta \frac{(1 + 13.33s)}{(1 + 0.374s)(1 - 0.389s)(1 - 93s)(1 + 0.14s + 0.01s^2)}$$

$$H_1 = 1$$

Flexible Body

$$G = 0.0224k_\theta \frac{\begin{array}{c}(s + 0.076)(s^2 + 6.31s + 26900) \\ \times (s^2 + 3.38s + 6820)(s^2 + 1.175s + 833)\end{array}}{\begin{array}{c}(s + 2.68)(s - 2.6)(s - 0.01068)(s^2 + 6.36s + 27000) \\ \times (s^2 + 3.34s + 6870)(s^2 + 1.173s + 891)(s^2 + 14s + 100)\end{array}}$$

$$= 2.27 \times 10^{-4}k_\theta \frac{\begin{array}{c}(1 + 13.16s)(1 + 0.234 \times 10^{-3}s + 0.372 \times 10^{-4}s^2) \\ \times (1 + 0.495 \times 10^{-3}s + 0.1466 \times 10^{-3}s^2) \\ \times (1 + 0.1411 \times 10^{-2}s + 0.1201 \times 10^{-2}s^2)\end{array}}{\begin{array}{c}(1 + 0.374s)(1 - 0.386s)(1 - 93.6s) \\ \times (1 + 0.236 \times 10^{-3}s + 0.370 \times 10^{-4}s^2) \\ \times (1 + 0.486 \times 10^{-3}s + 0.1457 \times 10^{-3}s^2) \\ \times (1 + 0.1316 \times 10^{-2}s + 0.1122 \times 10^{-2}s^2) \\ \times (1 + 0.14s + 0.01s^2)\end{array}}$$

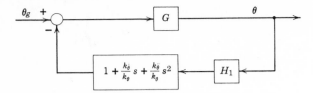

Fig. 7-1   Block diagram for missile of Example 1-2.

$$H_1 = -46.8 \frac{(s + 0.0745)(s - 23.8)(s + 22.9)(s^2 - 146.6s + 8400)}{(s + 0.0760)(s^2 + 6.31s + 26900)}$$
$$\times (s^2 + 150.5s + 8440)$$
$$\times (s^2 + 3.38s + 6820)(s^2 + 1.175s + 833)$$

$$= 0.997 \frac{(1 + 13.44s)(1 - 0.0420s)(1 + 0.0436s)}{(1 + 13.16s)(1 + 0.234 \times 10^{-3}s + 0.372 \times 10^{-4}s^2)}$$
$$\times (1 - 0.1744 \times 10^{-1}s + 0.119 \times 10^{-3}s^2)$$
$$\times (1 + 0.1784 \times 10^{-1}s + 0.1185 \times 10^{-3}s^2)$$
$$\times (1 + 0.495 \times 10^{-3}s + 0.1466 \times 10^{-3}s^2)$$
$$\times (1 + 0.1411 \times 10^{-2}s + 0.1201 \times 10^{-2}s^2)$$

7.2 Inflexible Missile

Usually the effect of body flexibility is to intensify the stability problem, rather than to relieve it, so an inspection of the rigid-body system should cast some light on minimum requirements, after which the effects of flexibility can be examined. Accordingly, the rigid-body missile forward transfer function is considered first. It is immediately evident (because of the negative factors in the denominator) that the open-loop system is unstable. This is expected because the aerodynamic center of this missile was located forward of the center of gravity, and static stability would have to be achieved by the automatic pilot.

Autopilot Parameter, k_θ. The next question to be determined is whether there is a value of k_θ which can insure closed-loop stability. This can be decided easily from either a complex plane plot or a root locus plot, neither of which would have to be actually plotted to scale for this purpose. Figure 7-2 shows a possible sketch of a

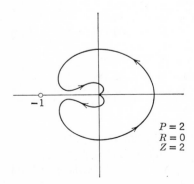

$P = 2$
$R = 0$
$Z = 2$

Fig. 7-2   Complex plane plot of G for rigid body missile, $k_{\dot\theta} = 0$.

complex plane plot of G for the rigid body for some value of k_θ ($k_{\dot\theta}$ and $k_{\ddot\theta}$ are assumed to be zero). Because there are two open-loop poles in the right half plane, the plot of G would have to encircle -1 twice in the counterclockwise direction in order for stability to result. However, the magnitudes of the various constants in G are such that the plot can never reach the negative real axis, so there cannot be a value of k_θ which would cause the -1 point to be encircled, and stability cannot be achieved by use of k_θ alone.

Figure 7-3 is a root locus plot of the closed-loop poles for the direct feedback system resulting when $k_{\dot\theta}$ and $k_{\ddot\theta}$ are assumed to be zero. It is again immediately evident that the system cannot be stabilized by a prudent selection of k_θ.

A frequency response plot of G would be misleading. It would seem at first glance that some value of gain constant k_θ could be selected so that the approximate straight-line plot of magnitude would cross zero decibels at -20 db per decade, and therefore some value of k_θ should insure a stable system. However, we must recall that the discussion of frequency response postulated a function, G, having the form of Equation 4-1, where all time constants and damping factors are positive, or a "minimum-phase" system. In this example two of the time constants are negative, and thus the frequency response plot, if used at all, must be used with the complex plane plot in mind in order to be sure that erroneous conclusions are not drawn.

Autopilot Parameter, $k_{\dot\theta}$. One way of increasing the stability would be to make a change which would cause a zero to be inserted in the left half plane of the root locus plot. This could be done by using a value of $k_{\dot\theta}$ different from zero, so that

$$H = 1 + \frac{k_{\dot\theta}}{k_\theta} s = \frac{k_{\dot\theta}}{k_\theta}\left(s + \frac{k_\theta}{k_{\dot\theta}}\right)$$

Physically, this is equivalent to adding viscous damping to the system, somewhat similar to the aerodynamic damping which might have been available from the use of tail surfaces. If the zero is arbitrarily selected to cancel the pole at -2.67 (not necessarily the best selection) the root locus plot appears as shown in Fig. 7-4 and it becomes

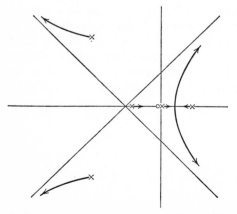

Fig. 7-3 Root locus plot for G in direct feedback system, $k_{\dot\theta} = 0$.

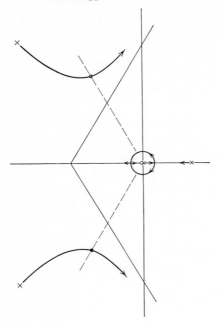

Fig. 7-4   Root locus, $k_\theta/k_{\dot\theta} = 2.67$.

possible to select a value of k_θ which would provide stability. (A value of k_θ of 48,000 locates the complex roots at 60 degrees from the negative real axis so that a reasonable value of damping factor results. Then $k_{\dot\theta}$ must be 18,000 to provide the zero at -2.67.) Reference to Fig. 7-2 also indicates that cancelling the $(s + 2.67)$ factor would allow the complex plane plot to reach the third quadrant, which would mean that a value of k_θ could be chosen which would insure encirclement of -1 in the counterclockwise direction, as required for stability in this instance.

The zero was inserted by use of a value of $k_{\dot\theta}$, which appears in the feedback transfer function. The block diagram could be redrawn as indicated in Fig. 7-5 to show this term as an interior feedback loop in a direct feedback system.

Now it may be possible to use the frequency response approach to this problem, even though G does contain negative time constants, if $|1/H| \ll |G|$ in the vicinity of zero crossover. Reference to the straight line attenuation plot of G and $1/H$ (Fig. 7-6) for the constants previously selected ($k_\theta = 48,000$, $k_{\dot\theta} = 18,000$) shows that the steep portion of the combined curve occurs quite close to zero crossover for the $1/H$ curve. This would seem to indicate that if the gain of G were raised without changing H, the system would be improved. It appears that the gain of G could be increased indefinitely as long as the $1/H$ line stays where it is.

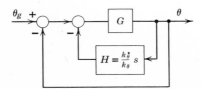

Fig. 7-5   Interior feedback.

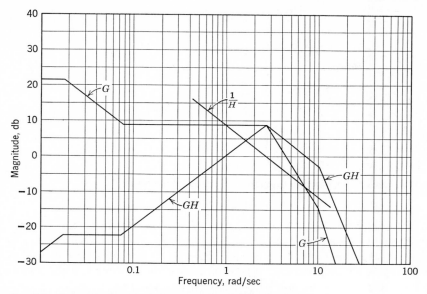

Fig. 7-6 Approximate attenuation curve for rigid body missile.

This is another instance in which the use of an equivalent forward transfer function composed of the lower of the two curves, G or $1/H$, can lead to an erroneous conclusion, for it is clear from the root locus plot that an indefinite increase in k_θ must force the roots along the 60 degree asymptotes into the unstable region. This failure of the frequency response method is not caused by the negative factors in G, but rather by the approximation that an "equivalent" forward transfer function can be formed from the lower of the two attenuation curves for G and $1/H$. (An example of two unity feedback systems for which the "equivalent" transfer functions are exactly the same, but with one system very stable and the other very unstable, is the following:

System 1

$$G = \frac{10}{(1 + 10s)(1 + 0.1s)^3}, \quad H = 0$$

System 2

$$G = \frac{10}{(1 + 0.316s)^4}, \quad H = s$$

H is internal feedback

The difficulty is caused by the fact that the function $GH/(1 + GH)$ is unstable in System 2.)

For the missile system to be stable, the complex plane plot of GH would have to encircle -1 in the counterclockwise direction because of the negative factors in G, as noted previously. On the Nichols chart this same requirement means that GH would have to encircle the origin in the clockwise direction to cause $G/(1 + GH)$ to pass from G to $1/H$ above the origin, down on the right side and back to G below the

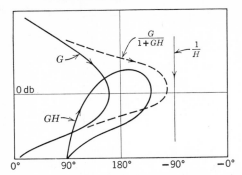

Fig. 7-7   Sketch of possible satisfactory transfer functions on Nichols chart.

origin. This is illustrated in Fig. 7-7 (not to scale). In addition to these requirements, the gain of G should be as large as possible for greater steady-state accuracy. In this regard it should be noted that the effective gain of G is related to the vertical location of the frequency response plot of G, regardless of the value of k_θ which causes this. Any effect which raises the plot of G raises the effective gain.

In order to cause the curves to assume a satisfactory form such as the one indicated in Fig. 7-7, it is necessary for the frequency response plot (Fig. 7-6) to vary as follows. GH should be relatively high at the frequency where $1/H$ crosses zero decibels and GH should cross zero decibels with -20 db/decade slope. Figure 7-6 shows that these objectives are accomplished with the gain constants selected, but the steep portion of GH starting at $\omega = 10$ is close to the cross-over frequency, and there is little prospect of increasing the gain of G although if the gain of H were decreased slightly, the performance might be somewhat improved. (This would mean $k_{\dot\theta}$ might be reduced slightly moving the corresponding zero on the root-locus plot a little farther to the left.) However, Fig. 7-6 does indicate that an increase in gain of G could be effected if another zero were added to H to reduce the steep slope of GH above $\omega = 10$. This investigation is left to the reader.

This discussion demonstrates how the various methods can be used in combination to achieve a clearer picture of the effects of various parameters on the system. It also shows that the frequency response method may be useful even for systems with negative time constants if it is used with the complex plane plot and Nichols chart in mind.

7.3 Flexible Missile

The discussion in Section 7.2 applies to the rigid-body missile. The transfer functions for the flexible missile are also given in Section 7.1. The root locus plot for the flexible missile is shown in Fig. 7-8. Only the loci in the upper half plane are shown. (Note that because there is a negative sign associated with H_1, the plot has the characteristics associated with regenerative feedback; that is, the angles to the open-loop poles and zeros sum to zero instead of 180 degrees, and in order for closed-loop poles to exist on the real axis there must be an even number of open-loop poles and zeros to the right instead of an odd number.) The similarity to the rigid body plot is readily noted and the three modes associated with body bending are easily identified. In this

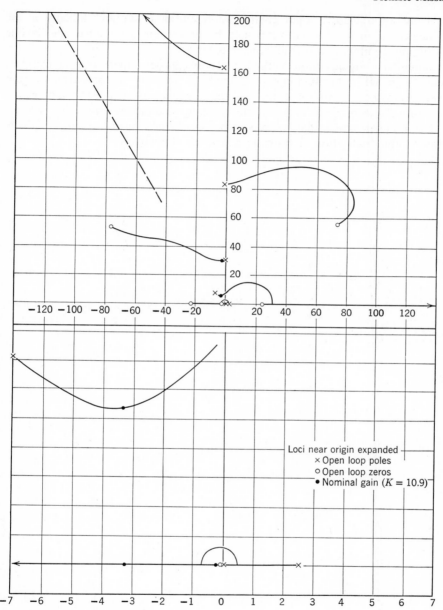

Fig. 7-8   Root locus, flexible body missile.

example the conclusions drawn from the rigid body analysis would not be altered significantly by body bending because the closed-loop poles associated with body bending are still near the open-loop poles at the gain values chosen. This might not be true of a system having different physical constants. For instance, in this example if the body stiffness were reduced, open-loop poles and zeros associated with body bending would approach the origin, creating more and more stability difficulty as the stiffness decreases, until eventually it would be impossible to stabilize the flexible missile with any combination of gain constants.

This chapter has shown how the methods and concepts developed in earlier chapters contribute to greater understanding of a complex system. The selection of gain parameters is not necessarily the optimum, and improvement could be made in the proposed control system. (Possible variations are suggested in the exercises.) However, one set of parameters which may be satisfactory has been determined with relatively little effort by the application of systematic methods of analysis.

CHAPTER 8

Digital Computers

8.1 Preliminary Comments

Many of the problems encountered in the analysis of vibrating systems must be solved by either digital or analogue computers; therefore, facility with these tools is important. In addition, computers of both types have become essential elements in control systems. This chapter deals with the use of digital computers, particularly in solving many of the problems developed in previous chapters.

Digital computers are especially useful in the solution of long problems involving numerous repetitive operations, problems which recur frequently enough so that the time required to write and "debug" a program can be amortized over a large number of applications, and problems which require a high degree of accuracy. Analogue computers, on the other hand, are usually more convenient to use when a problem requires numerous changes of variables during an investigation, where changes are suggested by results, so that there is a continuous interchange between the computer and the investigator, and where extreme accuracy is not a requirement.

The development of FORTRAN* and other similar coding methods which simplify the programming of digital computers has made it possible for anyone to make use of these computers with comparative ease. Excellent publications (Refs. 16 and 17) describe FORTRAN in great detail, including numerous simple examples which help the beginner to understand the system.

The approach used in this chapter is somewhat different. Instead of presenting the various aspects of FORTRAN programming and numerical analysis in isolated subsections that are convenient for explanation, a relatively complex problem is chosen which illustrates all important aspects of FORTRAN programming and many necessary details pertaining to numerical methods. In this way problems which arise in a numerical analysis are encountered in their natural order and the motivation for various procedures is better understood. FORTRAN statements are introduced as they become necessary or useful.

This approach also demonstrates that a novice who needs the capabilities of a

* Abbreviation for "formula translation."

computer to solve a problem which could not otherwise be solved can attack such a problem directly without a long learning period. This explanation is limited to FORTRAN in the interests of brevity and clarity (since FORTRAN is probably the most widely used coding method for scientific problems) and is directed to the beginner with an urgent "need to know," rather than the specialist in this field.

The objective, then, is to show by example various details of numerical analysis using the digital computer; to explain the FORTRAN language and clarify the procedures by which the problem is introduced to the computer, solved, and results reported by the computer; and to provide the necessary background so that the programs listed in the Appendix can be used to alleviate the more tedious numerical procedures of the earlier chapters.

The example chosen is part of a system set up for solving the various examples of the previous chapters. Although learning the FORTRAN language is quite easy, it still requires a great deal of time and patience to perfect a program, and especially a system of programs, to the point where problems can be easily solved. Therefore, in addition to the example which is explained in detail, listings of programs are given for solving most of the other problems of the previous chapters, and the programs are so devised that they can be used with each other by writing small connecting programs as desired. Programs are shown for determining normal modes of vibration, inverting matrices, obtaining flexibility matrices for some types of structures, obtaining the characteristic equation from a determinant whose elements are quadratics, factoring a high-order polynomial, and other problems. The programs were devised to use the Honeywell 800 at the computer facility of the University of Southern California. However, with appropriate modifications they can be used with any computer capable of using FORTRAN. The language used in these programs is known as FORTRAN II. Minor modifications would be required to convert these programs to FORTRAN IV.

8.2 Statement of Example Problem

This example demonstrates a method of determining the normal modes and frequencies of vibration by matrix iteration. The FORTRAN statements are referred to points on the flow chart and comments are included explaining the meaning of each statement. (The FORTRAN statements listed in Section 8.12 may be removed for greater convenience if desired. The same programs also appear in the Appendix.) The intention here is to show how to obtain a workable program, not necessarily the most efficient. The matrix equation to be solved is

$$\{x\} = \beta^2 [\delta][M]\{x\}$$

where $\{x\}$ is the column matrix or vector of variables
                    $[\delta]$ is the square matrix of influence coefficients
                    $[M]$ is the inertia matrix, often but not always diagonal
                    β is the natural frequency, rad/sec

The procedure is to assume $\{x\}$ to be used on the right side and calculate a new $\{x\}$ which will then be used again on the right side to calculate a more refined $\{x\}$, and so on.

The data which will be put into the program will be the elements of $[\delta]$ and $[M]$, the number of coordinates, number of modes desired, number of iterations permitted, and the required accuracy. The output will be the values of $\{x\}$, the corresponding values of β, and the number of iterations required to obtain the specified accuracy. Intermediate values of $\{x\}$ will also be printed in order to see how the process is converging for some examples, although in the use of the program this printing would be optional.

Block Diagram. In any problem involving a rather extensive calculation, as this one would probably be, it is almost mandatory that a block diagram (or information flow diagram) be made. The purpose of the diagram is to display the flow of information in such a way that the FORTRAN coding can be more easily written without the programmer becoming lost. It is not necessary for the block diagram to have any prescribed format, since it is for the benefit of the programmer himself, and it may contain as much detail as he desires. Often the diagram is changed as the program progresses. Although the diagram may take any form desired (many programmers prefer a vertical display to the horizontal display used here), it is advisable to include arrowheads on the lines connecting the blocks to indicate the direction of the flow of information.

Program Utilization. In the use of this program, data for the problem might be fed into the computer by a data card deck, or it might be computed by some other program. Also, the results of the computation might be needed in some other program. Therefore, in order to maintain as much flexibility as possible, the problem will be divided into three parts, an input portion, the computation itself, and an output portion. The input and output portions are relatively short, and different input and output programs can be written for different purposes. For the purpose of this example it will be assumed that data will be supplied in the form of cards and that the results will simply be printed. There will be three programs; an input program, designated A38INP1; the main computation, A38NM; and an output program, A38OUT1. The input program will read data from cards and store them on Tape 1, where the main program will read them. The results of the computation will also be stored on Tape 1, where the output program will read them and cause them to be printed. Both the input and output could be accomplished in the main program if it were not for the desirability of providing flexibility referred to earlier. (This flexibility could be provided by use of subroutines instead of separate main programs if the computer had a large capacity.) The rest of this chapter will be devoted to an explanation of the programs mentioned, and to a general discussion of FORTRAN programming. A listing of these three programs can be found at the end of the chapter, and the discussion refers to these listings and to the block diagrams which are also at the end of the chapter.

Source Program. A "source program" is a series of statements which instruct the computer as to how it shall solve a problem. Each statement is punched on a card in accord with a set of conventions which has been established, only one statement per card. The entire deck of cards, in the proper sequence, is read into the computer where the program is "compiled," or translated into instructions more suitable for the computer's use, and stored on a tape. This program is "executed" later; that is, data is fed into the computer using a separate data deck and the solution of the problem is accomplished according to the instructions in the source program. The source program is therefore of major interest at the present time, and most of the explanation which follows has to do with the preparation of a source program. The data deck used at the time of execution must be consistent with instructions contained in the source program.

8.3 Information Input to the Computer

Preliminaries. On the flow chart the first block, "Start," (usually using a square block) is represented in the listing of A38INP1 by the first 24 lines, which have the following significance. The first line, or card, has the word TITLE appearing, starting with the second column. The first column is left blank. The title in this example is A38INP1. The title may have as many as eight characters, either numbers or letters, but the first character must be a letter. However, these general comments may be modified to agree with the requirements of the particular computer facility where this program may be used. On the first line also may appear the programmer's name and the project number, as in this example. This depends on the conventions established by the computing facility to be used. The next 23 lines have a C entered in the first column. This signifies "comments," and these lines will be ignored by the compiler. These comments will appear in a listing of the souce program so that others who may wish to use the program will be able to do so intelligently. Comments may also appear later in the main body of the program. The comment cards may make use of all 80 columns on the card if desired. However, the rest of the statements in the program must not begin before Column 7 and must not extend past Column 72. Columns 2 to 5 may be used for statement numbers. Column 6 is left blank unless a statement is too long to fit within the 7 to 72 column limit. Then continuation cards may be used (as many as nine if necessary) and the number of the continuation card is inserted in Column 6. (An example appears later). Blanks in the statement itself will be ignored by the compiler, except for certain FORMAT statements discussed later, so it is permissible to include or omit blanks in the statement for greater clarity according to the programmer's wishes.

Variable Names. The second block on the flow diagram, "Read Data," requires a lengthy explanation. (An input or output operation is often indicated with an oval on the block diagram.) The data must be identified, or given a name. Lower-case letters and Greek letters are not used in FORTRAN. The name of a variable used in a program must begin with a capital letter and may consist of from one to six capital letters and/or numbers, except that the final letter should not be F unless the name is less than four characters long. The name should not be the same as a function, either, such as SIN, LOG, and other functions used in FORTRAN. A list of such functions appears in Section 8.9. The first letter in the name tells whether the number represented is a "fixed-point" number (integer) or a "floating-point" number (described later). If the first letter is I, J, K, L, M, or N, the number is a fixed-point number. If the first letter is any other letter except these, then the number represented is a floating-point number. Therefore, instead of $[\delta]$, the name DELTA will be used to designate this array of numbers, and instead of $[M]$, the name TMASS will be used. (MASS would indicate integer numbers and so should not be used.) The product $[\delta][M]$, the "dynamic matrix," will be designated DYN to indicate dynamic matrix.

Subscripted Variables and the DIMENSION Statement. In this problem the variables DELTA and TMASS are subscripted. (The word variable is used even if the quantity does not vary during the problem. A constant is simply a number, such as 3 or 24.2 used in the program, while any number defined by a name is termed a variable, regardless of whether it "varies" or not.) In order to indicate that a variable is a subscripted variable, a DIMENSION statement is used. This statement appears in the listing after the FORMAT statements, which will be discussed later. The DIMEN-SION statement specifies the possible size of the arrays of the variables defined, so that storage can be provided. As used here, the statement means that DELTA is a two-dimensional array which may be as large as 30 by 30, and similarly for TMASS. The name is followed by parentheses enclosing the numbers which indicate the possible size of the array. If the array is a one-dimensional array, only one number appears inside the parentheses. If it is a two-dimensional array, two numbers appear, separated by a comma. Provision is also made for three-dimensional arrays, in which case there are three numbers inside the parentheses, all separated by commas. If more than one variable appears in the DIMENSION statement, they are separated by commas as indicated. Every subscripted variable used in a program must be defined in a DIMEN-SION statement, and this statement must precede the use of the subscripted variable in the program. However, it does not have to be the first statement in the program, although it is good practice to put all DIMENSION statements at the beginning. This can be done by rearranging the cards after they have been punched.

READ and READ INPUT TAPE Statements and Statement Numbers. The first executable statement, READ INPUT TAPE 5, 18, INTPRT, IPRDTA causes transfer of two items into memory; namely, the numerical values of INTPRT and IPRDTA. The significance of the READ INPUT TAPE statement, rather than just READ, is that the data will be read from a magnetic tape rather than directly from data cards. It takes more computer time to read data cards than it does to read tape, so that if the input data is likely to involve many cards, it is better to transfer this data from data cards to tape first, which can be done without using valuable machine time. (This assumes that the computer facility has this capability.) The data in this example might involve as many as 1806 different numbers; consequently, tape is used. However, if data were to be read directly from cards, then instead of READ INPUT TAPE, only the statement READ would be used. The 5 after READ INPUT TAPE signifies the particular tape to be read. If Tape 1 were used, the 1 could be omitted and tape number one would be read anyway; however, if any other tape number were to be designated, the number (5, for instance) would have to appear.

The number following the 5, that is, 18, refers to the statement number of the FOR-MAT statement, which is described later. These statement numbers may be selected completely for convenience and need not be in sequence. There is always a FORMAT statement associated with a READ INPUT TAPE statement. Although the statement numbers need not be in sequence, it is desirable that they increase in some sort of systematic order so that later on it is easy to find a statement or a card when necessary. Therefore, it may be convenient to write the program so that there are perhaps five or ten numbers between each numbered statement. Then if it is necessary to insert additional numbered statements, the sequence is not destroyed.

The variable, INTPRT, is simply an indicator which is used to determine whether intermediate results will be printed before reaching the final results. If it is desired to see how the computation is progressing, this indicator can be given the value 1, otherwise zero. Of course, the program itself must make use of this indicator in this way. It is not itself a feature of FORTRAN, or of the computer. The variable IPRDTA is a similar indicator to control whether the original data should be printed.

After the first READ INPUT TAPE statement, there are five more READ INPUT TAPE statements, each introducing one item into the memory of the computer. These are the numerical values of N, M, ITER, ACC, and GMASS. N is the number of variables and also the order of the matrices, DELTA and TMASS. M is the number of modes desired, ITER the limiting number of iterations permitted, and ACC the required accuracy if the limiting number of iterations is not reached first. GMASS is the value of the generalized mass desired from the normalization of the modes.

The way these READ INPUT TAPE statements have been made, the numbers for the first two items, INTPRT and IPRDTA, will both appear on the same data card, whereas each of the next five items must appear on a separate data card, and in the order specified, when a problem is to be solved using this program (at the time of execution of the program). It would have been possible to have written one statement

READ INPUT TAPE 5, 25, INTPRT, IPRDTA, N, M, ITER, ACC, GMASS

in which the variables following the number 25 form a "list," and the FORMAT statement (discussed later) would be modified to the following:

25 FORMAT (I1, I1, I2, I2, I4, E17.9, E17.9)

If this had been done, then the five numbers would all be punched on one data card to agree with this FORMAT statement, as explained later.

Read Statements for Subscripted Variables. Some discussion of the next two READ INPUT TAPE statements is necessary. These statements cause the transmission from tape to memory of all of the elements of DELTA and TMASS which are actually used in the calculation, N^2 elements in all for each array. Instead of the statement used to transmit DELTA, the following statement might have been used: READ INPUT TAPE 5, 40, DELTA. When an array such as DELTA is named in such a statement without parentheses, all of the elements are transmitted. If the matrix were always the same size, such a statement would be used. However, in this instance it would complicate the preparation of the data to use this statement. If it had been desired to transmit only one element, for example, DELTA(1,3), then the parentheses enclosing the 1,3 indicate which element is transmitted. If only the third row of one of the matrices were to be transmitted, this could be accomplished with the statement READ INPUT TAPE 5, 40, (DELTA(3,J), J = 1,N). Here, the parenthesis which precedes DELTA and the one following N have a special significance. The first parenthesis indicates that more than one element is to be transmitted. The first element is transmitted, for J = 1, then the second parenthesis is encountered, which says to go back to the first parenthesis mark and do it again with J increased by 1 (unless otherwise indicated with a third number following J) and so on, until J = N. Statements of this type are often referred to as "Implied DO" statements; the significance of this name will be appreciated after the discussion of the DO statement.

Similarly, if the first, third, and fifth rows were to be transmitted, the statement would have been READ INPUT TAPE 5, 40, ((DELTA(I,J), J = 1,N), I = 1,5,2) Here, the two opening parentheses indicate that two indices will vary. When the second closing parenthesis is encountered, the indication is to go back to the first opening parenthesis and do everything as before but with 1 increased by 2 (the third number). This will be continued until I = 5. It is clear now that the entire DELTA matrix is transmitted with the statement

READ INPUT TAPE 5, 40, ((DELTA(I,J),J = 1,N), I = 1,N)

It is recalled that N has a specific value at the time this statement is executed, established by the data and a preceding statement.

Input Floating-Point FORMAT Statement. The FORMAT statements describe how the data cards will be punched and also give information to the computer as to how to interpret the numbers received from the data cards. The data must be punched on the cards so as to agree with these statements. Statement 40 is discussed first. Statement 40 is FORMAT (E17.9)

The significance of this statement is as follows. The numbers in the parentheses following FORMAT mean that there will be one number punched on each data card as floating-point numbers (designated by the E). It will take a total of 17 columns on each card to describe each number, or the width of the "field" is 17. The number will be understood to have 9 digits to the right of the decimal point if no decimal point is punched on the card. (This number, 9, could have been specified as any other number up to 9, if desired, but should not exceed 9.) The E also has another significance. It means that the number will be expressed with a multiplying factor of 10 to some exponential power, which will modify the position of the decimal point. As an example, the number -2431.58793 could be punched on the data card as $-243158793000E + 01$. [Notice that the decimal point for the number preceding the E is assumed to be just before the 1 because of the FORMAT statement which says that the number will have nine digits to the right of the decimal point. The E + 01 then states that this number is multiplied by 10^1. If the FORMAT statement had been FORMAT (E17.0), then the number -2431.58793 could be punched on the data card as $-243158793000E - 08$].

Floating-point numbers may also be specified on the FORMAT statement with an F, as in FORMAT (F11.8). This would describe a number requiring 11 spaces for its definition. It has 8 digits to the right of the decimal point if the data card does not specify the position of the decimal point. Thus, if the number punched on the card were $+2431587931$, the FORMAT statement means that the number intended is $+24.31587931$. However, if the number is punched on the data card with a decimal point indicated, then the position of the decimal point specified by the data card takes precedence over that specified by the FORMAT statement. That is, if the data card is punched $+2431.58793$, this is the number the computer would use rather than $+2.43158793$, which is what the computer would use if no decimal point were specified on the data card. This is true with either E or F designation.

In either floating-point designation there can be no more than 12 digits,* not counting the sign, decimal point, or exponential designation. However, the computer may only retain 8 significant figures* in computation, so there may be no need to specify numbers with more significant figures than 8 or 9. All floating-point numbers must be between 10^{-38} and 10^{+38}.* Some computers may retain 12 significant figures

---

* These ranges for either fixed- or floating-point numbers are typical but by no means universal. Consult the appropriate computer manual for exact information on this point.

with a range from 10^{-76} to 10^{+76}.* The plus sign in front of numbers may be omitted. (Fixed-point numbers may have any value between -32767 and $+32767$.)* It is not necessary to use all of the spaces provided in the field width designated in the FORMAT statement.

If more than one number is to be punched on each card, each with the same specification, it is necessary to indicate the number of fields needed—for example, FORMAT (4E17.9) would mean four numbers would be punched on each card. Each designation has advantages. If four elements are punched on each card the data deck is smaller, but if one number is punched on each card, corrections or changes may be facilitated. In a problem of this type it is more desirable to use the E specification than the F specification because of the possibility of large variations in the magnitudes of the elements of the matrices.

Input Fixed Point FORMAT Statements. The FORMAT statement, 18 FORMAT (I1,I1) has the following significance. The I designates an integer or fixed point number and the 1 states that the number consists of one digit. Similarly, 20 FORMAT (I2) indicates a two-digit fixed point number, etc. Only two digits are needed for N and M since they will never exceed 30 and since they will always be positive. If fixed-point numbers might have negative signs, then it would be necessary to provide a space for the sign too. For instance, if N could have been -86 it would have been necessary to use I3 in the FORMAT statement in order to allow for the sign. If fixed-point numbers may have any value between -32767 and $+32767$ for the computer used, the field width for a fixed-point number need not exceed six. Of course there is no decimal point, so no provision need be specified in the FORMAT statement. Also, when the data cards are punched, it is necessary that the decimal point shall not be punched, even at the end of the figures.

Additional Input Information. If the six statements had been combined into one, as indicated previously, so that the FORMAT statement would be

25 FORMAT (I1, I1, I2, I2, I4, E17.9, E17.9)

then all seven numbers would have to be punched on one data card, the first number, INTPRT, to agree with I1, the second, IPRDTA, to agree with I1, the third, N, to agree with I2, etc.) The data card must be prepared with the values in the proper order and positions to agree with the fields of the FORMAT statement. The statement 25 FORMAT (2I1, 2I2, I4, 2E17.9) is equivalent to the previous FORMAT statement, and the statement 25 FORMAT (5I4, 2E17.9) could also be used, with proper care in the preparation of data cards. Although FORMAT statements may appear anywhere in the program, it is customary to rearrange the deck after punching so that the FORMAT statements come at the beginning of the program.

When an array is transmitted without the use of subscripting parentheses as in READ INPUT TAPE 5, 40, DELTA and FORMAT (E17.9), it may be necessary to know the convention of how the numbers in DELTA are related to the various spaces defined in the FORMAT statement. The answer is that the number designated as DELTA(1,1) will be the first number followed by the number designated as DELTA(2,1), and so on to DELTA(30,1), after which will come DELTA(1,2), DELTA(2,2), etc. It may not be necessary to know this correspondence, but if it is,

---

* These ranges for either fixed- or floating-point numbers are typical but by no means universal. Consult the appropriate computer manual for exact information on this point.

this will explain it. The first number in the parenthesis varies first, then the second, and then the third (if the array is three-dimensional).

Use of a Work Tape. All the information necessary for the computation has now been read into the computer memory. The next three statements store this information on a "work tape," designated as Tape 1, so that the following program (A38NM) can read the information from this tape rather than from an input tape or cards. This allows A38NM to be more general than would be the case if the input data were read in A38NM, because other programs rather than data cards may be used to generate the information stored on Tape 1. Statement 100 says that a list composed of N, M, ITER, ACC, INTPRT, IPRDTA, GMASS, in that order, is stored on Tape 1 by one WRITE TAPE statement. This is one "logical record." Statement 110 says that a total of $2N^2$ numbers are stored in the next logical record. These are the elements of DELTA and TMASS. The parentheses and indices have the same significance as they had in the READ INPUT TAPE statements. Tape 1 was rewound with the statement REWIND 1 before these WRITE TAPE statements were made.

This is the end of the input program, A38INP1, so the statements STOP and END appear. These are both necessary. (However, the computer facility may prefer the statement CALL EXIT instead of STOP.)

In the next program (A38NM) the first executable statements (after rewinding the tapes) cause this information to be recovered from Tape 1 by READ TAPE 1 statements which are exactly like the WRITE TAPE 1 statements. (The comment, DIMENSION, COMMON and FORMAT statements at the beginning of A38NM are not executable statements, but just furnish information to the compiler.) The reason for the next statement, MC = N, will become clear later.

8.4 Information Output from the Computer

When the results of a computation are received by the interested individual, he may wish to know what numbers were used by the computer in solving the problem. It is often desirable to have the data used by the computer printed on the same sheet with the results. On the other hand, a very large amount of printing might be a nuisance. Consequently, the next block on the diagram, which calls for the data to be printed, may be avoided or not, according to the wishes of the individual using the program. In fact, most of the printing in the program can be avoided if desired, and so several of these blocks are cross hatched. This is not a general convention, but is used here to indicate that wherever one of these blocks is encountered, a bypass to avoid these blocks will be provided. In this program the use of the bypass will depend on the value of INTPRT, a variable whose name suggests "intermediate printing," and whose value is part of the data and is in the memory of the computer at this time. If the value of INTPRT is 1, the intermediate results are supposed to be printed; if it is zero the printing is supposed to be bypassed. A similar index, IPRDTA, will be used to control whether the original data will be printed.

The IF Statement. An IF statement can be used to instruct the computer as to how it should select among alternatives. Although the IF statement is a control statement, rather than an output statement, it is convenient to discuss it at this time because the problem logic requires its use. The statement, IF(IPRDTA) 280, 280, 200, means that if the quantity within the parentheses, IPRDTA, is negative, the computer will go to

Statement 280 to find out what to do next. If the value of IPRDTA is positive, control will pass to Statement 200, and if the value of IPRDTA is zero, control will pass to Statement 280. The three numbers following the closing parentheses are the numbers of the statements to which transfer is made if the value of IPRDTA is negative, zero, or positive, respectively. Although the value of IPRDTA by definition should never be negative, and therefore there is no logical need to specify a number for this possibility, it is still necessary to provide a number or the compiler will indicate an error. Therefore, either 200 or 280 would be equally satisfactory for the first of the three numbers.

The PRINT Statement and Output FORMAT Statements. If there is to be printing, the next statement to be executed is Statement 200, which says PRINT 210. Here the number following PRINT is again a statement number, this time a FORMAT statement. This FORMAT statement will specify how a particular line of printing will appear. The three characters 75H following the opening parenthesis in Statement 210 mean that the next 75 spaces after the H will be printed exactly as they appear in the statement, including blanks. (Here is an instance where blanks will not be ignored by the compiler.) In this statement these 75 spaces form a single line of printing, which conveys the information that the data will follow and also indicates how the elements of the matrices will be identified. This whole statement could not be punched on a card in the first 72 columns, and thus a continuation card is used, and the number, 1, appears in Column 6, since this is the first continuation card in this statement. Notice that all blanks are counted in determining the width of the field: that is, the 75 spaces required for this printing. The letter, H, following the 75 stands for "Hollerith," and is used whenever descriptive text is to be printed. The three slashes are outside of the Hollerith field and mean that there will be triple spacing after this line of printing. (Two slashes would mean double spacing, etc.) It is possible to print up to 120 characters on one line. If more than 120 characters were to be printed, another PRINT and FORMAT statement would be necessary.

After Statement 200 is another PRINT statement, this time with a "list." Again, as with all PRINT statements, the number immediately following PRINT is the number of the appropriate FORMAT statement. Then come the names of several variables whose values are to be printed, the list, separated by commas as shown. The associated FORMAT statement, 220, describes the line of print in which these variables will appear. This time the Hollerith fields are mixed with the fields describing the numbers. Also, the first group of characters, 1H2, determines how many lines are skipped before this or the next line of printing, an alternate method to the slashes used in the previous statement. These points are explained in more detail later.

There are several ways to get the matrices printed. For instance, the two statements

PRINT 60, DELTA

60   FORMAT (E14.7)

would print the elements of DELTA. However, it would print all 900 elements of the possible 30 by 30 matrix, even if the actual matrix were only 3 by 3. Also, there would be only one element printed on each line. Obviously, this would result in a great deal of unnecessary paper. An improvement over this method would be the two statements:

PRINT 60, ((I, J, DELTA(I,J), J = 1, N), I = 1,N)

60   FORMAT (1H0, 3HI = I4, 3HJ = I4, E20.7)

This would have the effect of printing each element of the actual matrix along with its row number and column number, and therefore would avoid the printing of all the blanks if the actual matrix is not 30 by 30. However, there is still only one element printed on each line, which would mean much paper for large matrices. In this program and in others it will often be necessary to require the printing of a matrix, and when this occurs, it would be preferable if the line of print were fully utilized. Although this could be accomplished with a number of statements whenever such a printing is required, it is convenient to devise a subroutine for this purpose (thereby providing an opportunity to examine this important subject). First, some discussion of the two methods already described is necessary.

Probably the simplest form of a PRINT statement is one such as the following, where L, B, C, D would be previously defined variables.

PRINT 60, L, B, C, D
60 FORMAT (I4, 2E20.7, F20.7)

Whenever a PRINT statement is used, there must be an accompanying FORMAT statement, which will specify how the printed information will appear on the line. Each PRINT and FORMAT statement defines one line of print. Here the L must be a fixed-point variable, and B, C, and D must be floating-point to agree with the respective four fields indicated in the FORMAT statement. The field for the fixed-point variable is four spaces wide, so L must have four or less digits. If L has fewer than four digits, the numbers will be printed as far to the right in the field as possible. The floating-point numbers for B, C, and D are also printed as far as possible to the right in their respective fields, which are 20 spaces wide. One line of printing can accommodate up to 120 characters or spaces so that the sum of the field widths must not exceed this number, and usually it is desirable to arrange the field widths in relation to the numbers to be printed therein in such a way that spaces will appear between the numbers for easy reading. In this example there will be spaces between numbers, since the field widths are wider than the numbers to be printed. The number following the decimal point (7 in this example) specifies the number of figures which will be printed following the decimal point. Therefore, the number 123.45678 in the memory of the computer would appear as 0.1234567E03 when printed subject to the control of the specification E20.7. It would appear as 0.123E03 if printed under control of E20.3. The specification 1PE20.7 would cause this number to be printed as 1.2345678E02 and the specification 4PE20.3 would cause the number to appear as 1234.567E−01. (The 1P or 4P causes the decimal point to be moved one or four places to the right with the exponent of 10 reduced accordingly.)

PRINT Statements for Subscripted Variables. As indicated in connection with the READ statement, when a subscripted variable is to be printed, specific elements may be picked out to be printed by indicating the subscripts in the parentheses, or the whole array will be printed if the parentheses are omitted. However, the two statements

PRINT 60, DELTA
60 FORMAT (E14.7)

would cause DELTA(1,1) to be printed on the first line, DELTA(2,1) on the second line, etc. to DELTA(30,1), after which DELTA(1,2), DELTA(2,2), DELTA(3,2), etc., would be printed each on a separate line until the entire 30 by 30 matrix is printed out, each element on a separate line. If most of these were zero, too much paper would be generated.

Several features are illustrated in the two statements

$$\text{PRINT 60 ((I, J, DELTA(I,J), J = I,N), I = I,N)}$$
$$\text{60   FORMAT (1H} \odot \text{, 3HI} \odot = \text{I4, 6H} \odot \odot \odot \text{J} \odot = \text{I4, E20.7)}$$

(Whenever the symbol $\odot$ is used in this text it is to be interpreted as a blank. It is not a symbol to be punched. It is a space to be left unpunched. Ordinarily, the compiler will ignore blanks, so it does not matter whether the programmer provides blanks for better legibility. However, in the Hollerith statement blanks are significant, and when the card is punched care must be taken to provide exactly the specified number of unpunched columns.) The PRINT and FORMAT statements specify that there will be three numbers printed on each line, the value of I, of J, and of DELTA(I,J). I and J would both be 1 for the first line. Then J is increased by 1 and the printing is repeated on the second line. (If J were to be increased by any number other than 1, the number would appear as the third number in J = 1, N, 2 for instance.) J is increased again and a new printing made, and this process is continued until after J = N. Then I is increased by 1 and the whole process is repeated starting with J = 1 again. This continues until I also reaches N. The parentheses and commas in the PRINT statement are necessary. As in the similar READ statement, this PRINT statement could be called an "implied DO" statement. (The significance of the name will be better appreciated after the discussion of the DO statement.)

The FORMAT statement demonstrates the method used to print letters or words intermingled with the numbers, and also shows one way to control the spacing of the lines of printing. The first symbols following the opening parenthesis indicate how many spaces should follow the line being printed. That is, the expression 1H$\odot$ indicates that the next line* of print will follow with single spacing. The expression 1H0 (zero) means that double spacing occurs after the current line is printed. The symbol 1H1 means that the next information after the current line will be printed at the top of the next sheet. 1H2, 1H3, etc. to 1H9 mean that 2, 3, etc., to 9 lines will be skipped before the next printing. 1H+ means that no spacing will occur after the current line is printed. A comma is necessary after this first set of symbols. The next set of symbols are 3HI$\odot$ = I4. As explained previously, the H here stands for "Hollerith" and means that the next symbols which appear will be printed just as they appear, including blanks, for as many spaces as the number which precedes the H. In this example, then, there are three spaces. The letter I will be printed in the first space, the second space will be blank, and in the third space an equals sign will be printed. This uses up the Hollerith field. The next field is four spaces wide (the 4 in I4). A fixed point number, the value of I, will be printed at the right of this field. Since I is at most a number of two digits, there will be a space between the equal sign and the value of I. It is seen that the previous two statements would cause a line of printing such as the following:

$$\text{I} = 12, \quad \text{J} = 16 \qquad 0.2647019\text{E} - 02$$

---

* These are the conventions followed by the programs of the Appendix. However, the spacing convention for most computers refers to the spacing between the current line and the *previous* line rather than the following line.

WRITE OUTPUT TAPE Statements. The entire discussion concerning PRINT statements applies also to writing the output on a tape to be printed from the tape in a separate operation. Replace the word PRINT with WRITE OUTPUT TAPE 3, (if tape 3 is to be used). A typical statement similar to one of the previously described PRINT statements is

WRITE OUTPUT TAPE 3, 60, ((I, J, DELTA(I,J), J = 1,N), I = 1,N)
60   FORMAT (1H⊙,3HI⊙ = I4, 6H⊙ ⊙ ⊙J⊙ = I4, E20.7)

Requirements for the Matrix Print-Out. With these preliminaries understood, it is possible to devise a subroutine which would print several elements in each line instead of just one. Suppose it is desired to print five elements in each line, with the corresponding value of I and J. Therefore, suppose a typical row might appear as

(12,11) −0.123456789E + 03/(12,12) + 0.314279842E − 02/(12,13), etc.

In the parentheses are the row and column number, respectively. The elements are separated by the slashes for greater clarity. Five such elements can be printed on each line. Since one row might contain as many as 30 elements, it might take six lines of print for each row of the matrix. These six lines, or as many lines as are necessary for one row of the matrix, should be single spaced, with double spacing between the matrix rows. Also, if the matrix is smaller than the maximum possible (30 by 30), it would be desirable not to print all the zeros. Although this could be accomplished easily with DO statements in the main program as described later, logic based on IF statements is used for purposes of illustration, a small flow chart is constructed to keep track of the logic, and the printing is accomplished with a subroutine instead of the main program.

8.5 Subroutines

A subroutine is a separate source program, almost the same as a main program. It has its own title and FORTRAN statements, and its variables are completely independent of the variables in the main program unless specific action is taken to relate these variables. The subroutine source program is not included in the main program, and it is compiled separately.

Probably the most important reason for using subroutines is that a particular sequence of computations, or other action, is often useful in many different investigations, and it is convenient to write the program once as a subroutine and then call for its use in the various main programs where it may be applicable (or even in various locations in a single main program). Also, it is often convenient to break a large, complex problem into smaller parts for reasons of efficiency and sometimes because of computer limitations on the number of some types of statements which may be used in a single program. It may be that some problems are so large that even the use of subroutines is not sufficient to overcome capacity limitations, and the investigation must be broken into separate main programs. (The A55 series in the appendix is an example.)

In the example of this chapter a matrix inversion is needed at one point. Since this is useful in many other applications, and is a rather lengthy computation, a matrix inversion subroutine (A37IMS) is used. However, the simpler printing subroutine described in this section is more convenient for explanation purposes. This printing could be accomplished more easily using implied DO statements, but the subroutine is written to demonstrate use of logic based on IF statements.

Subroutine Name and Variables. The first statement in the subroutine program is SUBROUTINE A37PM starting in Column 7. This establishes that the name of this subroutine is A37PM (the "PM" for "print matrix"). The name of a subroutine may be any combination of six or less letters or numbers, the first of which must be a letter and the last of which must not be F if the name is more than three characters long. Since a subroutine program is completely independent of the main program, the variables and statement numbers in the subprogram might or might not be the same as variables and statement numbers in the main program. There is no necessity to avoid duplication.

The next statement in the subroutine is DIMENSION PM(30,30). This establishes the fact that PM may be a 30 by 30 array of floating-point numbers. The next statement, COMMON NPM, MPM, PM, will be discussed later.

It is now necessary to discuss the logic of the subroutine, which is most conveniently described by the block diagram. The variables NPM and MPM are fixed-point numbers, the number of columns and rows respectively of the matrix to be printed. These numbers are data as far as the subroutine is concerned. The fixed-point variables, I, J, NT, are defined in the three statements following the FORMAT statements and in the first three blocks of the diagram. Then, four more variables, J1, J2, J3, J4, are defined. The statements defining these variables are "arithmetic statements" and are like algebraic equations, with certain differences to be discussed later. The only precaution necessary is that the new variables be fixed-point variables, since they are defined in terms of fixed-point variables and constants. (It would be wrong to write $R = J + 1$, for instance, because R would be a floating-point variable, unless it were really desired to change from fixed to floating point variables.

Control Statements and Logic Based on the IF Statement. If there are exactly five elements in one row of PM, these five elements are supposed to be printed and then double spacing provided before the next five elements are printed. If there are more or less than five elements, different action must be taken. This requires a decision. A new variable is defined, IND1 (for "Index 1"), which is the number of columns less the variable NT (which is now 5). If this variable is zero, the first row is to be printed, followed by double spacing. If IND1 is positive, there are more than five elements, and transfer is made to a different line of action. If it is negative, there are less than five elements and still different action is required. This is all accomplished by an IF statement. As described previously, the statement

IF (IND1) 11, 4, 9

means that if IND1 is negative, transfer is made to statement 11, if IND1 is zero, transfer is made to statement 4, and if IND1 is positive, transfer is made to statement 9. These numbers are also used on the block diagram in order to make the correspondence between the block diagram and the program statements more easily recognized. Usually, however, the numbers on the block diagram do not correspond with the program statement numbers because the block diagram is constructed first. A decision is usually indicated by a diamond-shaped box on the block diagram.

If there are five elements in the first row, transfer is to Statement 4, as explained above. Statements 4 and 5 describe how the printed line will appear. There is nothing new in these two statements. A continuation statement is needed, as indicated in column 6, since all of one statement will not fit in the 72 spaces available for each statement. Note that parentheses and commas are called for by use of the Hollerith field specification and that the first Hollerith specification in the FORMAT statement specifies that double spacing will occur after the current line is printed.

The next thing to do is to find out if this is the last row of the matrix to be printed. (So far, I is still 1.) Another index is defined, IND2 = MPM − 1. If this index is zero, there are no more rows to be printed and control should be returned to the main program. If it is positive, there are more rows to be printed, so I will be increased by one and the entire process will be repeated. Although in this example it is not possible for IND2 to be negative, it is necessary to provide a statement number for this possibility as far as the IF statement is concerned. Accordingly, the statement number 21 is used for this possibility in IF (IND2) 21, 21, 7. If control is transferred to Statement 7 (that is, there are more rows to be printed), then I = I + 1 has the effect of increasing I by one. This arithmetic statement (which is obviously erroneous from an algebraic point of view) means that the new value of I will be the old value increased by 1. In this respect arithmetic statements differ somewhat from algebraic equations. The same result could have been achieved with two statements such as

$$IX = I + 1$$
$$I = IX$$

where IX is just a dummy variable; but the convention used allows this to be accomplished with the single statement, I = I + 1.

After I is increased by 1, a transfer is made by the statement GO TO 1. This statement causes the computer to refer to Statement 1 for its next instruction. It is clear now that each row of five elements will be printed with double spacing between rows until I = MPM, the total number of rows of the matrix, after which transfer will be made to a statement RETURN. This is necessary to return control to the main program. An END statement is also necessary to indicate the end of the subroutine. This is the last statement in the subroutine. IF, GO TO, and RETURN statements are examples of "control statements," which tell the computer where to look for the next instruction.

However, there were the other possibilities that the number of elements in the row might be either more or less than five. If there were more than five elements, transfer was to Statement 9. This statement, along with 10, is just like 4 and 5 except that single spacing occurs instead of double spacing. After the first line of print, J is increased by 5, so that the next line of print will print elements five to ten (or less if there are less than ten elements), and NT is increased by 5 in order that IND1 will tell whether there are exactly 5 more elements to be printed, or more or less than 5. If exactly 5 more elements remain to be printed, the procedure will be the same as if there were only 5 elements. If more than 5 elements remain to be printed, then control will come back to 9 again and J and NT will again be increased by 5 until eventually all the elements will be printed, or else IND1 will become negative.

If there were originally less than five elements, control would have transferred to Statement 11 (Block 11 on flow chart). IND1 would be negative for this to occur. IND1 is then increased by one and tested again. If it is zero, four elements are printed. If it is still negative, another one is added, and so on. Sooner or later IND1 is zero and the appropriate number of elements are printed followed by double spacing, since this is certain to be the last of the first row of the matrix. After this, it is necessary to know if there are more of the matrix rows to be printed, so control is transferred to Statement 6 so that this can be determined. If there are more rows, I is increased by one and the entire procedure is repeated.

Output FORMAT Statements. The subroutine as written makes use of several FORMAT statements (Statements 5, 13, 15, 18, and 20) where actually one (Statement 5) would have been sufficient. The only difference between these FORMAT statements is that the number of fields is different for each statement. If the print statements that refer to Statements 13, 15, 18, or 20 had referred to Statement 5, the presence of the excess number of fields would cause no difficulty. On the other hand, if Statement 4 had referred to Statements 13, 15, 18, or 20, the five elements designated by Statement 4 would not all have been printed on the same line, but on as many lines as necessary with the FORMAT statement used (five lines for Statement 20, three lines for Statement 18, two lines for Statements 15 or 13).

Printing with DO and Implied DO Statements. As mentioned earlier, the entire subroutine could have been written using DO statements, instead of IF statements, but another portion of the program is used to illustrate the use of the DO statement. However, as an illustration of the power of the DO statement and the "implied" DO statement, the entire matrix could have been printed in the desired format with the statements

```
      DO 30 I = 1, MPM
      PRINT 10, (I, J, PM(I,J), J = 1, NPM)
   30 PRINT 50
   10 FORMAT (1H⊙, 5(1H(I2, 1H, I2, 1H) E16.9, 1H/))
   50 FORMAT (1H⊙, 1H⊙)
```

The DO statement is discussed later and the implied DO statement (PRINT 10, etc.) was discussed earlier. Statement 30 merely causes an extra line to be skipped after one row of the matrix is printed in order to achieve the required double spacing between matrix rows.

The COMMON and DIMENSION Statements. This completes the discussion of the subroutine, except for the COMMON statement at the beginning. The COMMON statements in the main program and the subroutine are the links which connect the two programs. What these two statements do is identify variables in the main program and in the subroutine program as being identical. Thus, the statement COMMON N, MC, DYN in the main program and the statement COMMON NPM, MPM, PM in the subroutine establish the fact that N and NPM are the same (and, in fact, occupy the same location in the computer memory), and MC and MPM are the same, and the arrays DYN and PM are identical. It should be noted that the COMMON statement is used even if the variables in the main program and in the subroutine both have the same name. It is best to keep these variables in corresponding order, as indicated here, but actually the arrays are assigned to one area of memory and the single variables to another area so that the order N, DYN, MC or DYN, N, MC will be satisfactory. In the main program the number of rows and columns are both N, but the subroutine can have different numbers for the rows and columns. Therefore, a new variable, MC, is defined in the main program. This variable is the number of rows of the matrix, and it is identified with MPM in the subroutine by the COMMON statement. MC is set equal to N before the subroutine is called.

It is necessary that the DIMENSION statement in the subroutine shall specify the same size and shape array as the corresponding variable in the main program. DYN is a 30 × 30 array in the main program (maximum dimensions). PM must also be specified as a 30 × 30 array in the subroutine, since these variables correspond to each other because of the COMMON statement. If PM were given dimensions of 40 × 40, for instance, an error would result in the selection of elements to be printed.

Calling the Subroutine. When it is desired that the computer should refer to a subroutine for its next instructions, a CALL statement is used. An example occurs in Program A38NM immediately after Statement 240, where this printing subroutine is called with the statement CALL A37PM. At that point the subroutine takes command, and the computer receives instructions from the subroutine until the RETURN statement in the subroutine is reached. The computer then returns to the statement in the main program immediately following the CALL statement, which must be an executable statement. (In this instance the statement is PRINT 250.)

A subroutine may call another subroutine, to any depth, but it cannot call itself.

Subroutine with Arguments. Another way to link a subroutine and main program together is to use "arguments." The arguments are enclosed in parentheses in the title of the subroutine. In this example the title statement could be

SUBROUTINE A37PM(NPM, MPM, PM)

Then the statement which calls the subroutine could be

CALL A37PM(N, MC, DYN)

The arguments, or parameters, of the two statements are matched in the same order, and the necessary exchange of information between the main program and subroutine can occur.

The arguments of the SUBROUTINE statement must not appear in the COMMON statement in the subroutine if there is one, and they must not possess subscripting parentheses, but an argument may be the name of an array such as PM in this instance. It is permissible to use subscripting parentheses in an appropriate argument of the CALL statement, however. For instance, if N had been a dimensioned variable, then N(2) could be used as an argument in the CALL statement (but not in the SUBROUTINE statement).

8.6 The Matrix Iteration

The DO Statement. Attention is now directed back to the main program. The statement PRINT 230 and the accompanying FORMAT statement identify the next printing, which will be the matrix DELTA. Since it is the matrix DYN which is identified with the matrix PM in the subroutine through the COMMON statement, it is necessary to move the matrix DELTA into the space occupied by DYN before calling the subroutine to print this matrix (a step which could be avoided by using arguments in the subroutine instead of the COMMON statement). This is accomplished by the three statements,

DO 240 I = 1,N
DO 240 J = 1,N
240   DYN(I,J) = DELTA(I,J)

The DO statement is very powerful and easy to use when it is necessary to do an operation repeatedly. Consider the statement

$$DO\ 240\ J = 1,N$$
$$240\quad DYN(1,J) = DELTA(1,J)$$

This means that everything from the DO statement down to statement 240 (in this instance the very next statement) will be done once with J = 1 and then with J = 2, J = 3, etc., to J = N. If J were to be increased more than one each time, there would be a comma after the N and another number would appear which would specify how much J would be increased each time. The previous two statements then say that DYN(1,1) = DELTA(1,1) and DYN(1,2) = DELTA(1,2), etc., or each element in the first row of DYN is equal to the corresponding element in the first row of DELTA.

These DO statements can be nested as in this example. The statement

$$DO\ 240\ I = 1,N$$

causes first I = 1 and the second DO statement executed, which has the effect of setting the first row of DYN equal to the first row of DELTA, and then I = 2 and the second DO statement executed again, which would cause the second row of DYN to be set equal to the second row of DELTA. This continues until I = N. It is recalled that N itself has a definite numerical value at this time. The numbers which follow the = in the DO 240 statement must be fixed-point, unsigned constants or nonsubscripted variables, and the second number must not be less than the first number. The third number may be omitted if the increment by which I or J is increased is one. Of course it is not necessary to use I, J, or N for these indices. Any fixed point variable can be used. However, the indices must not be altered by any statement within the range of the DO statement.

The statement, CALL A37PM, causes control to pass to the subroutine, where DELTA is printed, after which control is returned to the next statement after the CALL statement by the RETURN statement in the subroutine. In order to print TMASS, these elements must be moved into the DYN locations. This is done and TMASS printed, and an indication is made that all the data has been recorded.

Matrix Multiplication. The series of DO statements ending with Statement 290 causes the multiplication of the matrix DELTA by the matrix TMASS. First I = 1, then J = 1, then DYN(I,J) = 0.0 means DYN(1,1) = 0.0. Element DYN(I,J) is to be computed by accumulation of a number of products. Each time a multiplication is performed, the product is added to the previous sum. Therefore, DYN(I,J) must be zero before this process is started. This is often termed "initialization." Now, since I and J are both 1, the statements

$$DO\ 290\ K = 1,N$$
$$290\quad DYN(I,J) = DYN(I,J) + DELTA(I,K) * TMASS(K,J)$$

mean

$$DO\ 290\ K = 1,N$$
$$290\quad DYN(1,1) = DYN(1,1) + DELTA(1,K) * TMASS(K,1)$$

which says that

$$DYN(1,1) = 0.0 + DELTA(1,1) * TMASS(1,1)$$
$$+ DELTA(1,2) * TMASS(2,1)$$
$$+ etc.$$

(The symbol * indicates multiplication.) After this one element is calculated, J becomes 2 with I still 1, and the process is repeated to obtain the numerical value of DYN(1,2). This is repeated for all the J's with I = 1. Finally, I is changed to 2 and everything is repeated. This continues until I has ranged through all its values, 1 to N in this instance. This is the actual dynamic matrix and is now printed out (by calling the subroutine again) if INTPRT is positive.

Later on it is discovered that DYN and TMASS need to be saved on tape for subsequent use and that DELTA should be made into the unit matrix. This is explained later. However, for the present the series of statements from 320 to 340 will be ignored.

Statement 350, a DO statement, merely says that all of the rest of the program down to Statement 880 will be repeated for modes 1 through M. The variable, MODE, is the mode number. The block on the flow chart indicated by ① corresponds to Statement 350. Some printing follows, which needs no explanation.

The block, ASSUME{X} = {1}, is accomplished by statements

$$\text{DO 390 I} = 1,\text{N}$$
$$390 \quad \text{X(I)} = 1.0$$

This simply means that the first assumed values of the variables, X(I), are unity. The next statement is a DO statement corresponding to the diamond block on the diagram. This statement causes the series of statements from immediately after 390 to 500 to be executed repeatedly a total of ITER times. This is the limiting number of iterations allowed. It may be that the accuracy required will be satisfied before this number of iterations occurs. If so, a transfer out of the DO loop will occur, as explained later. In each iteration a new modal column will be calculated from the old column. Therefore, after the new column is computed, it must be moved to a different location, and becomes the old column for the next iteration. On the block diagram this is indicated by the block {XA} = {X} and accomplished in the source program with the two statements ending with Statement 400.

Computation of the Normal Mode. The block{X} = [DYN]{XA} means to make the matrix multiplication indicated. This is accomplished in a way similar to the multiplication of DELTA and TMASS with the four statements ending with Statement 410. This new modal column must then be normalized as discussed below.

In the text, normalization was accomplished by dividing all the coordinates by the value of the Nth one. In most problems this would be satisfactory. However, it is possible that in some problem the deflection of the Nth coordinate in some mode might be zero. In fact any coordinate might be zero in some mode. Therefore, division by any particular coordinate could conceivably encounter difficulty. Since all coordinates could not be zero, one possible way to circumvent this difficulty might be to search for a nonzero coordinate and divide by that coordinate. However, this might lead to normalization on different coordinates in different iterations and cause convergence difficulties and also other possible troubles. Another alternative might be to divide by the sum of the absolute values of the coordinates. However, the method of normalization selected here is to divide by a number so selected that the generalized mass is equal to a value specified in the data. This is often chosen to be equal to the sum of all masses involved in the calculation, but causing the value to be obtained from input data allows for possible deviation in instances where such a convention would be awkward. This normalization will be accomplished if the coordinates are all divided by

$$\sqrt{\frac{\{\tilde{X}\}[M]\{X\}}{\text{generalized mass}}}$$

This number is computed by the series of nine statements beginning with the statement following 410 and ending with the statement following 420. The coordinates are then normalized by dividing, which is accomplished by the two statements ending with 430. (The slash in an arithmetic statement denotes division.) There is nothing new in these eleven statements except the use of SQRTF, which will be discussed later.

The original inertia matrix has to be used for this calculation, and so it was necessary to save TMASS on tape to avoid using memory. This was done previously with the WRITE TAPE 2 statement following Statement 320. Since Tape 2 had been rewound prior to writing (back at the beginning of the program), it must now be rewound before reading. Whenever a WRITE TAPE statement is made, a "logical record" is formed, and the list of variables in the WRITE TAPE statement comprises all the information contained in the logical record. Whenever a READ TAPE statement is used, it is necessary to be careful that the list of variables to be read does not exceed the list of variables in that particular logical record. In this instance the list of variables read is the same as the list written, and consequently no trouble should be encountered.

The square-root function is one of several functions often encountered in problems. The square root of a quantity can be indicated by simply enclosing the quantity in parentheses as indicated in the next statement after 420. The quantity in parentheses is the "argument" of the function. A more detailed discussion of functions is given in Section 8.9.

Accuracy. "Determine ACCUR" on the block diagram means to determine the present accuracy. The accuracy is supposed to indicate how close the variables are to their final theoretically correct values. However, since the final values are not known, a determination of the amount of change of the variables from one iteration to the next would provide equivalent information. The smaller the change from one iteration to the next, the nearer are the variables to their final values. One test which immediately suggests itself is to take the difference of the value of a coordinate for two successive iterations, divide the difference by one of the values, and then compare the absolute values of these fractions for different coordinates, choosing the largest as a measure of the accuracy. This would be satisfactory except for the possibility that one or more coordinates might be tending toward zero in some mode, and then difficulty would be encountered with the division. In order to avoid this, the accuracy will be defined in a manner similar to the one just described, except that the sum of the absolute values of the coordinates for the latest iteration will be used in the denominator, and the sum of the absolute values of the differences between iterations will be used in the numerator. That is,

$$\text{ACCUR} = \frac{\sum_{k=1}^{m} |X_{k\text{latest}} - X_{k\text{previous}}|}{\sum_{k=1}^{m} |X_{k\text{latest}}|}$$

(Perhaps a more descriptive name for this variable would be ERROR instead of ACCUR, but the implication is satisfactory.) Statements 431 through 441 accomplish this. The absolute value function. ABSF( ), is used here. Discussion of functions may be found in Section 8.9.

This relative error is more significant than an absolute error. Suppose two numbers of the order of magnitude of 10^{20} differ only in the 12th figure. They are obviously nearly equal; yet the difference between them is of the order of 10^8. This appears to be a large number, and an iteration depending on its magnitude would not stop if this number were compared with a required difference of perhaps 10^{-11}. On the other hand two numbers whose magnitudes are of the order of 10^{-20} and 10^{-15} are not even approximately equal, yet the difference between them would be less than the required 10^{-11}, and an erroneous impression of accuracy would be obtained. In most instances where the differences between floating-point numbers is being tested for approaching zero, it is the relative difference which must be tested. The required accuracy (or error) should not be specified as less than about 10^{-7} for computers which maintain eight significant figures or 10^{-11} for computers which use twelve significant figures.

In order to print the coordinate vector, it is necessary to use DYN, since this is the matrix which is common to the main program and the subroutine. However, because only one row is needed, MC is first set equal to 1 before calling the subroutine. Also, since the information in the first row of DYN is needed again later, these numbers are stored temporarily by transferring them to a subscripted variable, ST, and then recovering them after the printing is completed. All this is accomplished by the statements from one statement before 450 through 478. Nothing new is encountered here.

DO Loop Rules and the CONTINUE Statement. The accuracy is tested next to see if it is equal to or better than required. If ACC is the required accuracy, and ACCUR is the accuracy at this time, another iteration should be performed if ACC < ACCUR. The three statements ending with 500 accomplish this. Another variable, TEST2 (which is ACC-ACCUR), is formed, and tested to see if it is less than zero. If it is, the iteration should be performed again and transfer is to the CONTINUE statement. If it is equal to or greater than zero, transfer out of the DO loop is made. It would have been satisfactory to use the statement IF (ACC-ACCUR) 500, 510, 510 instead of forming the new variable, TEST2.

The only other item of interest in these three statements is the use of the CONTINUE statement. This is the last statement in the DO loop which was started one statement after 390. There are several rules about the use of DO loops which must be observed. The first statement in the range of a DO statement must be one which can be executed. This excludes DIMENSION and FORMAT, which only furnish information to the compiler and do not cause any action by the computer. Another rule about the use of DO statements is that no statement within the range of the DO is permitted which would have the effect of changing any of the indices of the DO (the numbers following the DO statement). Another rule is that the last statement in the DO loop must not be one which can transfer control, such as GO TO or IF. The CONTINUE statement is used in situations which might cause this rule to be violated. In this example it would be erroneous for the IF statement to cause transfer back to the DO statement, because this would simply start the DO loop all over again. Instead, transfer is made to the CONTINUE statement, which simply means that the DO loop will be continued. There are several other rules about the nesting of DO statements and permissible ranges and transfers into and out of DO loops. Usually, these can be deduced by logic. However, if an unusual application is encountered, the programmer must be alert to the fact that there is a possibility of trouble developing and must consult these rules in the manual of the computer or other appropriate sources.

The next phase is to print the final value of ITERNO (iteration number), ACCUR (accuracy), X (the modal column), and then calculate and print the value of BETA, the natural frequency. Immediately following Statement 500 is the statement ITERNO = ITER. This is inserted here because if the DO loop is completed ITERNO will have been given the value of (ITER +1) before comparison with ITER to see if the DO loop has been completed. Since ITERNO is printed, it is necessary to set ITERNO equal to ITER, if the DO loop is completed, in order to print the correct number of iterations. There is nothing new in the printing phase, and this will not be discussed. A discussion of Statement 560 is postponed for the present.

Work Tape Statements. Two statements after 560 is

$$\text{READ TAPE 1, ((DYN(I,J), J = 1,N), I = 1,N)}$$

The reason for this and the earlier WRITE TAPE statement corresponding to this, the two statements beginning with 320, is that it is desirable to use the original dynamic matrix in calculating the natural frequency. Then a comparison of natural frequency using each of the equations affords a measure of the loss of accuracy incurred in modifying the dynamic matrix for calculation of higher modes. Since the dynamic matrix is changed for each mode, it was necessary to store the original dynamic matrix somewhere. It was stored on tape to avoid using memory. The WRITE TAPE statement simply stores the numbers listed on a tape, but without any indication as to what variables are being stored. When the tape is rewound and read, the numbers are transmitted in the same order as they were written, but it is the programmer's responsibility to get these numbers transmitted to the correct location. The tape is rewound before the first writing. It must then be rewound before reading.

There is one possibility of error here. The READ TAPE statement must not have a longer list than the WRITE TAPE statement. That is, it is conceivable that the information could be stored on the tape with statements having the same effect as the following:

$$\text{DO 6 I = 1,N}$$
$$\text{DO 6 J = 1,N}$$
$$\text{6   WRITE TAPE 1, DYN(I,J)}$$

Then it would not be correct to use the statement

$$\text{READ TAPE 1, ((DYN(I,J), J = 1,N), I = 1,N)}$$

The writing was made one number at a time, while the READ statement assumes that there is a list of N^2 numbers to be read, and the computer can find only one number, so indicates an error and stops. The READ statements would have to be similar to the above three statements which stored the information or else the WRITE statements must be of the same form as the READ statement; namely,

$$\text{WRITE TAPE 1, ((DYN(I,J), J = 1,N), I = 1,N)}$$

Natural Frequency. After the original dynamic matrix is recovered, the value of BETA can be obtained from any of the algebraic equations represented by the matrix equation, $\{X\} = \beta^2[\text{DYN}]\{X\}$. If it is calculated from each of the N equations as suggested above, then BETA itself is a vector, or matrix with only one row or else one column. Accordingly, the four statements ending with Statement 570 make the above matrix multiplication and the seven statements ending with 600 calculate BETA from each of the algebraic equations. There is a division here, and as usual it is necessary to avoid division by zero or a small number. It is quite possible that one of the coordinates might be zero in a natural mode. Therefore a test of XA(I) is performed to see if its absolute value is less than some arbitrary value (10^{-30} in this instance). If it is, then the corresponding value of BETA is simply set equal to zero, although the corresponding frequency is clearly not zero. This simply avoids this coordinate and makes an indication of the fact that this coordinate was very small. Occasionally it might occur that for one of these coordinates the ratio X/XA might be negative. Then Statement 590, which calls for the square root of this ratio, could not be executed, and an error would occur. Consequently, Statement 574 requires that if this should happen, zero will be printed for BETA for this coordinate.

The statement following 600 stores BETA on Tape 3. There were also two other statements which stored information on Tape 3—Statement 560 and the statement immediately preceding it. Therefore, for each mode there are three logical records on Tape 3, the first a single variable ACCUR, the second the array, X(J), and the third the array, BETA(J). It will be necessary to read these off in the same order and with the same lists when these quantities are recovered from tape later on. Since Tape 3 was rewound before the first writing, it will be necessary to rewind before reading.

The nine statements ending with Statement 660 cause the first row of DYN to be temporarily stored, BETA to be moved to this row and then printed, and then the first row of DYN to be recovered. After this point BETA will not again be needed, so the memory locations of BETA can be used for other purposes. They will be used for the row matrix obtained from the multiplication

$$[B] = \{\tilde{X}\}[\text{TMASS}] = [\text{BETA}]$$

This matrix will be used shortly in the determination of the dynamic matrix for the higher modes, the next block on the flow chart.

Work Tapes and the BACKSPACE Statement. The six statements ending with Statement 670 accomplish the matrix multiplication indicated above. First, [TMASS] must be recovered from storage on tape. (It will soon be found necessary to use the memory locations of [TMASS] for other purposes, so that [TMASS] had to be stored on tape prior to Statement 350, the statement which causes repetition of subsequent steps for different modes.) [TMASS] was stored on a different tape from [DYN] simply to avoid complications in the reading of these matrices from tape. It is possible to use the same tape if care is taken that the correct matrix is always being used. However, sometimes it is easier to use two tapes. The writing of [TMASS] on Tape 2 was accomplished with the second statement following Statement 320.

In more complicated programs it is often necessary to store more than one matrix on the same tape, and sometimes it is inconvenient to rewind the tape to the beginning. It may be desirable to use the backspace statement, such as BACKSPACE 2, which would have the effect of rewinding the tape by only one logical record, instead of all the way back to the beginning. (A logical record is generated every time a WRITE TAPE statement is encountered. In this example one logical record on Tape 2 contains N^2 numbers, since there were N^2 numbers in the list of the statement

WRITE TAPE 1, ((TMASS(I,J), J = 1, N), I = 1,N)

There are several precautions to be taken in connection with reading and writing on tape. It is unwise to write on a tape after reading from it. Writing should be accomplished only after rewinding or a previous writing or after a BACKSPACE statement. However, there are complications which may occur with the use of the BACKSPACE statement, and if this statement is used, the manual for the computer should be consulted in order to avoid difficulties. Usually it is possible to arrange the logic so that writing on tape can always follow a REWIND or a previous WRITE TAPE statement. It may be necessary to use more tapes, but this is better than errors resulting from either writing after reading or improper use of the BACKSPACE statement.

8.7 Higher Modes

The Sweeping Matrix. The formation of the sweeping matrix S, from which the dynamic matrix for the second mode will be determined, is now discussed. A slight variation from the method used in Chapter 2 will be used. It is recalled that the matrix equation $[B]\{X\} = 0$ is used, where [BETA] is now [B]. In Chapter 2, this equation was written in the form

$$X_1 = 0X_1 - \frac{B_2}{B_1} X_2 - \frac{B_3}{B_1} X_3 - \cdots$$

However, it is conceivable that B_1 might be zero or nearly zero. Therefore, it would be preferable to scan through the elements of [B] to find the largest, and solve for that variable. Suppose that B_3 had the largest absolute value of any of the elements of [B]. Then the equation would be written

$$X_3 = -\frac{B_1}{B_3} X_1 - \frac{B_2}{B_3} X_2 + 0X_3 - \frac{B_4}{B_3} X_4 - \cdots$$

and the sweeping matrix would become

$$[S] = \begin{bmatrix} 1 & 0 & 0 & 0 & 0 & \cdot \\ 0 & 1 & 0 & 0 & 0 & \cdot \\ -\dfrac{B_1}{B_3} & -\dfrac{B_2}{B_3} & 0 & -\dfrac{B_4}{B_3} & -\dfrac{B_5}{B_3} & \cdot \\ 0 & 0 & 0 & 1 & 0 & \cdot \\ 0 & 0 & 0 & 0 & 1 & \cdot \\ \cdot & \cdot & \cdot & \cdot & \cdot & \cdot \end{bmatrix}$$

To form [S], therefore, a unit matrix is first formed. Actually instead of using a different set of variables, [S], the matrix [DELTA] will be used, since [DELTA] is no longer needed once [DYN] is formed. The five statements ending with Statement 340 changed [DELTA] to the unit matrix. The three statements ending with 674 move the dynamic matrix to [TMASS] to be used later. The seven statements ending with 710 identify the element of [BETA] which has the largest absolute value. (The statement preceding 694 will be discussed shortly.) The element number is IDENOM and the value of the element is DENOM. Next the elements of BETA will be divided by DENOM and entered in row number IDENOM of [DELTA] by the two statements ending with 720. First, however, an escape is arranged in the unlikely event that all of the elements of [BETA] are near zero. The three statements following 710 accomplish this. Finally, the element of DELTA on the diagonal corresponding to IDENOM is set equal to zero, which would complete the formation of the sweeping matrix, if this were the first mode, except for a complication which will be explained presently.

The statement preceding 694 will now be explained. If more than one mode is to be eliminated (in order to cause convergence on some higher mode), there should be as many rows of the sweeping matrix modified as there are modes to be eliminated. It is conceivable that the coordinate having the largest absolute value in some specific mode might correspond to a row which has already been modified in a previous calculation. In this event it is necessary to choose a different coordinate, one which causes modification of a different row from any which have already been modified. Since all elements on the diagonal are unity except those in rows already modified, this fact can be used to eliminate the corresponding elements of BETA from the search for the element having the largest absolute value. This can all be accomplished with the single IF statement preceding 694.

The complication mentioned previously will now be discussed. When this program was tried, it was found that the calculation would converge properly only for the first mode, a result which probably should have been anticipated. The trouble arises because successive coordinates are not eliminated with each mode when the sweeping matrix is formed in this manner. For instance, suppose that after the first mode is computed, the matrix equation relating the coordinates so that the first mode amplitude is zero is

$$\{X\} = [S]\{X\}$$

or

$$\begin{Bmatrix} X_1 \\ X_2 \\ X_3 \\ X_4 \end{Bmatrix} = \begin{bmatrix} 1 & 0 & 0 & 0 \\ 0 & 1 & 0 & 0 \\ S_{31} & S_{32} & 0 & S_{34} \\ 0 & 0 & 0 & 1 \end{bmatrix} \begin{Bmatrix} X_1 \\ X_2 \\ X_3 \\ X_4 \end{Bmatrix}$$

This equation essentially states that each coordinate can be expressed in terms of only the coordinates X_1, X_2, X_4. Now, if the method for determining the sweeping matrix which was previously described is used, the matrix equation for the coordinates when both the first and second modes are to be eliminated might appear for instance, as follows.

$$\begin{Bmatrix} X_1 \\ X_2 \\ X_3 \\ X_4 \end{Bmatrix} = \begin{bmatrix} 0 & S_{12} & S_{13} & S_{14} \\ 0 & 1 & 0 & 0 \\ S_{31} & S_{32} & 0 & S_{34} \\ 0 & 0 & 0 & 1 \end{bmatrix} \begin{Bmatrix} X_1 \\ X_2 \\ X_3 \\ X_4 \end{Bmatrix}$$

Now all four variables are contained in the equations relating the coordinates. It is necessary to arrange the equations so that the variables will be expressed in terms of only two coordinates. If the equations were arranged as follows

$$X_1 - S_{12}X_2 - S_{13}X_3 - S_{14}X_4 = 0$$
$$0X_1 + 1X_2 + 0X_3 + 0X_4 = X_2$$
$$-S_{31}X_1 - S_{32}X_2 + 1X_3 - S_{34}X_4 = 0$$
$$0X_1 + 0X_2 + 0X_3 + 1X_4 = X_4$$

or by the matrix equation

$$\begin{bmatrix} 1 & -S_{12} & -S_{13} & -S_{14} \\ 0 & 1 & 0 & 0 \\ -S_{31} & -S_{32} & 1 & -S_{34} \\ 0 & 0 & 0 & 1 \end{bmatrix} \begin{Bmatrix} X_1 \\ X_2 \\ X_3 \\ X_4 \end{Bmatrix} = \begin{bmatrix} 0 & 0 & 0 & 0 \\ 0 & 1 & 0 & 0 \\ 0 & 0 & 0 & 0 \\ 0 & 0 & 0 & 1 \end{bmatrix} \begin{Bmatrix} X_1 \\ X_2 \\ X_3 \\ X_4 \end{Bmatrix}$$

it is clear that this could be solved as

$$\begin{Bmatrix} X_1 \\ X_2 \\ X_3 \\ X_4 \end{Bmatrix} = \begin{bmatrix} 1 & -S_{12} & -S_{13} & -S_{14} \\ 0 & 1 & 0 & 0 \\ -S_{31} & -S_{32} & 1 & -S_{34} \\ 0 & 0 & 0 & 1 \end{bmatrix}^{-1} \begin{bmatrix} 0 & 0 & 0 & 0 \\ 0 & 1 & 0 & 0 \\ 0 & 0 & 0 & 0 \\ 0 & 0 & 0 & 1 \end{bmatrix} \begin{Bmatrix} X_1 \\ X_2 \\ X_3 \\ X_4 \end{Bmatrix}$$

or a new matrix equation $\{X\} = [S]\{X\}$ in which the new matrix $[S]$ will simply be the second and fourth columns of the above inverse with zeros in the other columns. Therefore, the coordinates would all be expressed in terms of X_2 and X_4.

The program was modified to make this change. The statements from 1001 through 1080 accomplish this. [DYN] is used to form the matrix whose inverse is to be taken. Statements 1001 through 1010 clear [DYN]. Then the negative of the elements of [DELTA] are entered in [DYN], and finally the diagonal elements of [DYN] are set equal to unity. This is all accomplished with the six statements ending with 1050. [DYN] is then inverted with Subroutine A37IMS, which is not described here, although a listing of the subroutine appears. At the end of the inversion process, the inverted matrix appears at [DYN], and the proper columns of this matrix are selected for the new sweeping matrix by the five statements ending with 1080. Thus the new sweeping matrix is now located in [DELTA].

Dynamic Matrix for Next Mode. Next the original dynamic matrix is recovered from Tape 1 and stored in [TMASS], the sweeping matrix is moved to [DYN] for printing (Statements 730 to 770), and the new dynamic matrix for the next mode is formed by postmultiplying the original dynamic matrix by the sweeping matrix (Statements 770 to 780). The computation then proceeds to the next mode, since Statement 880 is the end of the DO loop starting with Statement 350.

8.8 Concluding Computations and the Output Program

This completes the main computation. The rest of the program is a check and also provides the proper storage of the results on tape so that the following program can make use of it. The statements from 883 to 890 recover the information stored on Tape 3; the next two statements recover the original inertia matrix; and then the generalized mass in each mode is computed with the eight statements ending with 910. (The value of generalized mass thus computed should agree with GMASS from input data.) The results of this computation are printed, and then all of the results written on Tape 1. The results which are here written do not correspond with the names of the variables used, of course. The names used in the READ TAPE 1 statements of the output program, A38OUT1, are more descriptive of the results which are written with these final statements.

STOP and END Statements. There is always an END card at the end of the program. The STOP card is often at the end of the program just ahead of the END card, as in this instance. However, there are occasions when the STOP card would logically occur elsewhere in the program, if the last statement causes a transfer to some other computation phase. However, there must be a STOP or CALL EXIT statement somewhere in the program, or at least a PAUSE statement, which causes the computer to stop so that the operator can take appropriate action. There may well be several STOP statements, as there were in this example, if there are logical stopping points in the computation. In a subroutine there may not be a STOP statement, but there must be a RETURN statement if there is no STOP statement.

Output Program. Program A38OUT1 reads the information written on Tape 1 and prints the results. Since there is nothing new here, no discussion of this program is given. Actually, this program is only included as an example output program, since the results are printed in A38NM. Some other output program might be written to make use of the results of A38NM in a subsequent calculation.

Arithmetic Statements and Expressions. There are statements available to the programmer besides those used in this program. However, this discussion has demonstrated many of the techniques employed, and with this as a framework and a good reference book (such as Ref. 17, or the manual of the particular computer to be used), any problem could be solved by the novice, even though he might not select the most efficient method of working the problem. A few more comments on arithmetic statements and expressions are in order. The most important rules regarding statements and expressions are repeated here for convenience.

1. Fixed-point and floating-point numbers must not be mixed in an expression. (Certain exceptions are permitted, notably the raising of a floating-point quantity to a fixed-point power.)

2. In an expression, exponentiation, or raising to a power, will be done first. The appropriate symbol is $**$; A^2 would be indicated by A$**$2, for example. Multiplication and division will be done next, and addition and subtraction last. Parentheses around parts of a statement have the same effect as in ordinary algebraic usage, except where they are used to denote subscripts.

3. If there are no parentheses shown, operations proceed from left to right; the expression A*B/C*D means (AB/C)D rather than (AB)/(CD), for instance. The latter could be accomplished with the expression A*B/C/D.

4. Two operational symbols may not appear in succession; it would be erroneous to write A/$-$B, for instance, although A/($-$B) would be all right. (Of course, $**$ is permitted, since this is really only one symbol, denoting exponentiation.)

5. In a statement, a single variable must appear on the left side of the equals sign, and this variable would then take the value of what appears on the right side. A*B = C/D is not permitted, for instance, although a new variable defined to be AB could be used so that AB = C/D is a legitimate statement. The statement

A = A + B means that the new value to be given to A is the sum of B and the old value of A.

8.9 Function Statements

The following discussion explains the use of some of the functions available to the programmer.

Y = LOGF(X) is a statement which will cause the natural logarithm of a floating-point variable, X, to be computed and stored as a floating-point variable at Y.

Y = SINF(X) is a statement which will cause sin X to be stored at Y. X is in radians.

Y = COSF(X) is equivalent to Y = cos X.

Y = EXPF(X) is a statement which will cause the result of the computation, e^x, to be stored at Y.

Y = SQRTF(X) is equivalent to Y = $\sqrt{X}$, and of course only the positive value is implied, and X must be positive and real.

Y = ATANF(X) is equivalent to Y = arctangent X, Y in radians.

Y = ABSF(X) is equivalent to Y = $|X|$, where both X and Y are real floating-point numbers.

Y = FLOATF(I) is a statement which will cause the floating-point equivalent of a fixed-point number, I, to be stored at Y.*

I = XFIXF(X) is a statement which will cause the fixed-point equivalent of a floating-point number, X, to be stored at I. I is not rounded to the nearest integer, but is computed by taking the algebraic sign of X times the largest integer which is equal to or less than X.*

Although other functions may be available in some versions of FORTRAN, the above functions are probably the most useful and most generally used. In these functions, the arguments may be other functions. For instance, the statement

$$A = ABSF(SINF(X))$$

would cause the absolute value of sin X to be stored at A.

A programmer may also invent his own function if he wishes. For instance, suppose the combination $A + Bx + Cx^2 + Dx^3$ occurs many times in a program. The programmer could define a function as follows:

$$POLYF(A,B,C,D,X) = A + B*X + C*X**2 + D*X**3$$

In this definition the name must begin with a letter and end with F and be from four to six characters long. The intermediate characters may be numbers. The arguments of the defining statement must be nonsubscripted variables, and there may be from one to perhaps forty of these, depending on the compiling provisions.

When the function is used later in the program, the quantities which appear as arguments do not necessarily have the same names as those which appeared in the definition, and they may be subscripted variables or other functions. Thus the statement

$$ZETA = POLYF(DEL(2,3), ABSF(Y), 2.0, F, Z)$$

would mean that DEL(2,3) would be used for A, ABSF(Y) would be used for B, 2.0 for C, F for D, and Z for X. ZETA would take the value computed by the defining equation when these variables are inserted into the equation.

---

* Conversion from one mode to the other can also be made by simple arithmetic statements, such as $I = F$ or $F = I$, where the desired form is at the left.

8.10 Compilation, Collection, Execution

After the source program has been written and punched on cards, there is still much to be done before answers may be expected from the computer. The source program must be "compiled" by the computer. This means that the computer itself will translate the source program into the computer language that it requires to solve the problem. This is a separate operation, and so the computer facility often finds it convenient to do all of the compiling of source programs at once. If there are illegal statements or omitted commas or parentheses or other similar difficulties, the program will not be compiled until these have been corrected. When, finally, the program is successfully compiled, it is stored on a collector tape. Subroutines used in the main program must also be compiled, and it is possible for either the subroutine or main program to be successfully compiled even though the other may not be. Of course, all subroutines and the main program must be compiled before a problem can be solved. If a program or subroutine has been compiled and if it is then desired to make a change in the program, it is necessary to compile the whole program or subroutine with the required alteration and then make sure that the old program is deleted if the new one has the same name as the old one.

After the main program and all subprograms have been compiled, it is necessary to "collect" or assemble them on a program tape. This is also a separate operation. If a change is made in a program after collection, it is necessary to compile, delete, and collect again in order that the change be incorporated in the program.

Preparation of Data Cards. After the program has been collected, it can then be "executed," or a problem can be solved using it. However, data must be prepared for use with the program. A card is prepared which identifies the program, then a "data" card, followed by the cards with the numbers properly punched to agree with the program, and finally an "end data" card. Many of the detailed procedures for compilation, collection, and execution depend on the computer facility, and these comments must be considered as representative rather than general.

The data cards must agree with the various FORMAT statements in the program. No identification of a particular number as to what variable it represents appears on the data card. The numbers are simply used in the order in which they appear. Therefore, it is necessary to use care in the preparation of the cards. Each card should have no more values of variables punched on it than the corresponding FORMAT statement allows, and these must be in exactly the correct locations on the card to agree with the field widths specified in the FORMAT statement. As an example, the statement

FORMAT (I2, I2, I4, E14.8)

means that the corresponding data card should have four numbers on it. The first three must not have decimal points punched in them. Suppose that the numbers desired are 8, 4, 50, 1.0×10^{-5}. The data card should be punched as follows:

08040050 + 100000000E − 05

All of the zeros could be left blank if desired, and the blanks would be interpreted as zeros. However, the numbers must be in the correct position. If the first position were 8 and the second position were left blank, the computer would interpret the number to be 80 instead of 8. The 1.0×10^{-5} could have been written 1.0E − 05 if desired, but if so, this should be at the right side of the field (positions 8 through 14) rather than at the left (positions 1 through 7) or in the center somewhere, because the computer may expect to find the exponential designated in the last four positions. The plus sign could be omitted if desired.

The statement FORMAT (E17.9) means that the corresponding data card should contain one number and, in fact, all of the elements of DELTA and TMASS would be punched one per card. If two or more numbers were punched on a card, an error would result, since only the first one would be read. Blank cards are interpreted as zeros.

There follows a list of cards which could be used to analyze the system of Example 1-1. The headings are the column numbers on the data cards. In this program, only one number is punched on each data card, except the indicators INTPRT and IPRDTA. These cards would be processed by the computer in order, so that the three programs would follow one after the other, each of the last programs using information obtained from the program preceding it.

```
 1  2  3  4  5  6  7  8  9 10 11 12 13 14 15 16 17 18 19 20 21 22 23 24 25 26 27 28 29 30 31 32 33 34 35
P R O G R A M        A 3 8 1 N P 1                      V E R N O N   0 1 0 1
D A T A              A 3 8 1 N P 1
1 1
0 3
0 1 0 0
        1 . 0                       E - 0 5
        6 . 0                       E
        1 . 0                       E
        1 . 0                       E
        1 . 0                       E
        2 . 0                       E
        2 . 0                       E
        1 . 0                       E
        2 . 0                       E
        3 . 0                       E
        1 . 0                       E
        0 . 0                       E
        0 . 0                       E
        0 . 0                       E
        2 . 0                       E
        0 . 0                       E
        0 . 0                       E
        0 . 0                       E
        3 . 0                       E
E N D   D A T A      A 3 8 1 N P 1
P R O G R A M        A 3 8 N M                          V E R N O N   0 1 0 1
P R O G R A M        A 3 8 O U T 1                      V E R N O N   0 1 0 1
```

8.11 Program Listings of the Appendix

The programs in the Appendix were written to accomplish some of the more tedious tasks described in the early chapters of this text. It is not to be supposed that programs like these can be written without errors, and these programs all went through a "debugging" process to remove errors in both the FORTRAN writing and the logic involved in the solutions.

It was intended that these programs would be used by the Honeywell 800 computer at the University of Southern California. This particular computer had about 8000 memory units at the time, so the programs were designed to fit this size memory storage. Consequently, some calculations which might logically be contained in one program, except for their size, were written as several independent programs to follow each other in succession. The DIMENSION statements can be altered, if desired, if these programs are executed by other computers with different capacities, and the input or output statements may be changed to suit the user.

Block diagrams are not provided for these programs, since the logic involved is not of particular interest. The purpose of providing the listings is to save the reader without access to such programs the time and effort of writing and debugging programs of his own, although he may have to make minor adjustments in input and output statements and dimensions of variables.

8.12 Block Diagram and Program Listings

The block diagrams for A38INP1, A38NM, and A37PM, and the listings for these programs and A38OUT1 appear next. The listings of these programs also appear in the Appendix, so that the reader may remove these listings from this position in the text for convenience if he wishes.

Block diagram for A38INP1 and A38NM

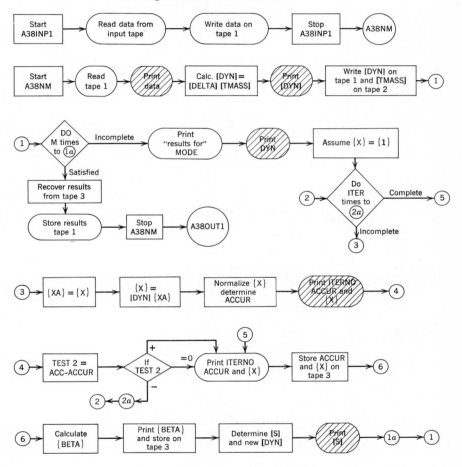

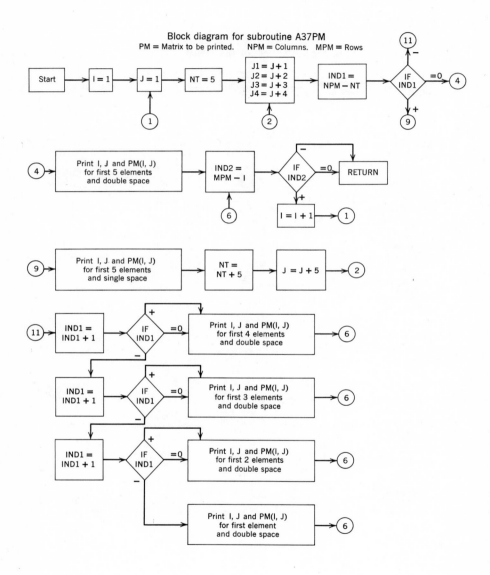

Block diagram for subroutine A37PM

PM = Matrix to be printed.   NPM = Columns.   MPM = Rows

```
      TITLE A38INP1              J.B.VERNON   0101
C           PROGRAM TO CALCULATE NORMAL MODES AND FREQUENCIES BY
C           MATRIX ITERATION. THIS PROGRAM USES DATA CARDS TO PREPARE
C           TAPE 1 FOR A38NM. IF SOME OTHER INPUT PROGRAM IS USED, IT
C           SHOULD ARRANGE TO LEAVE TAPE 1 IN THE SAME CONDITION AS THIS
C           PROGRAM, WHICH MAY BE DETERMINED FROM THE WRITE TAPE 1
C           STATEMENTS AT THE END OF THIS PROGRAM, STATEMENTS 100 AND
C           110. MAXIMUM NUMBER OF VARIABLES IS 30. DATA REQUIRED SHOULD
C           AGREE WITH THE READ TAPE 5 STATEMENTS IN THIS PROGRAM. N IS
C           NUMBER OF VARIABLES AND ORDER OF THE MATRICES. M IS THE
C           NUMBER OF MODES REQUIRED. ITER IS THE LIMITING NUMBER OF
C           ITERATIONS. ACC IS THE ACCURACY REQUIRED IF THE LIMITING
C           NUMBER OF ITERATIONS IS NOT REACHED FIRST. ACC IS SPECIFIED AS
C           THE FRACTION WHOSE DENOMINATOR IS THE SUM OF THE ABSOLUTE
C           VALUES OF ALL THE COORDINATES FOR THE LATEST ITERATION, AND
C           WHOSE NUMERATOR IS THE SUM OVER ALL THE COORDINATES OF
C           THE NUMBERS OBTAINED BY TAKING THE ABSOLUTE VALUE OF THE
C           DIFFERENCE FOR THE LATEST TWO ITERATIONS. (SEE STATEMENTS 431
C           THROUGH 441 OF PROGRAM A38NM.) INTPRT IS 1 IF IT IS DESIRED THAT
C           INTERMEDIATE PRINTING OF RESULTS SHOULD OCCUR DURING
C           EXECUTION OF PROGRAM A38NM. 1PRDTA IS 1 IF IT IS DESIRED THAT
C           THE DATA BE PRINTED. GMASS IS THE VALUE OF THE GENERALIZED
C           MASS DESIRED FROM THE NORMALIZATION OF THE MODES. TMASS IS
C           THE INERTIA MATRIX AND DELTA THE FLEXIBILITY MATRIX.
   18       FORMAT(I1, I1)
   20       FORMAT(I2)
   30       FORMAT(I4)
   40       FORMAT(E17.9)
            DIMENSION DELTA(30,30),TMASS(30,30)
            READ INPUT TAPE 5,18,INTPRT,IPRDTA
            READ INPUT TAPE 5,20,N
            READ INPUT TAPE 5,20,M
            READ INPUT TAPE 5,30,ITER
            READ INPUT TAPE 5,40,ACC
            READ INPUT TAPE 5,40,GMASS
            READ INPUT TAPE 5,40,((DELTA(I,J),J = 1,N),I = 1,N)
            READ INPUT TAPE 5,40,((TMASS(I,J),J = 1,N),I = 1,N)
            REWIND 1
  100       WRITE TAPE 1,N,M,ITER,ACC,INTPRT,IPRDTA,GMASS
  110       WRITE TAPE 1,((DELTA(I,J),J = 1,N),I = 1,N),((TMASS(I,J),J = 1,N),I = 1,N)
            REWIND 2
            REWIND 3
            STOP
            END
```

```
     TITLE A38NM                J.B.VERNON   0101
C         THIS PROGRAM USES DATA FROM TAPE 1, PREPARED BY PROGRAM
C         A38INP1 OR OTHER INPUT PROGRAM TO CALCULATE THE NORMAL
C         MODES AND FREQUENCIES OF A SYSTEM HAVING NO MORE THAN 30
C         COORDINATES AND ZERO DAMPING. TAPES 1, 2, AND 3 ARE USED
C         DURING THE COMPUTATION. THE OUTPUT OF THIS PROGRAM IS
C         STORED ON TAPE 1 BY STATEMENTS 950 THROUGH 960, AND MAY BE
C         USED BY AN OUTPUT PROGRAM SUCH AS A38OUT1. INTERMEDIATE
C         RESULTS OBTAINED DURING THE COMPUTATION WILL BE PRINTED IF
C         THE VALUE OF INTPRT IS 1. DATA USED WILL BE PRINTED IF THE VALUE
C         OF IPRDTA IS 1. FINAL RESULTS ARE ALSO PRINTED IN THIS PROGRAM.
          DIMENSION DELTA (30,30), TMASS(30,30), DYN(30,30),X(30),XA(30),ST(30)
          DIMENSION BETA(30)
          COMMON N,MC,DYN,TMASS,ST
210       FORMAT( 75H DATA  MATRIX ELEMENTS IDENTIFIED BY ROW AND CO
          1LUMN NUMBER IN PARENTHESES.///)
220       FORMAT(1H2, 4HN = I2, 6H M = I2, 9H ITER = I4, 8H ACC = E18.7,
          1 11H  GMASS =   E17.9)
230       FORMAT(1H0, 32H     FLEXIBILITY MATRIX, DELTA =)
250       FORMAT(1H0, 28H     INERTIA MATRIX, TMASS =)
270       FORMAT(1H2, 11HEND OF DATA)
310       FORMAT(1HO, 19H   DYNAMIC MATRIX =)
370       FORMAT(1H0, 31H     RESULTS FOR MODE NUMBER  I2)
380       FORMAT(1H0, 21H     DYNAMIC MATRIX =)
480       FORMAT(1H0, 21H  ITERATION NUMBER  I4, 13H  ACCURACY = E18.7)
490       FORMAT(1H , 22H   COORDINATE VECTOR X)
540       FORMAT(1HO, 26H   NUMBER OF ITERATIONS = I4,14H   ACCURACY = E
          1  18.7)
550       FORMAT(1H , 22H   COORDINATE VECTOR X)
640       FORMAT(1H0, 47H  BETA, CALCULATED FROM ORIGINAL DYNAMIC MA
          1TRIX)
714       FORMAT(1H0, 30HSWEEPING MATRIX FOLLOWING MODE I4,18H  CANN
          1OT BE FORMED)
760       FORMAT(1H0, 22H   SWEEPING MATRIX S =)
934       FORMAT(1H0,27HGENERALIZED MASS FOR MODE I2, 6H  IS E17.9)
          REWIND 1
          REWIND 2
          REWIND 3
          READ TAPE 1,N,M,ITER,ACC,INTPRT,IPRDTA
          READ TAPE 1, ((DELTA(I,J),J = 1,N),I = 1,N),((TMASS(I,J),J = 1,N),I = 1,N)
          MC = N
          IF(IPRDTA)280,280,200
200       PRINT 210
          PRINT 220,N,M,ITER,ACC,GMASS
          PRINT 230
          DO 240 I = 1,N
          DO 240 J = 1,N
240       DYN(I,J) = DELTA(I,J)
          CALL A37PM
          PRINT 250
          DO 260 I = 1,N
          DO 260 J = 1,N
260       DYN(I,J) = TMASS(I,J)
          CALL A37PM
          PRINT 270
280       DO 290 I = 1,N
```

```
        DO 290 J = 1,N
        DYN(I,J) = 0.0
        DO 290 K = 1,N
290     DYN(I,J) = DYN(I,J) + DELTA(I,K) * TMASS(K,J)
        MODE = 1
        IF(INTPRT)320,320,300
300     PRINT 310
        CALL A37PM
320     REWIND 1
        WRITE TAPE 1, ((DYN(I,J), J = 1,N), I = 1,N)
        WRITE TAPE 2, ((TMASS(I,J), J = 1,N), I = 1,N)
        DO 330 I = 1,N
        DO 330 J = 1,N
330     DELTA(I,J) = 0.0
        DO 340 I = 1,N
340     DELTA(I,I) = 1.0
350     DO 880 MODE = 1,M
        PRINT 370, MODE
        IF(INTPRT)364,364,360
360     PRINT 380
        CALL A37PM
364     DO 390 I = 1,N
390     X(I) = 1.0
        DO 500 ITERNO = 1,ITER
        DO 400 I = 1,N
400     XA(I) = X(I)
        DO 410 I = 1,N
        X(I) = 0.0
        DO 410 K = 1,N
410     X(I) = X(I) + DYN(I,K)*XA(K)
        REWIND 2
        READ TAPE 2,((TMASS(I,J),J = 1,N),I = 1,N)
        DUM1 = 0.0
        DO 420 J = 1,N
        DUM2 = 0.0
        DO 415 K = 1,N
415     DUM2 = DUM2 + TMASS(J,K) * X(K)
420     DUM1 = DUM1 + DUM2 * X(J)
        DUM1 = SQRTF(DUM1/GMASS)
        DO 430 I = 1,N
430     X(I) = X(I)/DUM1
431     DUM1 = 0.0
        DUM2 = 0.0
        DO 440 I = 1,N
        DUM1 = DUM1 + ABSF(X(I))
440     DUM2 = DUM2 + ABSF(XA(I) − X(I))
441     ACCUR = DUM2/DUM1
        DO 450 J = 1,N
450     ST(J) = DYN(1,J)
        DO 460 J = 1,N
460     DYN(1,J) = X(J)
        MC = 1
        IF(INTPRT)476,476,470
470     PRINT 480, ITERNO, ACCUR
        PRINT 490
        CALL A37PM
```

```
476    DO 478 J = 1,N
478    DYN(1,J) = ST(J)
       TEST2 = ACC − ACCUR
       IF(TEST2)500,510,510
500    CONTINUE
509    ITERNO = ITER
510    DO 520 J = 1,N
520    DYN(1,J) = X(J)
       MC = 1
530    PRINT 540, ITERNO, ACCUR
       PRINT 550
       CALL A37PM
       WRITE TAPE 3,ACCUR
560    WRITE TAPE 3,(X(J),J = 1,N)
       REWIND 1
       READ TAPE 1, ((DYN(I,J),J = 1,N),I = 1,N)
       DO 570 I = 1,N
       XA(I) = 0.0
       DO 570 K = 1,N
570    XA(I) = XA(I) + DYN(I,K)*X(K)
       DO 600 I = 1,N
       IF(ABSF(XA(I)) − 1.0E − 06)580,580,574
574    IF(X(I)/XA(I))580,580,590
580    BETA(I) = 0.0
       GO TO 600
590    BETA(I) = SQRTF(X(I)/XA(I))
600    CONTINUE
       WRITE TAPE 3,(BETA(J),J = 1,N)
       DO 610 J = 1,N
610    ST(J) = DYN(1,J)
       DO 620 J = 1,N
620    DYN(1,J) = BETA(J)
630    PRINT 640
       CALL A37PM
       MC = N
650    DO 660 J = 1,N
660    DYN(1,J) = ST(J)
       REWIND 2
       READ TAPE 2,((TMASS(I,J),J = 1,N),I = 1,N)
       DO 670 J = 1,N
       BETA(J) = 0.0
       DO 670 K = 1,N
670    BETA(J) = BETA(J) + X(K)*TMASS(K,J)
       DO 674 I = 1,N
       DO 674 J = 1,N
674    TMASS(I,J) = DYN(I,J)
       DENOM = 0.0
       DO 710 J = 1,N
       IF (ABSF(DELTA(J,J)) − 1.0E − 30)710,710,694
694    IF(ABSF(BETA(J)) − DENOM)710,710,700
700    IDENOM = J
       DENOM = ABSF(BETA(J))
710    CONTINUE
       IF(DENOM − 1.0E − 30)712,712,718
712    PRINT 714, MODE
       GO TO 882
```

```
718    DENOM = BETA(IDENOM)
       DO 720 J = 1,N
720    DELTA(IDENOM,J) = − BETA(J)/DENOM
       DELTA(IDENOM,IDENOM) = 0.0
1001   DO 1010 I = 1,N
       DO 1010 J = 1,N
1010   DYN(I,J) = 0.0
       DO 1050 K = 1,N
       IF (ABSF(DELTA(K,K)) − 1.0E − 30)1020,1020,1040
1020   DO 1030 J = 1,N
       DYN(K,J) = − DELTA(K,J)
1030   DELTA(K,J) = 0.0
1040   DYN(K,K) = 1.0
1050   CONTINUE
       CALL A37IMS
       DO 1080 K = 1,N
       IF(ABSF(DELTA(K,K)) − 1.0E − 30)1080,1080,1060
1060   DO 1070 I = 1,N
1070   DELTA(I,K) = DYN(I,K)
1080   CONTINUE
       REWIND 1
1090   READ TAPE 1,((TMASS(I,J),J = 1,N),I = 1,N)
730    DO 740 I = 1,N
       DO 740 J = 1,N
740    DYN(I,J) = DELTA(I,J)
       IF(INTPRT)770,770,750
750    PRINT   760
       CALL A37PM
770    DO 780 I = 1,N
       DO 780 J = 1,N
       DYN(I,J) = 0.0
       DO 780 K = I,N
780    DYN(I,J) = DYN(I,J) + TMASS(I,K) * DELTA(K,J)
880    CONTINUE
       GO TO 883
882    M = MODE − 1
883    REWIND 3
       DO 890 J = 1,M
       READ TAPE 3,X(J)
       READ TAPE 3,(DYN(I,J),I = 1,N)
       READ TAPE 3, (DELTA(I,J),I = 1,N)
 890   CONTINUE
       REWIND 2
       READ TAPE 2,((TMASS(I,J),J = 1,N),I = 1,N)
       DO 910 J = 1,M
       DUM1 = 0.0
       DO 907 I = 1,N
       DUM2 = 0.0
       DO 903 K = 1,N
903    DUM2 = DUM2 + TMASS(I,K) * DYN(K,J)
907    DUM1 = DUM1 + DUM2 * DYN(I,J)
910    ST(J) = DUM1
920    DO 930 J = 1,M
930    PRINT 934,J,ST(J)
940    REWIND 1
950    WRITE TAPE 1,N,M
```

```
          WRITE TAPE 1,((DYN(I,J),I = 1,N),J = 1,M)
          WRITE TAPE 1,((DELTA(I,J),I = 1,N),J = 1,M)
          WRITE TAPE 1,(X(J),J = 1,M)
960       WRITE TAPE 1,(ST(J),J = 1,M)
          STOP
          END


          SUBROUTINE   A37PM
C   THIS SUBROUTINE WILL CAUSE THE ELEMENTS OF A MATRIX TO BE
C   PRINTED. NPM IS THE NUMBER OF COLUMNS IN THE MATRIX, MPM THE
C   NUMBER OF ROWS, AND PM(I,J) THE ELEMENTS. FOR THE DIMENSION
C   STATEMENT GIVEN, THE MATRIX MAY BE AS LARGE AS 30 BY 30
          DIMENSION PM (30,30)
          COMMON NPM, MPM,PM
5         FORMAT(1H0,5(1H(I2,1H,I2,1H)E16.9,1H/))
10        FORMAT(1H ,5(1H(I2,1H,I2,1H)E16.9,1H/))
13        FORMAT(1H0,4(1H(I2,1H,I2,1H)E16.9,1H/))
15        FORMAT(1H0,3(1H(I2,1H,I2,1H)E16.9,1H/))
18        FORMAT(1H0,2(1H(I2,1H,I2,1H)E16.9,1H/))
20        FORMAT(1H0, (1H(I2,1H,I2,1H)E16.9,1H/))
          I = 1
1         J = 1
          NT = 5
2         J1 = J + 1
          J2 = J + 2
          J3 = J + 3
          J4 = J + 4
3         IND1 = NPM − NT
          IF(IND1)11,4,9
4         PRINT 5,I,J,PM(I,J),I,J1,PM(I,J1),I,J2,PM(I,J2),I,J3,PM(I,J3),I,J4
          1,PM(I,J4)
6         IND2 = MPM − I
          IF(IND2)21,21,7
7         I = I + 1
8         GO TO 1
9         PRINT 10,I,J,PM(I,J),I,J1,PM(I,J1),I,J2,PM(I,J2),I,J3,PM(I,J3),I,J
          14,PM(I,J4)
          NT = NT + 5
          J = J + 5
          GO TO 2
11        IND1 = IND1 + 1
          IF(IND1)24,12,12
12        PRINT 13, I, J,PM(I,J),I,J1, PM(I,J1),I,J2,PM(I,J2),I,J3,PM(I,J3)
          GO TO 6
24        IND1 = IND1 + 1
          IF(IND1)16,14,14
14        PRINT 15, I,J,PM(I,J),I,J1,PM(I,J1),I,J2,PM(I,J2)
          GO TO 6
16        IND1 = IND1 + 1
          IF(IND1)19.17,17
17        PRINT 18,I,J,PM(I,J),I,J1,PM(I,J1)
          GO TO 6
19        PRINT 20,I,J,PM(I,J)
          GO TO 6
21        RETURN
          END
```

```
        TITLE A38OUT1              J.B.VERNON  0101
C          THIS PROGRAM PRINTS THE RESULTS OF THE COMPUTATION OF A38NM.
C          IF SOME OTHER OUTPUT PROGRAM IS USED WITH A38NM, THE
C          NECESSARY INFORMATION MAY BE OBTAINED FROM TAPE 1 BY
C          STATEMENTS SIMILAR TO STATEMENTS 818 THROUGH 819 IN THIS
C          PROGRAM. THE VARIABLE, BETA, IS THE NATURAL FREQUENCY OF A
C          PARTICULAR MODE OF VIBRATION. THIS VALUE WAS COMPUTED USING
C          EACH OF THE N ALGEBRAIC EQUATIONS AND SHOULD BE THE SAME
C          FROM EACH EQUATION. THE COMPARISON OF THE N VALUES OF BETA
C          FOR A MODE THEREFORE AFFORDS A MEASURE OF THE ACCURACY OF
C          THE COMPUTATION. THE VARIABLE, X, IS THE RELATIVE DISPLACEMENT
C          OF THE COORDINATES IN A NATURAL MODE. THE VARIABLE, ACCUR,
C          IS THE ACCURACY, DEFINED IN A38INP1. THE VARIABLE, GMASS, IS THE
C          GENERALIZED MASS.
    820    FORMAT(1H0,34HRESULTS OF NORMAL MODE COMPUTATION)
    830    FORMAT(1H0,117HIN THE FOLLOWING MATRIX THE FIRST NUMBER INSIDE
           1THE PARENTHESES IS THE MODE NUMBER, THE SECOND THE COORDIN
           2ATE NUMBER.)
    840    FORMAT(1H0,29HCOORDINATE DISPLACEMENT, X(J))
    850    FORMAT(1H0,43HFREQUENCY COMPUTED FROM EACH OF N EQUATIONS)
    870    FORMAT(1H0,119HIN THE FOLLOWING ROW MATRIX THE FIRST NUMB
           1ER INSIDE THE PARENTHESES HAS NO SIGNIFICANCE, THE SECOND IS T
           2HE MODE NUMBER.)
    880    FORMAT(1H0,44HACCURACY AS DEFINED IN A38INP1 FOR EACH MODE)
    900    FORMATION(1H ,30HGENERALIZED MASS FOR EACH MODE )
    930    FORMATION (1H0,50HEND OF COMPUTATION OF NORMAL MODES AN
           1D FREQUENCIES)
           DIMENSION X(30,30), BETA(30,30),ACCUR(30),GMASS(30)
           COMMON NP,MP,X
    818    REWIND 1
           READ TAPE 1,N,M
           READ TAPE 1,((X(I,J),J = 1,N),I = 1,M)
           READ TAPE 1,((BETA(I,J),J = 1,N),I = 1,M)
           READ TAPE 1,(ACCUR(J),J = 1,M)
    819    READ TAPE 1,(GMASS(J),J = 1,M)
           PRINT 820
           NP = N
           MP = M
           PRINT 830
           PRINT 840
           CALL A37PM
           PRINT 830
           PRINT 850
           DO 860 I = 1,M
           DO 860 J = 1,N
    860    X(I,J) = BETA(I,J)
           CALL A37PM
           PRINT 870
           PRINT 880
           DO 890 J = 1,M
    890    X(1,J) = ACCUR(J)
           NP = M
           MP = 1
           CALL A37PM
           PRINT 870
           PRINT 900
```

```
        DO 920 J = 1,M
  920   X(1,J) = GMASS(J)
        CALL A37PM
        PRINT 930
        STOP
        END
```

CHAPTER 9

Analogue Computers

9.1 Preliminary Comments

Analogue computers may be used to solve many of the more difficult problems in engineering, especially in the fields of dynamics, vibration, or control systems. Non-linear problems may be solved, often with very little more effort than linear problems. One of the principal advantages of the use of analogue computers is the ease with which the important parameters can be varied and the effects observed. In this way the analogue computer becomes a valuable experimental tool. However, it must not be supposed that an understanding of theory is any less necessary because of the advent of either analogue or digital computers. Theory is required to guide the experiments.

For some problems an analogue computer is more appropriate than a digital computer, and for others the reverse is true, while many problems may be solved with either computer with approximately equal effort. Probably the best way to develop intuition as to which computer to use in a given situation is to become familiar with each type through actual use. However, as a general rule, if a digital program is already in existence for a given problem, or if there are very many variables in a problem, or extreme accuracy is required, then probably the digital computer should be selected, while if the problem is one involving continual adjustment of parameters and experimentation at the time of the computation, the analogue should be more efficient, provided that the problem is one for which the analogue can be used. Obviously, the matter of availability of a suitable computer and the expense involved would also have a bearing on which type should be used.

9.2 Operational Analogue Computer

The type of analogue computer which is explained here is the "operational analogue" computer. The heart of the computer is a d-c amplifier with very high gain. A small change in input voltage causes a very large change in output voltage. If the output is then connected to the input through a suitable impedance, various operations may be simulated.

157

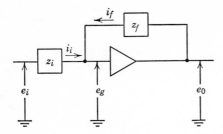

Fig. 9-1   Operational amplifier.

Multiplication by a Constant and Integration. In Fig. 9-1 the triangular symbol represents a high-gain d-c amplifier for which e_0 is many times greater than e_g (of the order of 10,000), so that e_g may be considered effectively zero in comparison with either e_i or e_0, both of which may be in the general vicinity of 1 to 100 volts. Also, the current entering the amplifier (grid current) is zero. Therefore, if z_i and z_f are impedances,

$$i_i + i_f = 0$$

or

$$\frac{e_i - e_g}{z_i} + \frac{e_0 - e_g}{z_f} = 0$$

or, with the assumption of $e_g = 0$,

$$\frac{e_0}{e_i} = -\frac{z_f}{z_i} \tag{9-1}$$

If the impedances, z_f and z_i, are both resistors, a straight multiplication is achieved by the amplifier. If z_i is a resistor and z_f a capacitor (for which $z_f = 1/cs$), the operation of integration and multiplication by a constant results. Other combinations of impedances produce other transfer functions.

Addition. The operation of addition is performed as indicated in Fig. 9-2. Here as before, if $e_g \rightarrow 0$,

$$i_1 + i_2 + i_3 + i_f = 0$$

$$\frac{e_1}{z_1} + \frac{e_2}{z_2} + \frac{e_3}{z_3} + \frac{e_0}{z_f} = 0 \tag{9-2}$$

$$e_0 = -z_f\left(\frac{e_1}{z_1} + \frac{e_2}{z_2} + \frac{e_3}{z_3}\right)$$

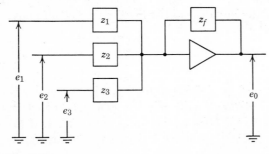

Fig. 9-2

If the impedances are all resistors, the operations of multiplication and addition are performed. If z_f is a capacitor, then multiplication, integration, and addition is achieved. More complex networks could be used for either the input or feedback circuits to achieve certain specific results.

Simulation of Differential Equations. If a differential equation is to be solved, it is written in such a way that integrations are performed; that is, the differential equation

$$\frac{d^2x}{dt^2} + \frac{dx}{dt} + x = u(t)$$

could be solved on the analogue computer as

$$\frac{d^2e_0}{dt^2} + \frac{de_0}{dt} + e_0 = e_i(t)$$

where $e_i(t)$ would be a step-input voltage. However, these equations are first rewritten to solve for the highest derivative term.

$$\frac{d^2x}{dt^2} = -\frac{dx}{dt} - x + u(t)$$

or

$$\frac{d^2e_0}{dt} = -\frac{de_0}{dt} - e_0 + e_i(t)$$

Since

$$\frac{dx}{dt} = \int_0^t \frac{d^2x}{dt^2}\, dt$$

and

$$x = \int_0^t \frac{dx}{dt}\, dt$$

(or, in operational form, $\dot{X} = \ddot{X}/s$ and $X = \dot{X}/s$), the above equations can be solved as indicated in Fig. 9-3.

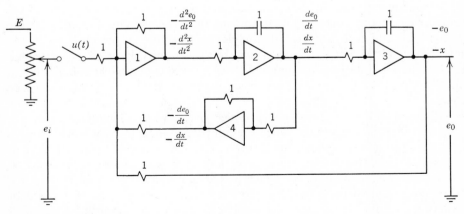

Fig. 9-3 Solution of $\dfrac{d^2x}{dt^2} + \dfrac{dx}{dt} + x = u(t)$.

9.3 Selection of Resistors and Capacitors

In Fig. 9-3 the numerical values indicated for the resistors and capacitors are in terms of megohms and microfarads. Normally, values of resistors would range from 0.1 to 10 megohms and capacitors from 0.01 to 1.0 microfarads, although values outside these limits may occasionally be used if necessary. In constructing Fig. 9-3, it is assumed that the voltage which simulates d^2x/dt^2 is available; this is then integrated twice (Amplifiers 2 and 3) to obtain voltages capable of simulating dx/dt and x, and then these voltages are all added, together with the input voltage, which is to represent the step function, by Amplifier 1 to form the voltage simulating d^2x/dt^2. Amplifier 4 is used merely to obtain the correct sign for the voltage which simulates dx/dt. The summing function and first integration could have been combined and performed by one amplifier (Amplifier 2) instead of two if a record of d^2x/dt^2 were not required. This would reduce the total number of amplifiers required by one. In this problem such a saving would probably be of no advantage, but in problems where many amplifiers are necessary it might be useful. If this change were made, however, the signs of dx/dt and x would be reversed from that shown in Fig. 9-3, and thus the sign-reversing amplifier would have to be moved from the dx/dt signal to the feedback from x.

Amplifier Saturation. In determining the sizes of the resistors and capacitors required for a given problem, it is necessary to consider the range of linear operation of the amplifiers. The amplifiers saturate at some value of output, so that an increased voltage input would not result in an increased output once this saturation limit is reached. If simulation of a problem requires a linear relationship between input and output, such saturation would spoil the results of the experiment. On the other hand, most physical problems involve elements which have a saturation limit so that the saturation characteristic of the amplifier might be used to better simulate a physical problem if proper care is exercized in relating the physical quantity with the voltage simulating it. However, if it is assumed that saturation is to be avoided in the problem represented by Fig. 9-3, it is necessary to be careful in the selection of the values of resistors and capacitors. Suppose that the amplifiers saturate at 100 volts. Then the output of each amplifier should never exceed about 90 volts. It is also desirable to have each amplifier operate in such a manner as to use a reasonably large part of the permissible 90 volts at peak output. In this problem it is possible to anticipate the maximum output of each amplifier. In complex systems, the output probably would be unknown in advance of the solution, and so the output voltage of each amplifier should be monitored during the computation to be sure the amplifier is operating in the proper range. Also, the indicators which warn of amplifier saturation must be watched.

For the problem of Fig. 9-3, a second-order system with damping factor of 0.5, an overshoot of 16% is expected. Therefore, unit step function input would cause a maximum deflection of 1.16 times the steady-state value of x. If the unit step were to be represented by a 50-volt input and if one unit of x were also represented by 50 volts, then the maximum value of voltage output of Amplifier 3 would be 58 volts. The maximum value of dx/dt for unit step input is about 0.6 ft/sec. If 1 ft/sec of dx/dt were represented by 50 volts, the maximum value of the output of Amplifier 2 would be about 30 volts. Thus, if 50 volts were used to represent one unit of each of the variables at the output of the amplifiers, each amplifier would be working over a reasonable portion of its range. The values of resistors and capacitors indicated in Fig. 9-3 would yield satisfactory results.

Adjustment of Amplifier Gain. Since Amplifiers 2 and 4 would reach a maximum output of only 30 volts, it would be possible to increase the gain through Amplifier 2, if desired, by using input resistor of 0.5 instead of 1.0. This change would result in a voltage output for Amplifier 2 which would correspond to $2dx/dt$ instead of dx/dt, so in order to get the proper magnitude of the dx/dt signal for Amplifier 1, it would be necessary to counteract this change somewhere. If the resistor in the output circuit from Amplifier 4 were changed from 1.0 to 2.0, this would be accomplished, and the correct signal for dx/dt would be used. It would now be expected that Amplifiers 2 and 4 should reach a peak value of about 60 volts instead of 30, but of course it must be remembered that this voltage represents $2dx/dt$ rather than dx/dt if a record of dx/dt were required. The above change would also cause the output of Amplifier 3 to correspond to $2x$ instead of x, which at the peak ought then to be 116 volts. This would cause saturation, spoiling the computation, so the input resistor for Amplifier 3 should be changed from 1.0 to 2.0. (With this adjustment it is unnecessary to make another compensating change for the resistor in the circuit leading from Amplifier 3 to Amplifier 1, which otherwise would have to be changed to 2.0 so that the correct signal for x at the summing amplifier would result.) These changes are shown in Fig. 9-4, where the scale factors for each variable are also noted. It would have been possible to indicate the same information on Fig. 9-4 by labeling the output of Amplifiers 2 and 4 as dx/dt and $-dx/dt$ with scale factors of 100 volts per unit. However, it may be less confusing to use the same scale factor everywhere and keep track of the simulation with coefficients of the variables, as in Fig. 9-4. This also eliminates the need to insert a scale factor notation at each amplifier output. This discussion has shown how gain may be shifted from one amplifier to another in a circuit, but the total gain around all closed circuits must be consistent with the equation being simulated.

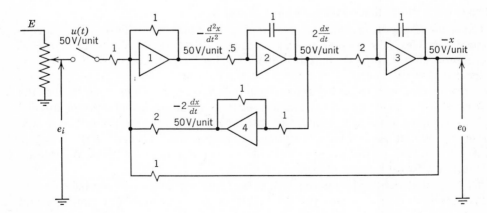

Fig. 9-4   Alternative solution of $\dfrac{d^2x}{dt^2} + \dfrac{dx}{dt} + x = u(t)$.

9.4 Time Scaling

Substitution of Variables. If the constants in an equation are not convenient for numerical solution, it may be necessary to time-scale the equation, or rewrite it in terms of more convenient variables. For instance, suppose the equation were

$$\frac{d^2x}{dt^2} + 100\,\frac{dx}{dt} + 10{,}000x = f(t)$$

This is recognizable as a second-order system whose natural frequency is somewhat less than 100 rad/sec. If this frequency is too high to be recorded properly with the available equipment, it might be necessary to slow the problem down as follows. Let $\tau = 100t$. Then

$$\frac{dx}{dt} = \frac{dx}{d\tau}\frac{d\tau}{dt} = 100\,\frac{dx}{d\tau}$$

$$\frac{d^2x}{dt^2} = \frac{d}{dt}\left(\frac{dx}{dt}\right) = \left[\frac{d}{d\tau}\left(\frac{dx}{dt}\right)\right]\frac{d\tau}{dt} = 10{,}000\,\frac{d^2x}{d\tau^2}$$

The differential equation then becomes

$$10{,}000\,\frac{d^2x}{d\tau^2} + 100 \times 100\,\frac{dx}{d\tau} + 10{,}000x = F(\tau)$$

Let $10{,}000x = z$. The following equation results:

$$\frac{d^2z}{d\tau^2} + \frac{dz}{d\tau} + z = F(\tau)$$

If $f(t)$ is the unit function, then $F(\tau)$ is also the unit function, and this equation can be simulated by either Fig. 9-3 or 9-4. (If $f(t)$ were some algebraic expression, $F(\tau)$ could be obtained from $f(t)$ by substituting for t in $f(t)$ the quantity $\tau/100$.)

When the results of the simulation are analyzed, 50 volts of input representing the unit function will result in a peak value of output of 58 volts, which corresponds to 1.16 units of z or 1.16×10^{-4} units of x. The period of oscillation of the computer voltage is 100 times that of the variable x in real time.

Capacitor Changes. In addition to rewriting the equations in terms of more convenient variables, it is possible to make a time-scale change by simply changing all capacitors. That is, suppose that a problem has been set up and when it is run it is suspected that the motion is too rapid for the recorder to follow properly, or else perhaps the motion is so slow that too much time and paper will be used. If all of the capacitors are changed by the same factor, the motion will be slowed down or speeded up by this factor. If 0.1 μf capacitors are changed to 1.0 μf, the motion will be slowed down and oscillations will require 10 times as long as the "correct" time. Changing from 0.1 μf to 0.01 μf will cause all motion to occur 10 times as rapidly. Magnitudes will not be affected by such changes.

This can be understood by noting that in the transform form a differential equation may be written in such a way that an "s" is always multiplied by a time constant which is the product of a resistance and capacitance. Changing capacitances would therefore change the time constants without changing gain. However, if time constants were changed by changing resistors, it would be necessary to be sure that possible gain changes were accounted for elsewhere. If *all* resistors were changed by the same factor, then of course the result would be the same as changing all the capacitors. It is often convenient to try to set up the problem using intermediate values of capacitors in case it later becomes desirable to make a change in the time scale.

9.5 Simulation of Transfer Functions

The previous discussion illustrated differential equation simulation. It is also possible to simulate entire transfer functions with a single amplifier. Reference to Equation 9-1, $e_0/e_i = -z_f/z_i$, shows that if the impedances are various combinations of resistors and capacitors, different transfer functions may be simulated. For example, the function

$$\frac{e_0}{e_i} = \frac{K}{1 + Ts}$$

could be simulated by the setup shown in Fig. 9-5.
Here,

$$z_f = \frac{1}{\dfrac{1}{R_f} + C_f s} = \frac{R_f}{1 + R_f C_f s}$$

so that

$$\frac{e_0}{e_i} = \frac{\dfrac{R_f}{1 + R_f C_f s}}{R_i} = \frac{R_f}{R_i} \frac{1}{1 + R_f C_f s}$$

Therefore, $T = R_f C_f$ and $K = R_f/R_i$. A numerator term $(1 + Ts)$ could be generated this way if the combination of R and C in parallel were used for the input impedance. More complicated functions may be generated with various circuits. A good summary is contained in Reference 14.

Although the transfer function method of simulation may require fewer amplifiers than the differential equation method, the latter is probably more useful because of its relative flexibility and the ease with which adjustments can be made. It is often easier, except for simple functions such as that of Fig. 9-5, to convert a transfer function to the equivalent differential equation and simulate the differential equation than it is to determine the combination of impedances necessary to simulate the transfer function (see Example 9-2).

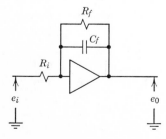

Fig. 9-5 Simulation of $\dfrac{K}{1 + Ts}$.

9.6 Coefficient Potentiometers

In many problems the coefficients of the variables are not readily simulated by standard values of resistors and capacitors. Of course, if the computer were an integral part of some control system and a particular value of a resistor were required, which would thereafter always remain the same, a special resistor or capacitor could be

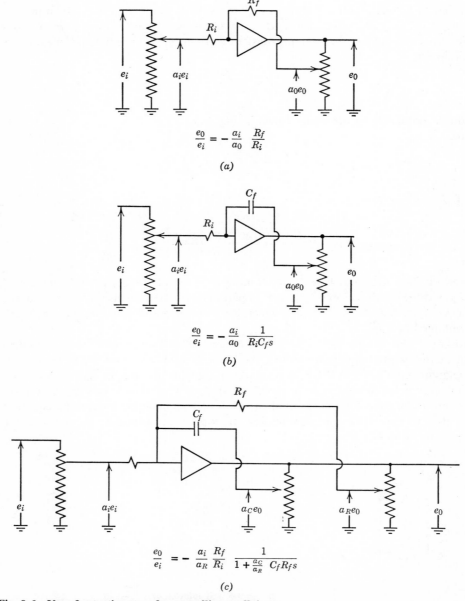

$$\frac{e_0}{e_i} = -\frac{a_i}{a_0}\frac{R_f}{R_i}$$

(a)

$$\frac{e_0}{e_i} = -\frac{a_i}{a_0}\frac{1}{R_iC_fs}$$

(b)

$$\frac{e_0}{e_i} = -\frac{a_i}{a_R}\frac{R_f}{R_i}\frac{1}{1+\frac{a_C}{a_R}C_fR_fs}$$

(c)

Fig. 9-6   Use of potentiometers for controlling coefficients.

provided. However, for applications of the type considered here, more flexibility is desired. It is customary to use potentiometers to vary coefficients easily. Figure 9-6 shows how this can be done for the simpler functions. Although Fig. 9-6 shows several potentiometers for each amplifier, ordinarily only one would be used. The purpose of showing several is merely to show how a particular position for a potentiometer would affect the final expression. For instance, the constant, 2.45, could be generated with $R_i = 0.1$, $R_f = 1.0$, $a_i = 0.245$, and $a_0 = 1.0$ (or no potentiometer in the output), or with $R_i = 1.0$, $R_f = 1.0$, $a_0 = 0.408$, and $a_i = 1.0$ (no potentiometer in the input). Notice that these potentiometers are used as voltage dividers and not as adjustable resistors in the input or feedback impedances.

The functions of Fig. 9-6 are derived as follows. Consider the circuit of Fig. 9-6a. The sum of currents entering the amplifier is zero, and the sum of voltages at that point is approximately zero, so that

$$\frac{a_i e_i}{R_i} + \frac{a_0 e_0}{R_f} = 0$$

or

$$\frac{e_0}{e_i} = -\frac{a_i}{a_0}\frac{R_f}{R_i}$$

The same procedure could be used for the other circuits of Fig. 9-6, and for more complex circuits.

Potentiometer Setting. A potentiometer is often indicated on a computer diagram as a circle. The value of the potentiometer setting is usually indicated in the circle. Since the voltage ratio for a potentiometer is not exactly the same as the resistance ratio, and depends on the load impedance (the impedance between the potentiometer arm and ground), it is customary to set the potentiometer with the actual load circuit in place by balancing the voltage output against that of a reference potentiometer, as indicated in Fig. 9-7. The reference potentiometer is set to the desired value and the computer potentiometer adjusted until the null voltmeter reads zero. The reference potentiometer and voltmeter are usually part of the computer, so that the necessary circuit is easily and speedily formed. Some computers have automatic balancing circuits so that the correct potentiometer setting is obtained simply by setting the desired voltage ratio and pressing a button to actuate the circuit balancing servomotor. The important consideration, with any potentiometer-setting method, is that the loading circuit actually to be used in the problem must be in place when the balancing is accomplished.

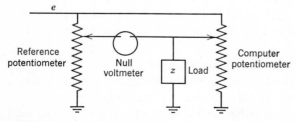

Fig. 9-7 Potentiometer setting.

9.7 Initial Conditions

Most computers are equipped with a switching arrangement so that initial conditions in a differential equation may be simulated. These are essentially initial charges on capacitors obtained from initial condition potentiometers. For instance, suppose that the equation to be simulated was

$$\frac{d^2x}{dt^2} + \frac{dx}{dt} + x = 0$$

with initial conditions

$$x_0 = 3, \qquad \left(\frac{dx}{dt}\right)_0 = 2$$

The setup of Fig. 9-3 or 9-4 could be used except that there would not be an input voltage, and there must be initial voltages on the capacitors of Amplifiers 2 and 3 to

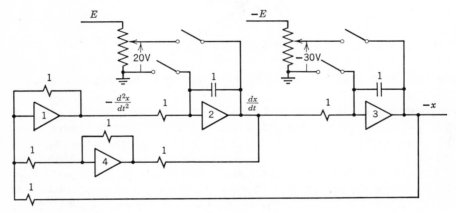

Fig. 9-8 $\dfrac{d^2x}{dt^2} + \dfrac{dx}{dt} + x = 0$ with $x_0 = 3$ and $\dot{x}_0 = 2$.

simulate the initial conditions. When the problem is turned on, the voltage source which charges these capacitors must be disconnected. Figure 9-8 shows such a setup. The switches indicated are initially closed and then opened when the computation starts. The switching mechanism is contained within the computer.

It would be necessary to use less than 50 volts per unit of x in order to avoid saturation if the initial value of x is to be 3. If the scale factor selected is 10 volts per unit of x, then the initial voltage on the capacitor of Amplifier 3 (Fig. 9-3) should be 30 volts, and on the capacitor of Amplifier 2, 20 volts. If the setup of Fig. 9-4 were used, the initial voltage on the capacitor of Amplifier 2 should be 40 volts instead of 20.

9.8 Saturation Characteristic for Simulation of Nonlinearities

The previous discussion referred primarily to linear systems. Nonlinear systems may be simulated if the proper equipment is available. A function multiplier provides a means of multiplying two variables together, and a function generator can be used to simulate an element whose output is some nonlinear function of input. These auxiliary pieces of equipment are not described here. However, certain nonlinear functions may be generated without auxiliary equipment simply by careful management of the saturation characteristic of the amplifiers. Obviously, saturation is one of these. A saturating amplifier can be followed by a gain reduction amplifier or potentiometer to provide saturation at the desired voltage with the desired gain. For instance, suppose that the amplifier saturates at 100 volts, but it is desired to simulate an element having a gain of 5 but saturating at 50 volts. The signal could be passed through an amplifier having a gain of 10 and then through another amplifier with a gain (or

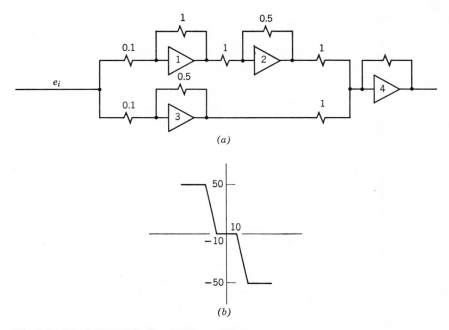

(a)

(b)

Fig. 9-9 Simulation of deadband with amplifiers.

attenuation) of 0.5 (or through a potentiometer with voltage ratio of 0.5). The combination would produce the desired result.

Deadband (or free play) can be simulated by using four amplifiers as indicated in Fig. 9-9a. Amplifiers 1 and 2 are the ones described in the previous paragraph which produce a gain of 5 and saturate at 50 volts. Amplifier 3 has a gain of 5 but of opposite sign. Therefore the output, e_0, remains zero until the input reaches 10 volts, after which it increases (negatively) at 5 to 1 slope until 50 volts is reached, after which the output remains constant because Amplifier 3 has reached 100 volts and saturated. Amplifier 4 is indicated as a summing amplifier, but it could be an integrator or another gain element or transfer function, if desired, in order to save one amplifier in the overall problem simulation. A relay with deadband could be simulated in the same way by using very high gains. Functions having two or more slopes can also be simulated this way. Simulation of nonlinearities by deliberate saturation of amplifiers is an expedient and is not recommended if a suitable function generator is available for this purpose.

9.9 Examples

Example 9-1. Simulate simple transfer functions and relate these to their block diagrams and differential equations (Figs. 9-10 and 9-11). Let the input be a step for each computation. For Fig. 9-11, let T be fixed at $T = 1$ and let K vary. This will provide a correlation between the response of a second-order system and the roots on a root locus plot. The root locus of the function $K/[s(1 + s)]$ is also shown in Fig. 9-11. Let $K = 0.1, 0.25, 0.5, 1, 4, 16, 100$.

The results of the computation for these setups are shown in the analogue records given in Fig. 9-12.

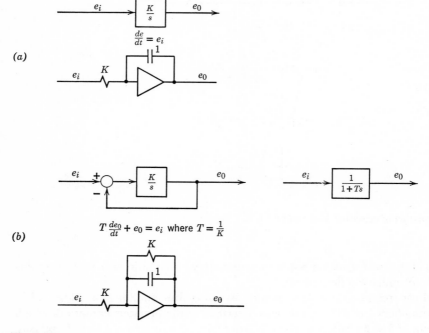

Fig. 9-10

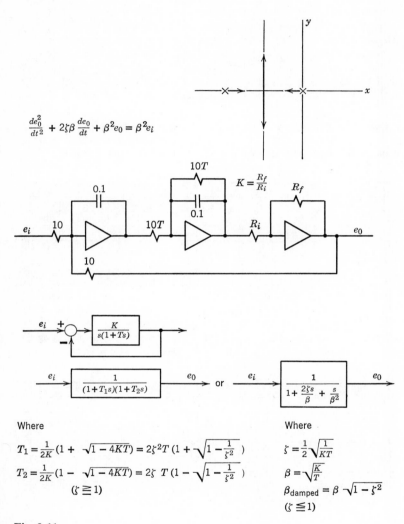

$$\frac{de_0^2}{dt^2} + 2\zeta\beta\frac{de_0}{dt} + \beta^2 e_0 = \beta^2 e_i$$

Where

$$T_1 = \frac{1}{2K}(1 + \sqrt{1 - 4KT}) = 2\zeta^2 T\left(1 + \sqrt{1 - \frac{1}{\zeta^2}}\right)$$

$$T_2 = \frac{1}{2K}(1 - \sqrt{1 - 4KT}) = 2\zeta\ T\left(1 - \sqrt{1 - \frac{1}{\zeta^2}}\right)$$

$$(\zeta \geqq 1)$$

Where

$$\zeta = \frac{1}{2}\sqrt{\frac{1}{KT}}$$

$$\beta = \sqrt{\frac{K}{T}}$$

$$\beta_{damped} = \beta\sqrt{1 - \zeta^2}$$

$$(\zeta \leqq 1)$$

Fig. 9-11

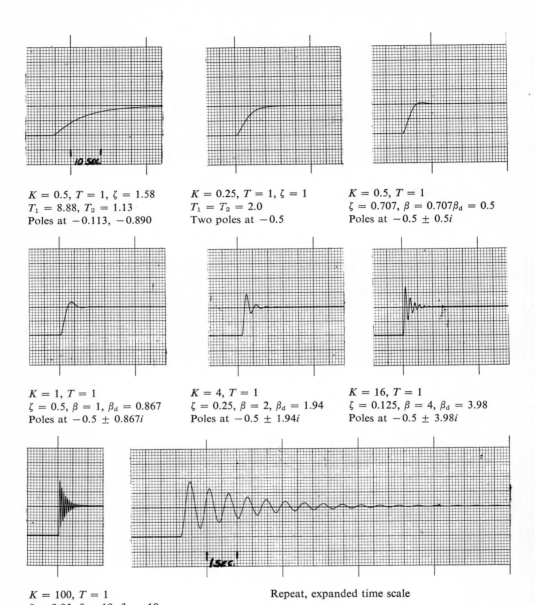

$K = 0.5$, $T = 1$, $\zeta = 1.58$
$T_1 = 8.88$, $T_2 = 1.13$
Poles at -0.113, -0.890

$K = 0.25$, $T = 1$, $\zeta = 1$
$T_1 = T_2 = 2.0$
Two poles at -0.5

$K = 0.5$, $T = 1$
$\zeta = 0.707$, $\beta = 0.707\beta_d = 0.5$
Poles at $-0.5 \pm 0.5i$

$K = 1$, $T = 1$
$\zeta = 0.5$, $\beta = 1$, $\beta_d = 0.867$
Poles at $-0.5 \pm 0.867i$

$K = 4$, $T = 1$
$\zeta = 0.25$, $\beta = 2$, $\beta_d = 1.94$
Poles at $-0.5 \pm 1.94i$

$K = 16$, $T = 1$
$\zeta = 0.125$, $\beta = 4$, $\beta_d = 3.98$
Poles at $-0.5 \pm 3.98i$

$K = 100$, $T = 1$
$\zeta = 0.05$, $\beta = 10$, $\beta_d = 10$
Poles at $-0.5 \pm 10i$

Repeat, expanded time scale

Fig. 9-12   Analogue records.

Example 9-2. Simulate the transfer function

$$\frac{e_0}{e_i} = \frac{1 + 2s}{1 + 3s + 4s^2}$$

This transfer function can be expressed as a differential equation as follows

$$e_0(1 + 3s + 4s^2) = (1 + 2s)e_i$$

$$4\frac{d^2e_0}{dt^2} + 3\frac{de_0}{dt} + e_0 = 2\frac{de_i}{dt} + e_i$$

Integrating once to avoid differentiating the input,

$$4\frac{de_0}{dt} + 3e_0 + \int_0^t e_0\,dt = 2e_i + \int_0^t e_i\,dt$$

If this is solved for de_0/dt,

$$\frac{de_0}{dt} = \frac{1}{2}e_i + \frac{1}{4}\int_0^t e_i\,dt - \frac{3}{4}e_0 - \frac{1}{4}\int_0^t e_0\,dt$$

A tentative circuit is shown in Fig. 9-13.

In this circuit Amplifiers 1 and 2 simulate the first two terms on the right side of the equation. Instead of using a separate summing amplifier to generate de_0/dt, Amplifier 3 sums and integrates to yield e_0. Amplifier 4 integrates and Amplifier 5 changes sign and provides correct gain for output of Amplifier 4. A potentiometer is used in the feedback from e_0 to obtain the proper magnitude for this signal.

However, if this circuit were to be tried on the computer, it would be found that Amplifier 2 would quickly saturate. Amplifier 2 is an integrating amplifier, so that even a small input voltage would cause the output voltage of Amplifier 2 to increase indefinitely. The saturation of Amplifier 2 would affect the rest of the circuit and spoil the simulation.

It is necessary to feed back a voltage into the input of Amplifier 2 from downstream, which would have the effect of limiting the output of Amplifier 2. Since Amplifier 4 is also an integrator, its function could be performed by Amplifier 2. There still must be two amplifiers between the output of Amplifier 3 and the input to Amplifier 3 for this circuit,

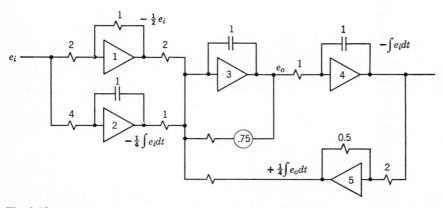

Fig. 9-13

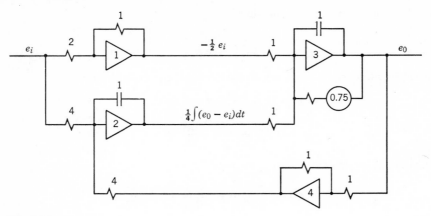

Fig. 9-14

however, in order to achieve the proper sign, so Amplifier 5 cannot be eliminated. However, the input and output resistors in this circuit must provide the correct gain for the circuit. Figure 9-14 shows the altered setup. The amplifier which was Amplifier 5 in Fig. 9-13 is Amplifier 4 in Fig. 9-14, and Amplifier 4 of Fig. 9-13 has been eliminated.

The transfer function of this example could also be simulated with one amplifier with the setup shown in Fig. 9-15. The circuits and values of components were taken from Table 16.4-1 of Reference 14.

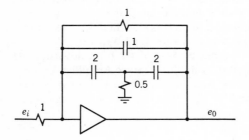

Fig. 9-15

Neither of the methods shown for simulating this transfer function would be useful if the constants were general decimal numbers. In this event, the first method could be modified to make use of potentiometers, an investigation left to the reader (Problem 9.2).

Problems

Chapter 2

2.1 (a) Write equations governing the behavior of the hydraulic servomotor whose schematic diagram is shown in Fig. P2-1.

(b) Draw a block diagram showing the feedback aspects of the device, and labeling all blocks with their appropriate transfer functions and input and output variables. Assume negligible load, inertia, and structure flexibility.

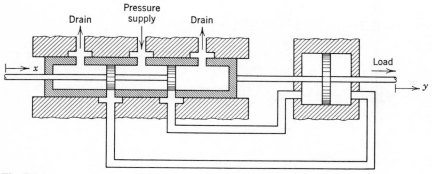

Fig. P2-1

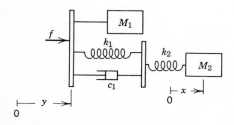

Fig. P2-2

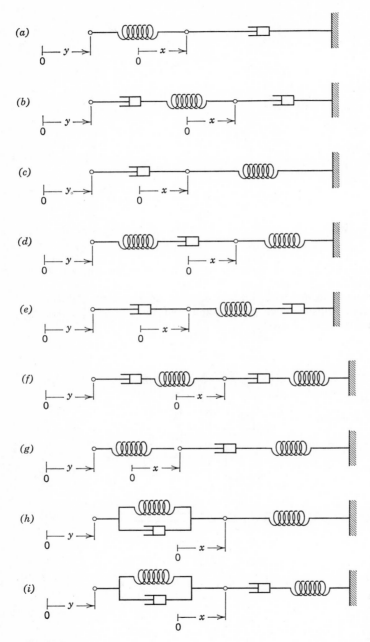

Fig. P2-3

(c) Determine transfer function Y/X.

(d) What physical factors affect the time constant for the servomotor?

(e) What is the effect of the load? Incorporate the load in the block diagram of Part b. Discuss the appropriateness of considering the effects of the position, x, and the load separately and independently by assuming zero for one of these variables while the other is being considered, and vice versa.

2.2   Make a block diagram and determine transfer functions X/F and X/Y for the mechanical system shown in Fig. P2-2.

2.3   Make block diagrams and determine transfer functions X/Y for the systems shown in Fig. P2-3.

2.4   Make a block diagram for the engine speed control system indicated in the schematic (Fig. P2-4) including transfer functions for the various blocks. Make whatever linearizations and assumptions seem appropriate to the problem. Indicate on the block diagram how a change in engine torque demanded (load) could be handled.

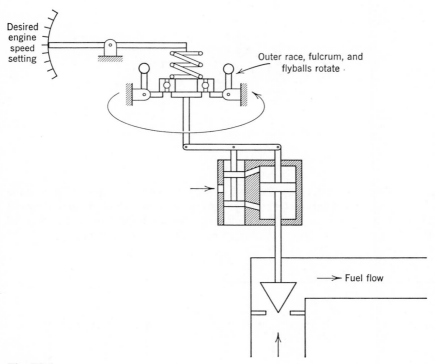

Fig. P2-4

2.5   Simplify the system shown in Fig. P2-5 three different ways and compare the results.

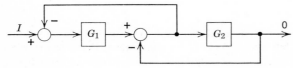

Fig. P2-5

2.6 Simplify the block diagram of Fig. P2-6 and obtain the transfer function O/I.

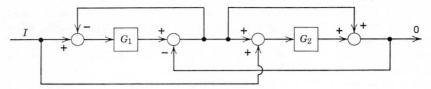

Fig. P2-6

2.7 Determine C/R and C/U for the system represented by the block diagram of Fig. P2-7.

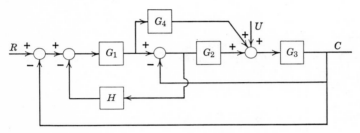

Fig. P2-7

2.8 Specific changes in the block diagram of Fig. P2-8a are suggested as possible methods of simplifying the diagram. Only the part of the diagram which is affected by the change is shown (Fig. P2-8b), the rest of the diagram remaining the same as the original diagram. If there is an error in one of the suggested changes, indicate the error.

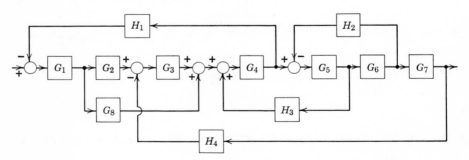

Fig. P2-8a

2.9 For the flexible missile example of the text (Example 1-2) develop a block diagram from which the effect of a gust could be studied. Assume for convenience that all aerodynamic disturbing loads are applied at Station 3 of Example 1-2. What changes in the analysis would be required if aerodynamic loads developed at other stations?

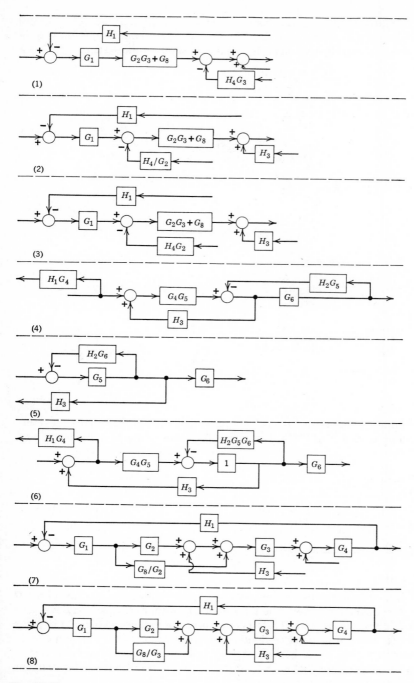

Fig. P2-8*b*

Chapter 3

3.1 Make a stability analysis, using a complex plane (Nyquist) diagram, of a control system represented by the block diagram (Fig. P3-1), where GH assumes the forms indicated below, and discuss the effect of changes of gain constant on the system.

$$\text{(a)} \quad GH = \frac{10}{s(1 + 0.1s)(1 + s)}$$

$$\text{(b)} \quad GH = \frac{10}{s(1 + s + s^2)}$$

$$\text{(c)} \quad GH = \frac{10(1 + s)}{(1 + s + s^2)(1 + s + 2s^2)}$$

$$\text{(d)} \quad GH = \frac{10}{1 + s^2}$$

$$\text{(e)} \quad GH = \frac{10}{s(1 + s^2)}$$

$$\text{(f)} \quad GH = \frac{10(1 + s)}{s(1 + s^2)}$$

$$\text{(g)} \quad GH = \frac{10s}{1 + s^2}$$

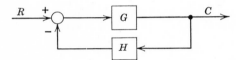

Fig. P3-1

3.2 Does the addition of the internal feedback element, $0.5s$, improve or harm the stability of the closed-loop system (Fig. P3-2)? Investigate by means of the complex plane plot.

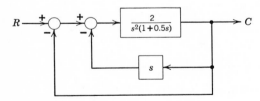

Fig. P3-2

3.3 Figure 3-4 shows the complex plane plots of a system whose transfer function GH possesses a free s in the denominator. The plots apparently approach the imaginary axis as an asymptote as s approaches $i0^+$. This is a consequence of visualizing the plot in terms of polar coordinates without actually computing and plotting to scale. The plot should approach an asymptote parallel to, but in general displaced from, the imaginary axis.

(a) Develop an expression for the point at which this asymptote intersects the real axis in terms of appropriate parameters of the transfer function, GH.

(b) What does the plot of GH approach for $s \rightarrow i0^+$ in a system whose transfer function GH possesses a free s^2 in the denominator?

3.4 In Fig. 3-4 the portion of the plot corresponding to s following the semicircle with infinite radius (Fig. 3-3) is the single point at $GH = 0$. Make a sketch showing the variation of GH in the neighborhood of zero if s takes values on a semicircle of large, but finite, radius.

3.5 In a direct feedback system,

$$G = \frac{K(1 + 2s)}{s^2(1 + s)(1 + 4s)}$$

(a) Sketch a Nyquist plot.

(b) For what values of K is the closed-loop system unstable?

(c) What changes in the transfer function time constants would improve the performance of the system?

3.6 If $G = 10/(1 - s)$, suggest several functions for the feedback function H which would result in a stable system, using the complex plane plot for a guide. (At least one of these functions should represent a stable element.)

3.7 (a) In a direct feedback control system $G = 10/(1 - s)(1 - 5s)$. Is it possible to select a series compensating function, G_a, so that the resulting closed loop system will be stable? If so, determine a satisfactory G_a.

(b) Is there a function G_a that could cause the system to be stable open loop?

Chapter 4

4.1 In a direct feedback system,

$$G = \frac{1}{s(1 + 0.5s)(1 + 0.125s)}$$

What value of K would result in a marginally stable or neutrally stable system?

4.2 In a direct feedback system, with forward transfer function of

$$G = \frac{K(1 + 0.1s)}{s^2(1 + 0.025s)}$$

approximately what value of gain constant, K, should be used? Explain.

4.3 In a direct feedback system, $G = K/s^2$. Let a stabilizing network of the form $(1 + T_a s)/(1 + T_1 s)$ be used in series with G. A Phase Margin (phase margin at zero crossover) of 45 degrees is desired, and it is also required that zero crossover shall occur at $\omega = 10$ rad/sec, halfway between the two breaks. Determine T_a, T_1, and K.

4.4 Select values for K, T_a, T_1 (Fig. P4-4) so that the system will be satisfactory. Use a straight-line magnitude plot and give an explanation for your selections.

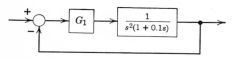

Fig. P4-4 $G_1 = \dfrac{K(1 + T_a s)}{(1 + T_1 s)}$.

4.5 (a) Make an exact frequency response plot of G_1 (Fig. P4-5) on graph paper, using the aids in the Appendix.

(b) Listed below are five proposed transfer functions representing possible stabilizing

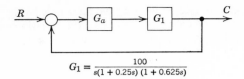

$$G_1 = \frac{100}{s(1 + 0.25s)(1 + 0.625s)}$$

Fig. P4-5

or "compensating" networks. For each, state what type of compensation it is, whether it will result in system stability, and if it will not, what is the reason for the failure.

$$\text{(a)} \quad G_a = \frac{1 + s}{1 + 10s}$$

$$\text{(b)} \quad G_a = \frac{1 + 10s}{1 + s}$$

$$\text{(c)} \quad G_a = \frac{1 + 0.01s}{1 + 0.1s}$$

$$\text{(d)} \quad G_a = \frac{1 + 0.1s}{1 + 0.01s}$$

$$\text{(e)} \quad G_a = \frac{(1 + 2s)(1 + 4s)}{(1 + s)(1 + 8s)}$$

4.6 If

$$G = \frac{100}{s(1 + s)(1 + 0.1s)}$$

in a direct feedback system, and it is proposed that the system be stabilized by internal feedback around this forward function, discuss briefly each of the following proposed functions for this internal feedback element.

$$\text{(a)} \quad H = \frac{0.25s^2}{1 + s}$$

$$\text{(b)} \quad H = 0.25(1 + s)$$

$$\text{(c)} \quad H = \frac{0.025s^2}{1 + s}$$

$$\text{(d)} \quad H = \frac{2.5s^2}{1 + s}$$

4.7 (a) Make a straight-line approximate attenuation plot for C/E, C/R, and C/U for three alternatives (Fig. P4-7):

$$G_1 = 1 \qquad G_2 = \frac{10(1 + 0.5s)}{(1 + 5s)} \qquad G_3 = \frac{4(1 + 0.1s)}{(1 + 0.005s)}$$

(b) Comment on the relative merits of the three functions, G_1, G_2, and G_3,

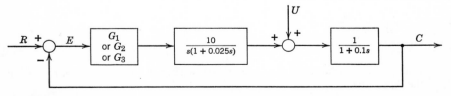

Fig. P4-7

4.8   Consider forward transfer function

$$G = \frac{10}{s(1 + 10s)(1 + s)^2}$$

in a direct feedback system.

(a) Draw an exact magnitude and angle frequency response plot.

(b) Determine suitable compensating transfer functions of the following general types; series lag, series lead, and internal feedback.

(c) If the term $(1 + s)^2$ in G were $(1 - s)^2$, would the curves of (a) change and in what way? Comment on the significance of these curves and upon the applicability of the compensating networks determined in (b). Would a series function of the form

$$\frac{s^2(1 + 10s)}{(1 + 0.1s)}$$

have a stabilizing or destabilizing effect and why?

4.9   The sketch (Fig. P4-9) represents a servomechanism having the transfer functions indicated. Use an approximate straight-line frequency response plot to determine whether the system with $H_1 = 0$ is satisfactory. If it is not, suggest a value for the constant of H_1 which would result in a satisfactory system. Then check the final selection with an exact frequency response analysis.

$$G_1 = \frac{0.6\left(1 + \frac{s}{0.04}\right)\left(1 + \frac{s}{0.3}\right)\left(1 + \frac{s}{0.6}\right)}{s\left[1 + \frac{1.2}{1.5}s + \left(\frac{s}{1.5}\right)^2\right]}$$

$$G_2 = \frac{26.3s}{\left(1 + \frac{s}{0.6}\right)\left(1 + \frac{s}{2.5}\right)^2\left(1 + \frac{s}{7}\right)\left(1 + \frac{s}{20}\right)}$$

$$H_2 = \frac{0.355s^2\left(1 + \frac{s}{5}\right)}{\left(1 + \frac{s}{0.3}\right)}$$

$$H_1 = \frac{K_H s^2\left(1 + \frac{s}{40}\right)}{\left(1 + \frac{s}{0.2}\right)}$$

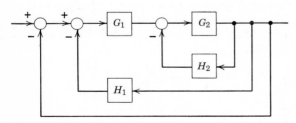

Fig. P4-9

4.10   Determine the exact frequency response curve of magnitude and angle of C/R for Example 4-1 if the internal feedback transfer function is the function suggested at the end of the example.

4.11   Using the frequency response curves of Problem 4.10, numerically determine the transient response to unit step input by applying the inverse Fourier transform.

Chapter 5

5.1   Investigate the stability of the systems of Problem 3.1 by means of root locus sketches.

5.2   In a direct feedback system with forward transfer function

$$G = \frac{10}{s(1 + s^2)}$$

is it possible to stabilize the system by gain change, simple lead or lag functions, or lag-lead function in the forward path? Investigate with complex plane sketch, frequency response sketch, and root locus sketch. Suggest a possible useful internal feedback transfer function.

5.3   The position of open-loop poles for a direct feedback system is shown in Fig. P5-3. It is proposed to add an open-loop pole and zero on the real axis in an attempt to improve the system.

(a) Discuss the feasibility of location of the zero in the regions (1), (2), (3), (4), (5), keeping in mind the necessity of also adding a pole.

(b) For zero locations which show promise, suggest suitable locations for the pole.

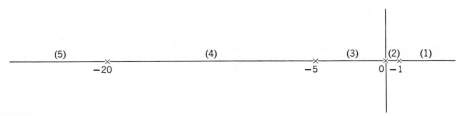

Fig. P5-3

5.4

$$G = \frac{2600}{(s + 10)(s^2 + 2s + 26)}$$

in a direct feedback system.

(a) Sketch a root locus plot for the system.

(b) Comment on gain change as a method of improving the performance of the system.

(c) Shown below are four transfer functions suggested as possible series compensating functions for improving the performance. From their effect on the root locus, which is most likely to improve performance? Explain.

$$(1) \quad K\frac{1 + s}{1 + 10s} \qquad\qquad (3) \quad K\frac{1 + s}{1 + 0.01s}$$

$$(2) \quad K\frac{1 + 10s}{1 + s} \qquad\qquad (4) \quad K\frac{1 + 0.01s}{1 + s}$$

5.5   (a) Make an accurate root locus for $GH = -1$ with variable gain for G (Fig. P5-5).

(b) Obtain the factored form of C/E from (a).

(c) Sketch a root locus for $C/E = -1$ with variable gain of the outer loop.

(d) Determine the factored form of C/R from (c).

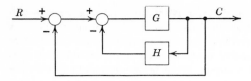

Fig. P5-5 $G = \dfrac{40}{s\left(1 + \dfrac{s}{4}\right)\left(1 + \dfrac{s}{16}\right)}$ $H = \dfrac{1 + 4s}{1 + 80s}$.

5.6

$$GH = \dfrac{-K}{s(1 - s)(1 + 0.2s)}$$

and K is positive.

$$G = \dfrac{1 + 10s}{1 + 0.1s}$$

(a) Sketch the root locus of the closed-loop system without G and with G in the forward path (series compensation).

(b) Does G help or would it be better inverted?

(c) Would it be better if G were in the feedback path instead of the forward path as far as stability is concerned?

5.7   Relations between significant parameters for a simple direct feedback system are desired, in order that more complex systems can be judged by comparison with the simple system. Let

$$G = \dfrac{K}{s(1 + Ts)}$$

and determine the following functional relationships between variables. Plot the various functions in dimensionless form for convenient reference. Definitions of variables used are:

β = closed-loop undamped natural frequency

ζ = closed-loop damping factor

$c/r|_m$ = maximum value of closed loop $|c/r|$ for sinusoidal input

$c/r|_p$ = peak value of c/r for step input

t_p = time for $c/r|_p$

ω_c = frequency where the straight-line attenuation plot intersects the 0-db line

ω_m = frequency for $c/r|_m$

ω_n = damped natural frequency

ω_T = break point frequency corresponding to T

β_0 = Phase Margin

N_0 = Gain Margin

ϕ = angle between negative real axis and closed-loop root

(a) $\beta(K, T)$ $\zeta(K, T)$ $\zeta(\omega_T, \omega_C)$

(b) $\dfrac{c}{r}\Big|_m (\omega_T, \omega_C)$ $\omega_m(\omega_T, \omega_C)$

(c) $\dfrac{c}{r}\Big|_p (\omega_T, \omega_C)$ $t_p(\omega_T, \omega_C)$ $\omega_n(\omega_T, \omega_C)$

(d) $\beta_0(\omega_T, \omega_C)$ $N_0(\omega_T, \omega_C)$

(e) $\phi(\zeta)$ $\phi(\beta_0)$ $\omega_n(\omega_T, \phi)$ $\beta(\omega_T, \phi)$

a force, is a graphical or tabular function of x, a distance. Therefore, let the problem be the following. Determine by use of the trapezoidal rule the integral,

$$z = \int_{x_1}^{x_2} y \, dx$$

where y is a single valued function of x, or a function with finite discontinuities. Since the problem might arise in the solution of a more comprehensive problem, let this determination be made in a subroutine. For this problem, assume that the values of x and y are furnished to the main program as input data, and the output will be printed by the main program. There may be various ranges for which the integral is required, therefore let desired combinations of x_1 and x_2 also be furnished to the main program as input data.

(b) Repeat (a), but let the integral be computed from a quadratic equation for y as a function of x, where the quadratic equation matches the tabular function at three successive values of x, not necessarily evenly spaced. The integral of the function between two successive values of x can be taken as the average of the integral when that interval is the left interval and when it is the right interval. (The integral between x_4 and x_5 is the average of the integral when the quadratic fits at Stations 3, 4, and 5 and when it fits at Stations 4, 5, and 6 in Fig. P8-6).

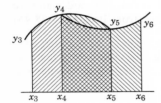

Fig. P8-6

8.7   The numerical analysis of many problems in engineering requires the solution of linear differential equations, which often can be converted to the solution of a set of simultaneous linear algebraic equations. If the set is very large with relatively few variables in each equation and if each equation is dominated by a different variable, it may be advantageous to solve the set by the Gauss-Seidel iteration method.

(a) Program this method. Input will be as follows. On each card will be the number of the equation, the number of the variable, and the coefficient of that variable in accordance with FORMAT (2I4, E17.9). The numbers on the right side of the equations will be indicated in the same way, except that the number of the variable will be designated as zero. Output will be the values of the variables.

It is desired that the data cards not necessarily be restricted to any particular order, that the dominant variable not necessarily be located on the coefficient matrix diagonal, and that the off-diagonal elements not necessarily be clustered about either the diagonal or the dominant variable. The program should determine the dominant variable in each equation by surveying the data, but there should be a mechanism for overriding this in the event that an attempt is made to use the system when one or more equations are solved for other than the dominant variable (see text).

(b) Modify (a) to invert a matrix.

8.8   (a) Write a program to reduce a determinant whose elements are complex numbers.

(b) Write a program to invert a matrix whose elements are complex numbers.

8.9   Program the method of normal mode determination illustrated by Equations 1-32, with the number of degrees of freedom general. Work Example 1-1 with this program if a computer is available.

8.10   (a) Program the method of obtaining the flexibility matrix of a rectangular variable thickness plate described in Section 1.5 but with general boundary conditions. Arrange the lattice so that stations will be located where mass elements are conveniently concentrated.

(b) Repeat (a) using the higher order polynomials of Ref. 1 and compare accuracy of (a) and (b) for the same lattice and plate.

8.11   (a) Equations 1-49 and 1-50 describe a method of factoring high-order polynomials into quadratics. Develop and program a similar method in which the polynomial is first factored into quartics, thence to quadratics, and determine by experimentation on a computer whether polynomials which cannot be factored into quadratics (by Program A86FP) because of convergence difficulties can be factored into quartics.

(b) Extend this idea by factoring the original polynomial into all of its quadratic factors simultaneously and using Equations 1-50(a) to find the unknown coefficients. Then determine by experimentation whether this is superior to (a) above or to Program A86FP.

8.12   Write a set of connecting programs and use programs given in this chapter in such a way that the minimum possible amount of necessary missile data is furnished the first program and the final output is information for a root locus plot similar to Fig. 7-8, without any intermediate human manipulation being required. Then use this sequence of programs to investigate the effect of varying missile stiffness on the stability of the flexible missile.

8.13   (a) Consider the application of Equation 1-77 to the solution of the equation $\partial^2 u/\partial x^2 + \partial^2 u/\partial y^2 = -1$ in a square region with $u = 0$ on the edges. It is desired to investigate the effect of both lattice size and polynomial order on the accuracy of the solution. Write a program to accomplish this.

(b) Repeat (a) for the deflection of a square plate of constant thickness with simply supported edges subjected to uniform lateral pressure.

Chapter 9

9.1   (a) Set up Example 9-1 on an analogue computer and verify the results shown in the traces.

(b) Set up Example 9-2 on an analogue computer, using both setups shown, and compare the results for a step input.

9.2   (a) Determine a configuration of elements such that the transfer function,

$$\frac{1}{1 + \dfrac{2\zeta s}{\beta} + \dfrac{s^2}{\beta^2}}$$

can be simulated using only nominal values of resistance and capacitance ($R = 1.0$ or 0.1 megohm, $C = 1.0$, 0.1, or 0.01 microfarad). It should be possible to select ζ and β by use of potentiometer settings between 0.1 and 1.0 so that $0.0 < \zeta < 1.0$ and $0.01 < \beta < 100$.

(b) Repeat (a) for transfer function

$$\frac{1 + T_a s}{1 + \dfrac{2\zeta s}{\beta} + \dfrac{s^2}{\beta^2}}$$

(c) Repeat (a) for transfer function

$$\frac{1 + T_1 s}{1 + T_2 s}$$

9.3 Determine a configuration of elements, as in Problem 9.2, so that a cosine function of time will be generated as an output for analysis of forced vibration. Therefore, it will be desirable that the output frequency and amplitude be easily changed with potentiometers and that a change of frequency or amplitude will not cause a change in the other characteristic, also, that the oscillation be centered on the (initially) zero value of output. (This will require use of the initial condition circuit.)

9.4 Suppose that it is desired to simulate on an analogue computer a geared shaft having a spring rate of 1000 lb-ft/rad, but with a free play region of 0.002 radians (total). It is anticipated that the maximum torque in the shaft will be 1 lb-ft. Show how to simulate this with saturating amplifiers, giving scaling factors and values of capacitors and resistors.

9.5 Investigate Problem 4.9 on an analogue computer and determine the effect of changes in the feedback parameters.

9.6 Simulate the control system represented by the block diagram shown in Fig. P9-6.

(a) Using K_0 alone ($K_1 = 0$), increase K_0 until about 1.4 overshoot to step input of R occurs. Determine the response to step disturbance, sinusoidal disturbance, and sinusoidal input of R.

(b) Repeat (a) using K_1/s alone ($K_0 = 0$).

(c) Combine K_0 and K_1 in an effort to decrease the response to U. Select values of K_0 and K_1 guided by theory and then modify as may be indicated by the experiment.

(d) Attempt further reduction in error by addition of $(1 + T_a s)/(1 + T_1 s)$ function in either the forward or feedback circuits as indicated by theory.

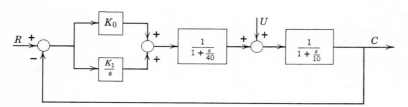

Fig. P9-6

9.7 Investigate Problem 6.6 with an analogue computer.

9.8 Investigate the control problem shown, using an analogue computer, as follows: The block diagram of a system for controlling the speed of a d-c motor is shown in Fig. P9-8a.

(a) The functional block diagram for a specific system is as shown in Fig. P9-8b.

(b) Make a root locus analysis to determine the factored form of C/R.

(c) Determine an approximate transfer function from a straight-line attenuation plot.

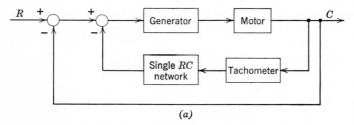

(a)

Fig. P9-8a

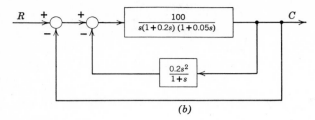

$$\frac{100}{s(1+0.2s)(1+0.05s)}$$

$$\frac{0.2s^2}{1+s}$$

(b)

Fig. P9-8*b*

(d) Compare the response to step input of R as determined by analogue computer for (a), (b), and (c).

(e) For (a) above determine the effect of changing both gain and time constant of the feedback element.

9.9 (a) Determine the natural modes and frequencies for Example 1-1 by use of the computer. Use the circuit of Problem 9.3 to force the system. (A slight amount of damping should be introduced in order to avoid the infinite response at the resonant frequencies.)

(b) Record the response to a step force and a ramp force applied to the third mass.

9.10 Determine the natural modes and frequencies for a cantilever beam with the analogue computer

(a) Using lumped elements directly.

(b) Using the matrix equations.

9.11 Devise a method of inverting a matrix experimentally, using the analogue computer. Check the method with simple matrices such as $[\delta]$ and $[K]$ for Example 1-1.

9.12 Construct an analogue simulation of the flexible missile (Example 1-2) and experimentally investigate the effect of changes in the autopilot parameters.

Answers to Problems

2.1 (c, d) $Y/X = 1/(1 + Ts)$, $T = A/C$,

$$A = \text{piston area}$$
$$C = \text{fluid flow rate per unit valve opening}$$

2.3 (a) $\dfrac{X}{Y} = \dfrac{1}{1 + \dfrac{c}{k}s}$

(d) $\dfrac{X}{Y} = \dfrac{\dfrac{c}{k_2}s}{1 + \dfrac{k_1 + k_2}{k_1}\dfrac{c}{k_2}s}$

(g) $\dfrac{X}{Y} = \dfrac{1 + \dfrac{c}{k_2}s}{1 + \dfrac{k_1 + k_2}{k_1}\dfrac{c}{k_2}s}$

(i) $\dfrac{X}{Y} = \dfrac{\left(1 + \dfrac{c_1}{k_1}s\right)\left(1 + \dfrac{c_2}{k_2}s\right)}{1 + \left(\dfrac{c_1}{k_1} + \dfrac{c_2}{k_1} + \dfrac{c_2}{k_2}\right)s + \dfrac{c_1 c_2}{k_1 k_2}s^2}$

2.7 $\dfrac{C}{R} = \dfrac{G_1 G_2 G_3 + G_1 G_3 G_4}{1 + G_1 H + G_2 G_3 + G_1 G_2 G_3 + G_1 G_3 G_4 - G_1 G_3 G_4 H}$

$\dfrac{C}{U} = \dfrac{G_3 + G_1 G_3 H}{1 + G_1 H + G_2 G_3 + G_1 G_2 G_3 + G_1 G_3 G_4 - G_1 G_3 G_4 H}$

2.8 Errors in b, c, and d.

3.1 (a) Two unstable roots for $K > 11.0$.
(b) Two unstable roots for $K > 1.0$.
(c) Two unstable roots for $K > 1.0$.
(d) Neutral stability for all positive K.
(e) Two unstable roots for all positive K.
(f) Two unstable roots for all positive K.
(g) Stable for all positive K.

3.3 (a) If GH has the form of Equation 4-1, with $n = 1$, if $s \to iO^+$

$$\mathscr{R}(GH) \to -K\left(T_1 + T_2 + \cdots + \frac{2\zeta_1}{\beta_1} + \frac{2\zeta_2}{\beta_2} + \cdots - T_a - T_b - \cdots \right.$$
$$\left. - \frac{2\zeta_a}{\beta_a} - \frac{2\zeta_b}{\beta_b} - \cdots \right)$$

(b) For $n = 2$ and $s \to iO^+$, $GH \to$ the parabola

$$K\left(T_1 + T_2 + \cdots + \frac{2\zeta_1}{\beta_1} + \frac{2\zeta_2}{\beta_2} + \cdots - T_a - T_b - \cdots - \frac{2\zeta_a}{\beta_a} - \frac{2\zeta_b}{\beta_b} - \cdots \right)$$
$$= -[\mathscr{I}(GH)]^2$$

3.6 It is necessary to encircle -1 once in the counterclockwise direction. $H = 1 + s$ would cause this. An unstable element which would cause two counterclockwise rotations about -1 and result in a stable system is $H = (1 + s)/(1 - 5s)$.

4.1 $K = 10$.

4.3 $T_a = 0.25$.
$T_1 = 0.04$.
$K = 40$.

4.6 (a) Straight line plot of $|1/H|$ crosses 0 db at -20 db/decade and maintains this slope to ± 12 db. Straight line plot of $|GH|$ has -40 db/decade at crossover, but phase margin is over $40°$. This function should be satisfactory.

(b) Conclusions are similar to those of (a) except that the system has the characteristics of $1/H$ at low frequency. This is the same as Type 0 with low gain, so the system is not as good as (a).

(c) System dynamic characteristics approach those of the same system without internal feedback. Further investigation would probably reveal instability. Gain constant for H is too low.

(d) Gain constant for H is too high. System is stable but too slow since $|1/H|$ crosses 0 db at an unnecessarily low frequency.

4.8 (c) $|G|$ would remain the same but $/G$ would change, and never become as negative as $-180°$, thereby apparently indicating stability for the system. This erroneous interpretation of the frequency response plot can be corrected by reference to the Nyquist plot. It is evident that stability cannot be assured unless the complex plane plot of GH encircles -1 twice in the counterclockwise direction. Insertion of the function, $s^2(1 + 10s)/(1 + 0.1s)$, either in the forward or feedback paths (not internal feedback), would produce this effect.

5.2 This function cannot be stabilized with gain change or the simple series circuits suggested. A possible internal feedback function is $H = s(1 + s)$, with variations.

5.4 (c) Functions (2) and (4) have unfavorable effects. Function (1) will allow a gain increase but the position of the lightly damped roots will not be improved. Function (3) shows the most promise because it can cause these roots to pull away from the imaginary axis for certain values of K.

5.7 (a) $\beta = \sqrt{K/T}$
$\zeta = 1/2\sqrt{KT}$
$\zeta = \omega_T/2\omega_C$ if $\omega_T < \omega_C$
$\zeta = \sqrt{\omega_T/\omega_C}/2$ if $\omega_T > \omega_C$

(b) $\left(\dfrac{c}{r}\right)_m = 1/2\zeta\sqrt{1 - \zeta^2}$, see (a) for ζ ($\zeta < \sqrt{2}/2$)

$\omega_m = \omega_T\sqrt{1 - 2\zeta^2}/2\zeta$, see (a) for ζ ($\zeta < \sqrt{2}/2$)

(c) $\left(\dfrac{c}{r}\right)_p = 1 + e^{-\pi\zeta/\sqrt{1-\zeta^2}}$, see (a) for ζ

$t_p = \pi/\sqrt{1 - \zeta^2}$, see (a) for ζ

$\omega_n = \omega_T\sqrt{1 - \zeta^2}/2\zeta$, see (a) for ζ

(d) $\beta_0 = 90 - \tan^{-1}\sqrt{\dfrac{\sqrt{1 + 1/4\zeta^4} - 1}{2}}$, see (a) for ζ

$N_0 \to \infty$

(e) $\phi = \cos^{-1}\zeta$

$\phi = \cos^{-1}\left\{\dfrac{1}{\sqrt{2}[(1 + 2/\tan^2\beta_0)^2 - 1]^{1/4}}\right\}$

$\omega_n = (\omega_T\tan\phi)/2$

$\beta = \omega_T/2\cos\phi$

6.1 Type 1, zero steady state error for step input, stable.

6.4 (a) Barely stable.

(b) Zero.

(c) Reduction of gain of G_2 would be favorable. If the system were more stable, increasing the time constant of G_2 would have a favorable effect. However, increasing the time constant without reducing gain makes the system less stable, so the net effect cannot be determined by casual inspection.

6.6 (a) System stable.

(b) -0.01 units of c.

7.4 (a) The block diagram will eventually reduce to one forward and one feedback block, where

$$G = \frac{k_e k_p[(k_L l - k_\alpha)k_\delta + MVk_\delta ls]}{s(s + k_p)[(k_L k_d + k_\alpha MV) + (k_d MV + Ik_L)s + IMVs^2]}$$

$$H = k_g s$$

(b) Yes.

(c) $\theta = 0.884 + 2.86t - 0.964e^{-4.26t}(0.079\cos 14.7t - 0.772\sin 14.7t)$.

The control position commands the angular velocity of the aircraft.

(d) $2.86°$, $3.24°$.

Appendix I

Index of FORTRAN Program Listings

A74 Series   Determination of characteristic polynomial from a determinant whose elements are quadratics

    A74INP1   Typical input data preparation

    A74PFD   Main program

    A74A86A   Program linking A74PFD with A86FP

A86 Series   Determination of the factors of a polynomial

    A86INP1   Typical input data preparation

    A86FP   Main program for factoring a polynomial

    A86FPS   Subroutine for factoring a polynomial

    A86RTS   Subroutine used in D91RTL for converting factors

    A87SHK   Main program for computing shock spectrum

    A87CXSK   Main program for computing the shock spectrum for a complex shock, zero damping

    D52FR   Main program for computing frequency response plot

    D52CN   Subroutine used in D52FR

    D86FT   Main program for computing either the coefficients of a Fourier series or the numerical Fourier transform

    D871FT   Main program for numerical computation of the inverse Fourier transform

    D91PRE   Main program for preparation of transfer functions for Programs E11TRN, D52FR, and D91RTL

    D91RTL   Main program for computing the root locus

    E11TRN   Main program for computing the inverse Laplace transform analytically and numerically and for numerically computing the response to an arbitrary transient input

    E11C4   Subroutine used in E11TRN

    E11SSB   Subroutine used in E11C4

```
      TITLEA37INP1         J.B.VERNON   0101
C THIS PROGRAM PREPARES TAPE 1 FOR USE BY PROGRAM A37IM60 OR A37ILM, USING DATA
C CARDS FOR INPUT.  THE DATA CARDS SHOULD BE PREPARED ACCORDING TO THE FORMAT
C STATEMENTS BELOW, WITH INTPM AND INTPI ON ONE CARD.  N AND THE ELEMENTS OF A
C ARE ALL ON SEPARATE CARDS.
  100   FORMAT(I1,I1)
  110   FORMAT(I3)
  120   FORMAT(E17.9)
        DIMENSION A(600)
        READ INPUT TAPE 5,100,INTPM,INTPI
        READ INPUT TAPE 5,110,N
        REWIND 1
        WRITE TAPE 1,INTPM,INTPI,N
        DO 130 I=1,N
        READ INPUT TAPE 5,120,(A(J),J=1,N)
  130   WRITE TAPE 1,(A(J),J=1,N)
        REWIND 2
        REWIND 3
        STOP
        END



      TITLEA37IM60         J.B.VERNON   0101
C THIS PROGRAM WILL INVERT A MATRIX, USING DATA STORED ON TAPE 1.  THIS DATA
C MUST BE PREPARED AND STORED ON TAPE 1 TO BE CONSISTENT WITH THE READ TAPE 1
C STATEMENTS AT THE BEGINNING OF THIS PROGRAM.  INTPM IS 1 IF THE ORIGINAL
C MATRIX IS TO BE PRINTED AND IS ZERO OTHERWISE.  N IS THE ORDER OF THE MATRIX.
C THE PRODUCT OF THE MATRIX AND ITS INVERSE IS COMPUTED AS A CHECK AND THE
C LARGEST ERROR PRINTED.  THE OUTPUT OF THIS PROGRAM IS STORED ON TAPE 1, AND
C CONSISTS OF N AND ISING, AN INDICATOR WHICH IS 1 IF THE MATRIX IS SINGULAR
C AND ZERO OTHERWUSE, FOLLOWED BY THE INVERSE MATRIX AND THE ORIGINAL MATRIX
C IN THAT ORDER AND STORED BY ROWS.
C AN OUTPUT PROGRAM MAKING USE OF THIS PROGRAM SHOULD HAVE READ TAPE 1 STATE-
C MENTS CONSISTENT WITH THE WRITE TAPE 1 STATEMENTS, 621, 622, 626.
C BOTH TAPE 1 AND TAPE 2 ARE USED IN THIS PROGRAM.  N CANNOT EXCEED 60 FOR THE
C DIMENSION STATEMENT USED.
  130   FORMAT(1H0, 73HDATA   MATRIX ELEMENTS IDENTIFIED BY ROW AND COLUMN
       1 NUMBER IN PARENTHESES)
  140   FORMAT(1H0, 16HMATRIX A FOLLOWS)
  250   FORMAT(1H0, 20HMATRIX A IS SINGULAR)
  580   FORMAT(1H0,20HINVERSE OF A FOLLOWS)
  640   FORMAT(1H0,80HMATRIX   A     POSTMULTIPLIED BY ITS INVERSE HAS BEEN
       1 COMPUTED. THE MAX ERROR IS E17.9,14H FOR ELEMENT (I3,1HI3,1H))
        DIMENSION A(60,60),B(60), C(60),IXIMAX(60), JXJMAX(60),
       1ICHK(60),JCHK(60)
        COMMON N,MC,A
        REWIND 1
        READ TAPE 1, INTPM, INTPI, N
        DO 100 I=1,N
  100   READ TAPE 1, (A(I, J), J=1,N)
        REWIND 1
        REWIND 2
        DO 120 I=1,N
  120   WRITE TAPE 1,(A(I,J),J=1,N)
        REWIND 2
        WRITE TAPE 2,((A(I,J),J=1,N),I=1,N)
        ISING = 0
        MC = N
        DO 132 J=1,N
        ICHK(J) = 0
  132   JCHK(J) = 0
        IF(INTPM)145,145,125
  125   PRINT 130
        PRINT 140
        CALL A37PM6
  145   DO 420 IXA = 1,N
        AMAX = 0.0
        DO 160 I=1,N
        IF(ICHK(I))146,146,160
  146   DO 158 J=1,N
```

```
      IF(JCHK(J))147,147,158
147   IF(AMAX - ABSF(A(I,J)))150,158,158
150   AMAX = ABSF(A(I,J))
      IMAX = I
      JMAX = J
158   CONTINUE
160   CONTINUE
      ICHK(IMAX) = 1
      JCHK(JMAX) = 1
      IXIMAX(IXA) = IMAX
      JXJMAX(IXA) = JMAX
      IF(AMAX - 1.0E-30)240,290,290
240   PRINT 250
      ISING = 1
      REWIND 1
      WRITE TAPE 1,N,ISING
      STOP
290   DUM = A(IMAX,JMAX)
      DO 310 J=1,N
      IF(JCHK(J))304,304,310
304   A(IMAX,J) = A(IMAX,J)/DUM
310   CONTINUE
      DO 380 I=1,N
      IF(I-IMAX)320,380,320
320   DO 340 J=1,N
      IF(JCHK(J))330,330,340
330   A(I,J) = A(I,J) - A(I,JMAX) * A(IMAX,J)
340   CONTINUE
380   CONTINUE
420   CONTINUE
      DO 430 J=1,N
      JT = JXJMAX(J)
430   WRITE TAPE 1,(A(I,JT),I=1,N)
      REWIND 1
      DO 434 I=1,N
434   READ TAPE 1,(A(I,J),J=1,N)
      DO 440 I=1,N
      DO 440 J=1,N
440   A(I,J) = 0.0
      DO 450 I=1,N
450   A(I,I) = 1.0
      DO 560 IXA = 1,N
      READ TAPE 1, (B(I),I=1,N)
      IMAX = IXIMAX(IXA)
      JMAX= JXJMAX(IXA)
      DO 460 J=1,N
460   A(IMAX,J) = A(IMAX,J)/B(IMAX)
      DO 558 I=1,N
      IF(I-IMAX)470,558,470
470   DO 480 J=1,N
480   A(I,J) = A(I,J) - B(I) * A(IMAX,J)
558   CONTINUE
560   CONTINUE
      DO 570 IXA = 1,N
      IMAX = IXIMAX(IXA)
      JMAX = JXJMAX(IXA)
      IF(IMAX - JMAX)565,570,565
565   DO 566 J=1,N
      DUM = A(IMAX,J)
      A(IMAX,J) = A(JMAX,J)
566   A(JMAX,J) = DUM
      DO 569 I=IXA,N
      IF(IXIMAX(I) - JMAX)569,567,569
567   IXIMAX(I) = IMAX
      GO TO 570
569   CONTINUE
570   CONTINUE
      IF(INTPI)600,600,575
575   PRINT 580
      CALL A37PM6
600   REWIND 1
      DO 620 I=1,N
      READ TAPE 1,(B(J),J=1,N)
      DO 610 J=1,N
```

```
        C(J) = 0.0
        DO 610 K=1,N
610     C(J) = C(J) + B(K) * A(K,J)
620     WRITE TAPE 2,(C(J),J=1,N)
        REWIND 1
621     WRITE TAPE 1,N,ISING
        DO 622 I=1,N
622     WRITE TAPE 1,(A(I,J),J=1,N)
        REWIND 2
        READ TAPE 2,((A(I,J),J=1,N),I=1,N)
        DO 630 I=1,N
630     READ TAPE 2,(A(I,J),J=1,N)
        DO 632 I=1,N
632     A(I,I) = A(I,I) - 1.0
        ERROR = -1.0
        DO 636 I=1,N
        DO 636 J=1,N
        IF(ABSF(A(I,J)) - ERROR)636,636,634
634     ERROR = ABSF(A(I,J))
        IMAXER = I
        JMAXER = J
636     CONTINUE
        PRINT 640,ERROR,IMAXER,JMAXER
        REWIND 2
        READ TAPE 2,((A(I,J),J=1,N),I=1,N)
        DO 626 I=1,N
626     WRITE TAPE 1,(A(I,J),J=1,N)
        STOP
        END




TITLEA37ILM        J.B.VERNON  0101
C THIS PROGRAM WILL INVERT A LARGE MATRIX BY USE OF TAPES. TAPES 1, 2, AND 3
C ARE USED.  FOR THE DIMENSION STATEMENT USED, THE ORDER OF THE MATRIX MUST
C NOT EXCEED 300.  SINCE TAPES ARE USED, THIS PROGRAM IS SLOW AND SHOULD NOT BE
C USED IF A FASTER PROGRAM IS AVAILABLE.  THE DATA FOR THIS PROGRAM IS READ
C FROM TAPES PREPARED BY ANOTHER PROGRAM WHICH SHOULD BE CONSISTENT WITH THE
C READ TAPE 2 AND READ TAPE 1 STATEMENTS AT THE BEGINNING OF THIS PROGRAM.
C NORMALLY ALL THE ELEMENTS OF THE MATRIX TO BE INVERTED AND THE INVERSE WOULD
C NOT BE PRINTED BECAUSE OF THE LARGE ORDER.  HOWEVER, IF IT IS DESIRED THAT
C EITHER OF THESE BE PRINTED THIS CAN BE ARRANGED BY GIVING THE VALUE, 1, TO
C THE VARIABLE,INTPM, IF THE ORIGINAL MATRIX IS TO BE PRINTED, AND THE VALUE 1,
C TO THE VARIABLE, INTPI, IF THE INVERSE IS TO BE PRINTED.  IF EITHER OF THESE
C MATRICES IS NOT TO BE PRINTED, THE APPROPRIATE VALUE IS ZERO.  THE MATRIX TO
C BE INVERTED MUST BE STORED BY ROWS ON TAPE 1.  N IS THE ORDER OF THE MATRIX.
C AT THE END OF THE PROGRAM N AND ISING, AN INDICATOR WHICH IS 1 IF THE MATRIX
C IS SINGULAR AND ZERO OTHERWISE, ARE STORED FIRST ON TAPE 1, FOLLOWED BY THE
C INVERSE MATRIX AND THEN THE ORIGINAL MATRIX STORED BY ROWS.  THE PRODUCT
C OF THE MATRIX POSTMULTIPLIED BY ITS INVERSE IS MADE AS
C A CHECK AND THE MAXIMUM ERROR PRINTED.  AN OUTPUT PROGRAM WOULD NORMALLY BE
C USED WITH THIS PROGRAM AND WOULD HAVE TO BE CONSISTENT WITH THESE TAPES.
90      FORMAT(1H6,12HSTART A37ILM)
100     FORMAT(1H0,32HPARITY ERROR.  THIS IS STATEMENT  I4,  14H COLUMN NU
       1MBER   I5,  42H     RETURNING TO PREVIOUS REWIND STATEMENT)
145     FORMAT(1H0,21HMATRIX TO BE INVERTED)
600     FORMAT(1H0,18HMATRIX IS SINGULAR)
607     FORMAT(1H ,16HSTARTING COLUMN   I4)
620     FORMAT(1H ,13HEND OF A37ILM)
626     FORMAT(1H1,30HEND OF TAPE--PROBLEM TOO LARGE)
        DIMENSION RIXA(300),RIXB(300),RMAXA(300),RMAXB(300),RIXBT(300)
        DIMENSION A(300),B(300),AT(300),BT(300),ICHK(300),RIXAT(300)
        COMMON N,I,AT,A,B,BT,RIXA,RIXB,RMAXA,RMAXB,INTPI,ISING,ITAPE
        PRINT 90
        IXA = 0
        DO 128 J=1,N
128     ICHK(J) = 0
        GO TO 131
130     IPARTY = 130
        PRINT 100,IPARTY,IXA
131     REWIND 1
```

```
        REWIND 2
        ISING = 0
        AMAX=0.0
        READ TAPE 1, INTPM, INTPI,N
        IF PARITY 130,132
132     IF(INTPM)150,150,140
140     PRINT 145
150     REWIND2
        REWIND 3
        I=1
151     IF(N-I)184,152,152
152     READ TAPE 1, (A(J), J=1,N)
        IF PARITY 130,153
153     IF(INTPM)158,158,154
154     DO 156 J=1,N
156     AT(J) = A(J)
        CALL A37PLM
158     DO 176  JX = 1,N
        IF(ABSF(A(JX))-AMAX)176,176,160
160     AMAX = ABSF(A(JX))
        IMAX = I
        JMAX = JX
        DO 174 J=1,N
        RMAXA(J)=A(J)
174     RMAXB(J)=0.0
        RMAXB(I)=1.0
176     CONTINUE
180     WRITE TAPE 3, (A(J),J=1,N)
        IF PARITY 130,181
181     I=I+1
        GO TO 151
182     IPARTY = 182
        PRINT 100,IPARTY,IXA
184     REWIND 1
        READ TAPE 1, INTPM, INTPI,N
        IF PARITY 182,185
185     I=1
186     IF(N-I)214,188,188
188     READ TAPE 1,(A(J), J=1,N)
        IF PARITY 182,189
189     DO 190 J=1,N
        B(J)=0.0
190     CONTINUE
        B(I)=1.0
        IF(I-JMAX)1903,1901,1903
1901    DO 1902 J=1,N
        RIXAT(J) = A(J)
1902    RIXBT(J) = B(J)
1903    WRITE TAPE 2, (A(J),J=1,N),(B(J),J=1,N)
        IF PARITY 182,191
191     IF END OF FILE 625,192
192     I=I+1
        GO TO 186
214     ITAPE=0
        ICK = 10
        ICHK(JMAX) = 1
        IXA=1
216     IF(N-IXA)610,218,218
218     IF(ITAPE)220,220,230
220     ITAPE=1
        GO TO 234
230     ITAPE=0
234     DUM1 = RMAXA(JMAX)
        AMAX = 0.0
        DO 240 J=1,N
        A(J) = RMAXA(J)/DUM1
        B(J) = RMAXB(J)/DUM1
        RIXA(J) = RIXAT(J)
        RIXB(J) = RIXBT(J)
240     CONTINUE
        GO TO 290
289     IPARTY = 289
        PRINT 100,IPARTY,IXA
290     REWIND 1
```

```
      REWIND 2
300   I=1
302   IF(N-I)400,304,304
304   IF(ITAPE)320,320,310
310   READ TAPE 2,(AT(J),J=1,N),(BT(J),J=1,N)
      IF PARITY 289,321
320   READ TAPE 1,(AT(J),J=1,N),(BT(J),J=1,N)
      IF PARITY 289,321
321   IF(I-JMAX)326,322,326
322   IF(ITAPE)324,324,323
323   WRITE TAPE 1,(A(J),J=1,N),(B(J),J=1,N)
      IF PARITY 289,325
324   WRITE TAPE 2,(A(J),J=1,N),(B(J),J=1,N)
      IF PARITY 289,325
325   IF(IMAX-JMAX)390,390,3251
3251  DO 3252 J=1,N
      RIXA(J) = AT(J)
3252  RIXB(J) = BT(J)
      GO TO 390
326   IF(I-IMAX)330,327,330
327   DO 328 J=1,N
      AT(J) = RIXA(J)
328   BT(J) = RIXB(J)
330   IF(ABSF(AT(JMAX))-1.0E-30)3501,3501,340
340   DUM1 = AT(JMAX)
      DO 350 J=1,N
      BT(J) = BT(J)  - DUM1 * B(J)
      IF(ABSF(A(J))-1.0E-30)350,350,342
342   AT(J)=AT(J)-DUM1*A(J)
      IF(ABSF(AT(J)/A(J)/DUM1)-1.0E-07)344,344,350
344   AT(J)=0.0
350   CONTINUE
3501  IF(ICHK(I))351,351,361
351   DO 354 J=1,N
      IF(ICHK(J))352,352,354
352   IF(ABSF(AT(J))-AMAX)354,354,353
353   AMAX = ABSF(AT(J))
      IMAXT = I
      JMAXT = J
354   CONTINUE
      IF(I-IMAXT)361,355,361
355   DO 356 J=1,N
      RMAXA(J) = AT(J)
356   RMAXB(J) = BT(J)
361   IF(I-JMAXT)369,362,369
362   DO 363 J=1,N
      RIXAT(J) = AT(J)
363   RIXBT(J) = BT(J)
369   IF(ITAPE)380,380,370
370   WRITE TAPE 1,(AT(J),J=1,N),(BT(J),J=1,N)
      IF PARITY 289,371
371   DO 372 J=1,N
372   AT(J)=BT(J)
      GO TO 390
380   WRITE TAPE 2,(AT(J),J=1,N),(BT(J),J=1,N)
      IF PARITY 289,381
381   DO 382 J=1,N
382   AT(J)=BT(J)
390   I=I+1
      GO TO 302
400   ICHK(JMAXT) = 1
      IMAX = IMAXT
      JMAX = JMAXT
      IF(N-IXA)401,401,4001
4001  IF(AMAX-1.0E-30)590,590,401
401   IXA = IXA + 1
      IF(IXA - ICK)216,402,216
402   PRINT 607, ICK
      ICK = ICK + 10
      GO TO 216
590   PRINT 600
      ISING = 1
      GO TO 5911
591   IPARTY = 591
```

```
       PRINT 100,IPARTY,IXA
 5911  REWIND 1
       WRITE TAPE 1,N,ISING
       IF PARITY 591,592
 592   STOP
 610   CALL A37LMS(AMAX)
       PRINT 620
       STOP
 625   PRINT 626
       STOP
       END




       SUBROUTINEA37LMS(AMAX)
 100   FORMAT(1H0,32HPARITY ERROR.  THIS IS STATEMENT  I4,  14H COLUMN NU
      1MBER  I5,  42H     RETURNING TO PREVIOUS REWIND STATEMENT)
 640   FORMAT(1H0,14HINVERSE MATRIX)
 800   FORMAT(1H0,80HMATRIX    A    POSTMULTIPLIED BY ITS INVERSE HAS BEEN
      1 COMPUTED. THE MAX ERROR IS E17.9,14H FOR ELEMENT  (I3,1H,I3,1H))
 7201  FORMAT(1H0,26HSTART MULTIPLICATION CHECK)
 7911  FORMAT(1H ,12HSTARTING ROW  I4)
       DIMENSION A(300), B(300), AT(300), BT(300)
       DIMENSION RIXA(300), RIXB(300), RMAXA(300), RMAXB(300)
       COMMON N,I,AT,A,B,BT,RIXA,RIXB,RMAXA,RMAXB,INTPI,ISING,ITAPE
       I=0
       GO TO 629
 628   IPARTY = 628
       PRINT 100,IPARTY, I
 629   REWIND 1
       REWIND 2
       REWIND 3
       IF(INTPI)650,650,630
 630   PRINT 640
 650   IF(ITAPE)660,660,690
 660   I=1
 662   IF(N-I)719,663,663
 663   READ TAPE 2,(B(J),J=1,N),(AT(J),J=1,N)
       IF PARITY 628,664
 664   WRITE TAPE 1,(AT(J),J=1,N)
       IF PARITY 628,667
 667   IF(INTPI)680,680,670
 670   CALL A37PLM
 680   I=I+1
       GO TO 662
 690   I=1
 692   IF(N-I)720,693,693
 693   READ TAPE 1,(B(J),J=1,N),(AT(J),J=1,N)
       IF PARITY 628,694
 694   WRITE TAPE 2,(A(J),J=1,N)
       IF PARITY 628,696
 696   IF(INTPI)710,710,700
 700   CALL A37PLM
 710   I=I+1
       GO TO 692
 718   IPARTY = 718
       PRINT 100,IPARTY,I
 719   REWIND 3
       ERROR = 0.0
       PRINT 7201
       PAUSE
       ICK = 10
       I=1
 721   IF(N-I)792,724,724
 724   DO 725 L=1,N
 725   BT(L)=0.0
       READ TAPE 3,(A(J),J=1,N)
       IF PARITY 718,7253
 7251  IPARTY = 7251
       PRINT 100,IPARTY,I
 7253  REWIND 1
```

```
7252  K=1
726   IF(N-K)762,728,728
728   READ TAPE 1,(B(J),J=1,N)
      IF PARITY 7251,750
750   DO 760 L=1,N
760   BT(L) = BT(L) + A(K)*B(L)
      K=K+1
      GO TO 726
762   BT(I)=BT(I)-1.0
      DO 790 J=1,N
      IF(ABSF(BT(J))-ERROR)790,790,780
780   ERROR=ABSF(BT(J))
      IMAXER=I
      JMAXER=J
790   CONTINUE
      I=I+1
      IF(I-ICK)721,791,721
791   PRINT 7911,ICK
      ICK = ICK + 10
      GO TO 721
792   PRINT 800,ERROR,IMAXER,JMAXER
      RETURN
720   IF(ITAPE)840,840,820
819   IPARTY = 819
      PRINT 100,IPARTY,I
820   REWIND 1
      REWIND 2
      WRITE TAPE 1,N,ISING
      IF PARITY 819,821
821   I=1
824   IF(N-I)860,826,826
826   READ TAPE 2,(A(J),J=1,N)
      IF PARITY 819,830
830   WRITE TAPE 1,(A(J),J=1,N)
      IF PARITY 819,831
831   I=I+1
      GO TO 824
839   IPARTY = 839
      PRINT 100,IPARTY,I
840   REWIND 1
      REWIND 2
      I=1
842   IF(N-I)854,844,844
844   READ TAPE 1,(A(J),J=1,N)
      IF PARITY 839,850
850   WRITE TAPE 2,(A(J),J=1,N)
      IF PARITY 839,851
851   I=I+1
      GO TO 842
854   REWIND 1
      REWIND 2
      GO TO 820
859   IPARTY = 859
      PRINT 100,IPARTY,I
860   REWIND 3
      I=1
862   IF(N-I)872,864,864
864   READ TAPE 3,(A(J),J=1,N)
      IF PARITY 859,870
870   WRITE TAPE 1,(A(J),J=1,N)
      IF PARITY 859,871
871   I=I+1
      GO TO 862
872   RETURN
      END



      TITLEA37OUT1       J.B.VERNON   0101
C THIS PROGRAM PRINTS THE OUTPUT OF PROGRAM A37IM60 OR A37ILM.
  65    FORMAT(1H0,18HMATRIX IS SINGULAR)
```

```
80      FORMAT(1H0,14HINVERSE MATRIX)
        DIMENSION A(600)
        COMMON N,I,A
        REWIND 1
        READ TAPE 1,N,ISING
        IF(ISING)70,70,60
60      PRINT 65
        STOP
70      PRINT 80
        DO 100 I=1,N
        READ TAPE 1,(A(J),J=1,N)
100     CALL A37PLM
        STOP
        END




        SUBROUTINE A37IMS
C       THIS SUBROUTINE MAY BE USED TO INVERT A MATRIX OF REAL NUMBERS.  BEFORE
C CALLING THE SUBROUTINE, IT IS NECESSARY TO HAVE ESTABLISHED THE ORDER OF THE
C MATRIX, A, WHICH IS TO BE INVERTED.  AT THE END OF THE SUBROUTINE  A  WILL
C HAVE BEEN REPLACED BY ITS INVERSE.  THIS SUBROUTINE IS USED IN PROGRAM A38NM.
250     FORMAT(1H0, 20HMATRIX A IS SINGULAR)
        DIMENSION A(30,30),B(30), C(30),IXIMAX(30), JXJMAX(30),
       1ICHK(30),JCHK(30),D(30,30)
        COMMON N,MC,A,D,B
        ISING = 0
        MC = N
        DO 132 J=1,N
        ICHK(J) = 0
132     JCHK(J) = 0
145     DO 420 IXA = 1,N
        AMAX = 0.0
        DO 160 I=1,N
        IF(ICHK(I))146,146,160
146     DO 158 J=1,N
        IF(JCHK(J))147,147,158
147     IF(AMAX - ABSF(A(I,J)))150,158,158
150     AMAX = ABSF(A(I,J))
        IMAX = I
        JMAX = J
158     CONTINUE
160     CONTINUE
        ICHK(IMAX) = 1
        JCHK(JMAX) = 1
        IXIMAX(IXA) = IMAX
        JXJMAX(IXA) = JMAX
        IF(AMAX - 1.0E-30)240,290,290
240     PRINT 250
        ISING = 1
        STOP
290     DUM = A(IMAX,JMAX)
        DO 310 J=1,N
        IF(JCHK(J))304,304,310
304     A(IMAX,J) = A(IMAX,J)/DUM
310     CONTINUE
        DO 380 I=1,N
        IF(I-IMAX)320,380,320
320     DO 340 J=1,N
        IF(JCHK(J))330,330,340
330     A(I,J) = A(I,J) - A(I,JMAX) * A(IMAX,J)
340     CONTINUE
380     CONTINUE
420     CONTINUE
        DO 430 J=1,N
        JT = JXJMAX(J)
        DO 430 I=1,N
430     D(I,J) = A(I,JT)
        DO 440 I=1,N
        DO 440 J=1,N
440     A(I,J) = 0.0
```

```
      DO 450 I=1,N
450   A(I,I) = 1.0
      DO 560 IXA = 1,N
      DO 452 I=1,N
452   B(I) = D(I,IXA)
      IMAX = IXIMAX(IXA)
      JMAX= JXJMAX(IXA)
      DO 460 J=1,N
460   A(IMAX,J) = A(IMAX,J)/B(IMAX)
      DO 558 I=1,N
      IF(I-IMAX)470,558,470
470   DO 480 J=1,N
480   A(I,J) = A(I,J) - B(I) * A(IMAX,J)
558   CONTINUE
560   CONTINUE
      DO 570 IXA = 1,N
      IMAX = IXIMAX(IXA)
      JMAX = JXJMAX(IXA)
      IF(IMAX - JMAX)565,570,565
565   DO 566 J=1,N
      DUM = A(IMAX,J)
      A(IMAX,J) = A(JMAX,J)
566   A(JMAX,J) = DUM
      DO 569 I=IXA,N
      IF(IXIMAX(I) - JMAX)569,567,569
567   IXIMAX(I) = IMAX
      GO TO 570
569   CONTINUE
570   CONTINUE
      RETURN
      END




      SUBROUTINE A37PM
C THIS SUBROUTINE WILL CAUSE THE ELEMENTS OF A MATRIX TO BE PRINTED.  NPM IS
C THE NUMBER OF COLUMNS IN THE MATRIX, MPM THE NUMBER OF ROWS, AND PM(I,J) THE
C ELEMENTS.  FOR THE DIMENSION STATEMENT GIVEN, THE MATRIX MAY BE AS LARGE AS 30
C BY 30.
      DIMENSION PM(30,30)
      COMMON NPM,MPM,PM
5     FORMAT(1H0,5(1H(I2,1H,I2,1H)E16.9,1H/))
10    FORMAT(1H ,5(1H(I2,1H,I2,1H)E16.9,1H/))
13    FORMAT(1H0,4(1H(I2,1H,I2,1H)E16.9,1H/))
15    FORMAT(1H0,3(1H(I2,1H,I2,1H)E16.9,1H/))
18    FORMAT(1H0,2(1H(I2,1H,I2,1H)E16.9,1H/))
20    FORMAT(1H0, (1H(I2,1H,I2,1H)E16.9,1H/))
      I=1
1     J=1
      NT=5
2     J1=J+1
      J2=J+2
      J3=J+3
      J4=J+4
3     IND1=NPM-NT
      IF(IND1)11,4,9
4     PRINT 5,I,J,PM(I,J),I,J1,PM(I,J1),I,J2,PM(I,J2),I,J3,PM(I,J3),I,J4
     1,PM(I,J4)
6     IND2=MPM-I
      IF(IND2)21,21,7
7     I=I+1
8     GO TO 1
9     PRINT 10,I,J,PM(I,J),I,J1,PM(I,J1),I,J2,PM(I,J2),I,J3,PM(I,J3),I,J
     14,PM(I,J4)
      NT=NT+5
      J=J+5
      GO TO 2
11    IND1=IND1+1
      IF(IND1)24,12,12
12    PRINT 13, I,J,PM(I,J),I,J1, PM(I,J1),I,J2,PM(I,J2),I,J3,PM(I,J3)
      GO TO 6
```

```
24      IND1=IND1+1
        IF(IND1)16,14,14
14      PRINT 15, I,J,PM(I,J),I,J1,PM(I,J1),I,J2,PM(I,J2)
        GO TO 6
16      IND1=IND1+1
        IF(IND1)19,17,17
17      PRINT 18,I,J,PM(I,J),I,J1,PM(I,J1)
        GO TO 6
19      PRINT 20,I,J,PM(I,J)
        GO TO 6
21      RETURN
        END




        SUBROUTINE A37PLM
C THIS SUBROUTINE CAN BE USED TO PRINT A ROW OF A MATRIX.  THE ROW TO BE PRINTED
C IS  I, THE NUMBER OF ELEMENTS IN THE ROW IS NPM, AND THE ELEMENTS ARE PM(J).
C UP TO 600 ELEMENTS CAN BE PRINTED WITH THE DIMENSION STATEMENT GIVEN.
        DIMENSION PM(600)
        COMMON NPM,I,PM
5       FORMAT(1H0,5(1H(I2,1H,I2,1H)E16.9,1H/))
10      FORMAT(1H ,5(1H(I2,1H,I2,1H)E16.9,1H/))
13      FORMAT(1H0,4(1H(I2,1H,I2,1H)E16.9,1H/))
15      FORMAT(1H0,3(1H(I2,1H,I2,1H)E16.9,1H/))
18      FORMAT(1H0,2(1H(I2,1H,I2,1H)E16.9,1H/))
20      FORMAT(1H0, (1H(I2,1H,I2,1H)E16.9,1H/))
1       J=1
        NT=5
2       J1=J+1
        J2=J+2
        J3=J+3
        J4=J+4
3       IND1=NPM-NT
        IF(IND1)11,4,9
4       PRINT 5,I,J,PM(J),I,J1,PM(J1),I,J2,PM(J2),I,J3,PM(J3),I,J4,PM(J4)
6       RETURN
8       GO TO 1
9       PRINT10,I,J,PM(J),I,J1,PM(J1),I,J2,PM(J2),I,J3,PM(J3),I,J4,PM(J4)
        NT=NT+5
        J=J+5
        GO TO 2
11      IND1=IND1+1
        IF(IND1)24,12,12
12      PRINT13,I,J,PM(J),I,J1,PM(J1),I,J2,PM(J2),I,J3,PM(J3)
        GO TO 6
24      IND1=IND1+1
        IF(IND1)16,14,14
14      PRINT15,I,J,PM(J),I,J1,PM(J1),I,J2,PM(J2)
        GO TO 6
16      IND1=IND1+1
        IF(IND1)19,17,17
17      PRINT18,I,J,PM(J),I,J1,PM(J1)
        GO TO 6
19      PRINT 20,I,J,PM(J)
        GO TO 6
        END




        SUBROUTINE A37PM6
C THIS SUBROUTINE IS THE SAME AS A37PM EXCEPT THAT THE DIMENSIONS OF THE
C MATRIX MAY BE AS GREAT AS 60 BY 60.
        DIMENSION PM(60,60)
        COMMON NPM,MPM,PM
5       FORMAT(1H0,5(1H(I2,1H,I2,1H)E16.9,1H/))
10      FORMAT(1H ,5(1H(I2,1H,I2,1H)E16.9,1H/))
13      FORMAT(1H0,4(1H(I2,1H,I2,1H)E16.9,1H/))
15      FORMAT(1H0,3(1H(I2,1H,I2,1H)E16.9,1H/))
```

```
18     FORMAT(1H0,2(1H(I2,1H,I2,1H)E16.9,1H/))
20     FORMAT(1H0, (1H(I2,1H,I2,1H)E16.9,1H/))
       I=1
1      J=1
       NT=5
2      J1=J+1
       J2=J+2
       J3=J+3
       J4=J+4
3      IND1=NPM-NT
         IF(IND1)11,4,9
4      PRINT 5,I,J,PM(I,J),I,J1,PM(I,J1),I,J2,PM(I,J2),I,J3,PM(I,J3),I,J4
      1,PM(I,J4)
6      IND2=MPM-I
       IF(IND2)21,21,7
7      I=I+1
8      GO TO 1
9      PRINT 10,I,J,PM(I,J),I,J1,PM(I,J1),I,J2,PM(I,J2),I,J3,PM(I,J3),I,J
      14,PM(I,J4)
       NT=NT+5
       J=J+5
       GO TO 2
11     IND1=IND1+1
       IF(IND1)24,12,12
12     PRINT 13, I,J,PM(I,J),I,J1, PM(I,J1),I,J2,PM(I,J2),I,J3,PM(I,J3)
       GO TO 6
24     IND1=IND1+1
       IF(IND1)16,14,14
14     PRINT 15, I,J,PM(I,J),I,J1,PM(I,J1),I,J2,PM(I,J2)
       GO TO 6
16     IND1=IND1+1
       IF(IND1)19,17,17
17     PRINT 18,I,J,PM(I,J),I,J1,PM(I,J1)
       GO TO 6
19     PRINT 20,I,J,PM(I,J)
       GO TO 6
21     RETURN
       END
```

```
TITLEA37EXP         101  J.B.VERNON
C      THIS PROGRAM USES SUBROUTINE A37RD(F) AND IS INTENDED AS AN EXAMPLE OF THE
C USE OF THAT SUBROUTINE.
       DIMENSION A(30,30)
       COMMON N,MPM,A
       READ INPUT TAPE 5,20,N
20     FORMAT(I2)
       READ INPUT TAPE 5,22,((A(I,J),J=1,N),I=1,N)
22     FORMAT(E17.9)
       MPM = N
       CALL A37PM
       CALL A37RD(F)
       PRINT 24,F
24     FORMAT(1H0,13HVALUE OF F =    E17.9)
       STOP
       END
```

```
       SUBROUTINE A37RD(F)
C      THIS SUBROUTINE WILL REDUCE A DETERMINANT OF REAL NUMBERS.  BEFORE
C ENTERING THE SUBROUTINE IT IS NECESSARY TO HAVE ESTABLISHED THE ORDER OF THE
C DETERMINANT, N, AND THE ELEMENTS OF THE MATRIX, A, WHOSE DETERMINANT IS BEING
C EVALUATED.  THE PARAMETER, F, IS THE OUTPUT, THE VALUE OF THE DETERMINANT.
C SEE PROGRAM A37EXP FOR AN EXAMPLE OF THE USE OF THIS SUBROUTINE.
       DIMENSION A(30,30)
       COMMON N,MPM,A
       NS = N
```

```
      F=1.0
480   IF(N)610,610,482
482   AMAX = 0.0
      DO 525 I=1,N
490   DO 520 J=1,N
500   IF(ABSF(A(I,J)) - AMAX)520,520,510
510   AMAX = ABSF(A(I,J))
      IMAX = I
      JMAX = J
520   CONTINUE
525   CONTINUE
      IF(AMAX - 1.0E-30)526,526,527
526   F=0.0
      N = NS
      RETURN
527   DUM = A(IMAX,JMAX)
      IF((IMAX + JMAX) - (IMAX + JMAX)/2 * 2)530,530,540
530   F = F * DUM
      GO TO 550
540   F = -F * DUM
550   DO 565 J=1,N
560   A(IMAX,J) = A(IMAX,J)/DUM
565   CONTINUE
      DO 600 I=1,N
      IF(I-IMAX)570,600,570
570   DO 590 J=1,N
      IF(J-JMAX)580,590,580
580   A(I,J) = A(I,J) - A(I,JMAX) * A(IMAX,J)
590   CONTINUE
600   CONTINUE
      I2 = 0
      DO 608 I=1,N
      J2 = 0
      IF(I-IMAX)602,608,602
602   I2 = I2 + 1
      DO 606 J=1,N
      IF(J-JMAX)604,606,604
604   J2 = J2 + 1
      A(I2,J2) = A(I,J)
606   CONTINUE
608   CONTINUE
      N=N-1
      GO TO 480
610   N=NS
      RETURN
      END
```

```
TITLEA38INP1        J.B.VERNON  0101
C        PROGRAM TO CALCULATE NORMAL MODES AND FREQUENCIES BY MATRIX
C        ITERATION.  THIS PROGRAM USES DATA CARDS TO PREPARE TAPE 1 FOR A38NM.
C        IF SOME OTHER INPUT PROGRAM IS USED, IT SHOULD ARRANGE TO LEAVE TAPE 1
C        IN THE SAME CONDITION AS THIS PROGRAM, WHICH MAY BE DETERMINED FROM
C        THE WRITE TAPE 1 STATEMENTS AT THE END OF THIS PROGRAM, STATEMENTS 100
C        AND 110.  MAXIMUM NUMBER OF VARIABLES IS 30.  DATA REQUIRED SHOULD
C        AGREE WITH THE READ TAPE 5 STATEMENTS IN THIS PROGRAM.  N IS NUMBER OF
C        VARIABLES AND ORDER OF THE MATRICES.  M IS THE NUMBER OF MODES REQUIRED.
C        ITER IS THE LIMITING NUMBER OF ITERATIONS.  ACC IS THE ACCURACY REQUIRED
C        IF THE LIMITING NUMBER OF ITERATIONS IS NOT REACHED FIRST.  ACC IS
C        SPECIFIED AS THE FRACTION WHOSE DENOMINATOR IS THE SUM OF THE ABSOLUTE
C        VALUES OF ALL THE COORDINATES FOR THE LATEST ITERATION, AND WHOSE
C        NUMERATOR IS THE SUM OVER ALL THE COORDINATES OF THE NUMBERS OBTAINED
C        BY TAKING THE ABSOLUTE VALUE OF THE DIFFERENCE FOR THE LATEST TWO
C        ITERATIONS.  (SEE STATEMENTS 431 THROUGH 441 OF PROGRAM A38NM.)  INTPRT
C        IS 1 IF IT IS DESIRED THAT INTERMEDIATE PRINTING OF RESULTS SHOULD
C        OCCUR DURING EXECUTION OF PROGRAM A38NM.  IPRDTA IS 1 IF IT IS
C        DESIRED THAT THE DATA BE PRINTED.  GMASS IS THE VALUE OF THE GENERALIZED
C        MASS DESIRED FROM THE NORMALIZATION OF THE MODES.  TMASS IS THE INERTIA
C        MATRIX AND DELTA THE FLEXIBILITY MATRIX.
18      FORMAT(I1,I1)
```

```
 20    FORMAT(I2)
 30    FORMAT(I4)
 40    FORMAT(E17.9)
       DIMENSION DELTA(30,30),TMASS(30,30)
       READ INPUT TAPE 5,18,INTPRT,IPRDTA
       READ INPUT TAPE 5,20,N
       READ INPUT TAPE 5,20,M
       READ INPUT TAPE 5,30,ITER
       READ INPUT TAPE 5,40,ACC
       READ INPUT TAPE 5,40,GMASS
       READ INPUT TAPE 5,40,((DELTA(I,J),J=1,N),I=1,N)
       READ INPUT TAPE 5,40,((TMASS(I,J),J=1,N),I=1,N)
       REWIND 1
100    WRITE TAPE 1,N,M,ITER,ACC,INTPRT,IPRDTA,GMASS
110    WRITE TAPE 1,((DELTA(I,J),J=1,N),I=1,N),((TMASS(I,J),J=1,N),I=1,N)
       REWIND 2
       REWIND 3
       STOP
       END
```

```
TITLFA38NM           J.B.VERNON   0101
C      THIS PROGRAM USES DATA FROM TAPE 1, PREPARED BY PROGRAM A38INP1 OR OTHER
C      INPUT PROGRAM TO CALCULATE THE NORMAL MODES AND FREQUENCIES OF A SYSTEM
C      HAVING NO MORE THAN 30 COORDINATES AND ZERO DAMPING.  TAPES 1, 2, AND 3
C      ARE USED DURING THE COMPUTATION.  THE OUTPUT OF THIS PROGRAM
C      IS STORED ON TAPE 1 BY STATEMENTS 950 THROUGH 960, AND MAY BE USED BY
C      AN OUTPUT PROGRAM SUCH AS A38OUT1.  INTERMEDIATE RESULTS OBTAINED
C      DURING THE COMPUTATION WILL BE PRINTED IF THE VALUE OF INTPRT IS 1.
C      DATA USED WILL BE PRINTED IF THE VALUE OF IPRDTA IS 1.  FINAL RESULTS
C      ARE ALSO PRINTED IN THIS PROGRAM.
       DIMENSION DELTA(30,30),TMASS(30,30),DYN(30,30),X(30),XA(30),ST(30)
       DIMENSION BETA(30)
       COMMON N,MC,DYN,TMASS,ST
210    FORMAT( 75H DATA   MATRIX ELEMENTS IDENTIFIED BY ROW AND COLUMN NU
      1MBER IN PARENTHESES.///)
220    FORMAT(1H2, 4HN = I2, 6H  M = I2, 9H  ITER = I4, 8H  ACC =  E18.7,
      1 11H  GMASS =   E17.9)
230    FORMAT(1H0, 32H     FLEXIBILITY MATRIX, DELTA =)
250    FORMAT(1H0, 28H     INERTIA MATRIX, TMASS =)
270    FORMAT(1H2, 11HEND OF DATA)
310    FORMAT(1H0, 19H  DYNAMIC MATRIX =)
370    FORMAT(1H0, 31H     RESULTS FOR MODE NUMBER   I2)
380    FORMAT(1H0, 21H     DYNAMIC MATRIX =)
480    FORMAT(1H0, 21H  ITERATION NUMBER  I4, 13H  ACCURACY =  E18.7)
490    FORMAT(1H , 22H    COORDINATE VECTOR X)
540    FORMAT(1H0, 26H  NUMBER OF ITERATIONS = I4,14H   ACCURACY = E18.7
550    FORMAT(1H , 22H    COORDINATE VECTOR X)
640    FORMAT(1H0, 47H   BETA, CALCULATED FROM ORIGINAL DYNAMIC MATRIX)
714    FORMAT(1H0,30HSWEEPING MATRIX FOLLOWING MODE  I4,18H  CANNOT BE FO
      1RMED)
760    FORMAT(1H0,22H     SWEEPING MATRIX S =)
934    FORMAT(1H0,27HGENERALIZED MASS FOR MODE  I2, 6H  IS  E17.9)
       REWIND 1
       REWIND 2
       REWIND 3
       READ TAPE 1,N,M,ITER,ACC,INTPRT,IPRDTA
       READ TAPE 1,((DELTA(I,J),J=1,N),I=1,N),((TMASS(I,J),J=1,N),I=1,N)
       MC=N
       IF(IPRDTA)280,280,200
200    PRINT 210
       PRINT 220,N,M,ITER,ACC,GMASS
       PRINT 230
       DO 240 I=1,N
       DO 240 J=1,N
240    DYN(I,J)=DELTA(I,J)
       CALL A37PM
       PRINT 250
       DO 260 I=1,N
       DO 260 J=1,N
```

```
260    DYN(I,J)=TMASS(I,J)
       CALL A37PM
       PRINT 270
280    DO 290 I=1,N
       DO 290 J=1,N
       DYN(I,J)=0.0
       DO 290 K=1,N
290    DYN(I,J)=DYN(I,J)+DELTA(I,K)*TMASS(K,J)
       MODE=1
       IF(INTPRT)320,320,300
300    PRINT 310
       CALL A37PM
320    REWIND 1
       WRITE TAPE 1, ((DYN(I,J), J=1,N), I=1,N)
       WRITE TAPE 2, ((TMASS(I,J), J=1,N), I=1,N)
       DO 330 I=1,N
       DO 330 J=1,N
330    DELTA(I,J) = 0.0
       DO 340 I=1,N
340    DELTA(I,I) = 1.0
350    DO 880 MODE=1,M
       PRINT 370, MODE
       IF(INTPRT)364,364,360
360    PRINT 380
       CALL A37PM
364    DO 390 I=1,N
390    X(I)=1.0
       DO 500 ITERNO=1,ITER
       DO 400 I=1,N
400    XA(I)=X(I)
       DO 410 I=1,N
       X(I)=0.0
       DO 410 K=1,N
410    X(I)=X(I)+DYN(I,K)*XA(K)
       REWIND 2
       READ TAPE 2,((TMASS(I,J),J=1,N),I=1,N)
       DUM1 = 0.0
       DO 420 J=1,N
       DUM2=0.0
       DO 415 K=1,N
415    DUM2 = DUM2 + TMASS(J,K) * X(K)
420    DUM1 = DUM1 + DUM2 * X(J)
       DUM1 = SQRTF(DUM1/GMASS)
       DO 430 I=1,N
430    X(I) = X(I)/DUM1
431    DUM1 = 0.0
       DUM2=0.0
       DO 440 I=1,N
       DUM1 = DUM1 + ABSF(X(I))
440    DUM2 = DUM2 + ABSF(XA(I) - X(I))
441    ACCUR = DUM2/DUM1
       DO 450 J=1,N
450    ST(J) = DYN(1,J)
       DO 460 J=1,N
460    DYN(1,J) = X(J)
       MC=1
       IF(INTPRT)476,476,470
470    PRINT 480, ITERNO, ACCUR
       PRINT 490
       CALL A37PM
476    DO 478 J=1,N
478    DYN(1,J) = ST(J)
       TEST2=ACC-ACCUR
       IF(TEST2)500,510,510
500    CONTINUE
509    ITERNO=ITER
510    DO 520 J=1,N
520    DYN(1,J) = X(J)
       MC=1
530    PRINT 540,ITERNO,ACCUR
       PRINT 550
       CALL A37PM
       WRITE TAPE 3,ACCUR
560    WRITE TAPE 3,(X(J),J=1,N)
```

```
      REWIND 1
      READ TAPE 1, ((DYN(I,J),J=1,N),I=1,N)
      DO 570 I=1,N
      XA(I)=0.0
      DO 570 K=1,N
570   XA(I)=XA(I)+DYN(I,K)*X(K)
      DO 600 I=1,N
      IF(ABSF(XA(I)) - 1.0E-06)580,580,574
574   IF(X(I)/XA(I))580,580,590
580   BETA(I) = 0.0
      GO TO 600
590   BETA(I) = SQRTF(X(I)/XA(I))
600   CONTINUE
      WRITE TAPE 3,(BETA(J),J=1,N)
      DO 610 J=1,N
610   ST(J)=DYN(1,J)
      DO 620 J=1,N
620   DYN(1,J)=BETA(J)
630   PRINT 640
      CALL A37PM
      MC = N
650   DO 660 J=1,N
660   DYN(1,J) = ST(J)
      REWIND 2
      READ TAPE 2,((TMASS(I,J), J=1,N), I=1,N)
      DO 670 J=1,N
      BETA(J)=0.0
      DO 670 K=1,N
670   BETA(J)=BETA(J)+X(K)*TMASS(K,J)
      DO 674 I=1,N
      DO 674 J=1,N
674   TMASS(I,J) = DYN(I,J'
      DENOM = 0.0
      DO 710 J=1,N
      IF(ABSF(DELTA(J,J))-1.0E-30)710,710,694
694   IF(ABSF(BETA(J))-DENOM)710,710,700
700   IDENOM = J
      DENOM = ABSF(BETA(J))
710   CONTINUE
      IF(DENOM-1.0E-30)712,712,718
712   PRINT 714, MODE
      GO TO 882
718   DENOM = BETA(IDENOM)
      DO 720 J=1,N
720   DELTA(IDENOM,J) = -BETA(J)/DENOM
      DELTA(IDENOM,IDENOM) = 0.0
1001  DO 1010 I=1,N
      DO 1010 J=1,N
1010  DYN(I,J) = 0.0
      DO 1050 K=1,N
      IF(ABSF(DELTA(K,K))-1.0F-30)1020,1020,1040
1020  DO 1030 J=1,N
      DYN(K,J) = -DELTA(K,J)
1030  DELTA(K,J) = 0.0
1040  DYN(K,K) = 1.0
1050  CONTINUE
      CALL A37IMS
      DO 1080 K=1,N
      IF(ABSF(DELTA(K,K))-1.0E-30)1080,1080,1060
1060  DO 1070 I=1,N
1070  DELTA(I,K) = DYN(I,K)
1080  CONTINUE
      REWIND 1
1090  READ TAPE 1,((TMASS(I,J),J=1,N),I=1,N)
730   DO 740 I=1,N
      DO 740 J=1,N
740   DYN(I,J)=DELTA(I,J)
      IF(INTPRT)770,770,750
750   PRINT 760
      CALL A37PM
770   DO 780 I=1,N
      DO 780 J=1,N
      DYN(I,J) = 0.0
      DO 780 K=1,N
```

```
780    DYN(I,J) = DYN(I,J) + TMASS(I,K) * DELTA(K,J)
880    CONTINUE
       GO TO 883
882    M=MODE-1
883    REWIND 3
       DO 890 J=1,M
       READ TAPE 3,X(J)
       READ TAPE 3,(DYN(I,J),I=1,N)
       READ TAPE 3,(DELTA(I,J),I=1,N)
890    CONTINUE
       REWIND 2
       READ TAPE 2,((TMASS(I,J),J=1,N),I=1,N)
       DO 910 J=1,M
       DUM1 = 0.0
       DO 907 I=1,N
       DUM2 = 0.0
       DO 903 K=1,N
903    DUM2 = DUM2 + TMASS(I,K) * DYN(K,J)
907    DUM1 = DUM1 + DUM2 * DYN(I,J)
910    ST(J)=DUM1
920    DO 930 J=1,M
930    PRINT 934,J,ST(J)
940    REWIND 1
950    WRITE TAPE 1,N,M
       WRITE TAPE 1,((DYN(I,J),I=1,N),J=1,M)
       WRITE TAPE 1,((DELTA(I,J),I=1,N),J=1,M)
       WRITE TAPE 1,(X(J),J=1,M)
960    WRITE TAPE 1,(ST(J),J=1,M)
       STOP
       END
```

```
TITLEA38OUT1          J.B.VERNON  0101
C       THIS PROGRAM PRINTS THE RESULTS OF THE COMPUTATION OF A38NM.  IF SOME
C       OTHER OUTPUT PROGRAM IS USED WITH A38NM, THE NECESSARY INFORMATION MAY
C       BE OBTAINED FROM TAPE 1 BY STATEMENTS SIMILAR TO STATEMENTS 818 THROUGH
C       819 IN THIS PROGRAM.  THE VARIABLE, BETA, IS THE NATURAL FREQUENCY
C       OF A PARTICULAR MODE OF VIBRATION.  THIS VALUE WAS COMPUTED USING EACH
C       OF THE N ALGEBRAIC EQUATIONS AND SHOULD BE THE SAME FROM EACH EQUATION.
C       THE COMPARISON OF THE N VALUES OF BETA FOR A MODE THEREFORE AFFORDS A
C       MEASURE OF THE ACCURACY OF THE COMPUTATION.  THE VARIABLE, X, IS THE
C       RELATIVE DISPLACEMENT OF THE COORDINATES IN A NATURAL MODE.  THE VARIABLE,
C       ACCUR, IS THE ACCURACY, DEFINED IN A38INP1.  THE VARIABLE, GMASS, IS THE
C       GENERALIZED MASS.
820    FORMAT(1H0,34HRESULTS OF NORMAL MODE COMPUTATION)
830    FORMAT(1H0,117HIN THE FOLLOWING MATRIX THE FIRST NUMBER INSIDE THE
      1 PARENTHESES IS THE MODE NUMBER, THE SECOND THE COORDINATE NUMBER.
      2)
840    FORMAT(1H0,29HCOORDINATE DISPLACEMENT, X(J))
850    FORMAT(1H0,43HFREQUENCY COMPUTED FROM EACH OF N EQUATIONS)
870    FORMAT(1H0,119HIN THE FOLLOWING ROW MATRIX THE FIRST NUMBER INSIDE
      1 THE PARENTHESES HAS NO SIGNIFICANCE, THE SECOND IS THE MODE NUMBE
      2R.)
880    FORMAT(1H0,44HACCURACY AS DEFINED IN A38INP1 FOR EACH MODE)
900    FORMAT(1H ,30HGENERALIZED MASS FOR EACH MODE   )
930    FORMAT(1H0,50HEND OF COMPUTATION OF NORMAL MODES AND FREQUENCIES)
       DIMENSION X(30,30), BETA(30,30),ACCUR(30),GMASS(30)
       COMMON NP,MP,X
818    REWIND 1
       READ TAPE 1,N,M
       READ TAPE 1,((X(I,J),J=1,N),I=1,M)
       READ TAPE 1,((BETA(I,J),J=1,N),I=1,M)
       READ TAPE 1,(ACCUR(J),J=1,M)
819    READ TAPE 1,(GMASS(J),J=1,M)
       PRINT 820
       NP=N
       MP=M
       PRINT 830
       PRINT 840
       CALL A37PM
```

```
      PRINT 830
      PRINT 850
      DO 860 I=1,M
      DO 860 J=1,N
  860 X(I,J)=BETA(I,J)
      CALL A37PM
      PRINT 870
      PRINT 880
      DO 890 J=1,M
  890 X(1,J)=ACCUR(J)
      NP=M
      MP=1
      CALL A37PM
      PRINT 870
      PRINT 900
      DO 920 J=1,M
  920 X(1,J)=GMASS(J)
      CALL A37PM
      PRINT 930
      STOP
      END



TITLEA55INP1        J.B.VERNON   0101
C THIS PROGRAM PREPARES TAPES FROM DATA CARDS. THIS PROGRAM, USED WITH PROGRAMS
C A55FMB1 THROUGH A55FMB7 AND AN OUTPUT PROGRAM SUCH
C AS PROGRAM A55OUT1 IN THAT ORDER,WILL CALCULATE THE FLEXIBILITY MATRIX FOR
C A BEAM.  AT EXECUTION TIME A DATA DECK WOULD BE PREPARED IN ACCORDANCE WITH
C THE FOLLOWING INSTRUCTIONS. IMMEDIATELY AFTER THE END DATA CARD WOULD COME
C PROGRAM CARDS FOR THE ABOVE MENTIONED PROGRAMS. THE DATA DECK IS PREPARED AS
C FOLLOWS.  EACH CARD CONTAINS ONLY ONE NUMBER.  AFTER THE DATA CARD COMES THE
C VALUE OF INTPRT,TO AGREE WITH FORMAT STATEMENT (I1), THEN THE VALUE OF N, TO
C AGREE WITH FORMAT(I2).  AFTER THESE CARDS COME THE VALUES OF FIXITY INDICA-
C TORS KFP(K), THEN KFR(K), ALSO IN ACCORDANCE WITH FORMAT(I1).  THEN COME THE
C VALUE OF SPRING CONSTANTS SPCP(K), SPCR(K), THEN D1K(K), DELK(K), EIK(K),
C QGIB(K) BMASSK(K), RHO2K(K), ALL IN ACCORDANCE WITH FORMAT(E17.9).  DEFINI-
C TIONS FOLLOW.  INTPRT IS 0 IF NO INTERMEDIATE PRINTING IS REQUIRED, AND 1
C OTHERWISE.  N IS THE NUMBER OF BEAM STATIONS.  KFP(K) IS SET TO 1 IF THERE
C IS A RIGID SUPPORT TO LINEAR DEFLECTION AT STATION (K), OTHERWISE IT IS ZERO.
C KFR(K) IS SET TO 1 IF THERE IS A RIGID SUPPORT TO ANGULAR ROTATION AT
C STATION (K), OTHERWISE IT IS ZERO.  SPCP(K) IS THE VALUE OF THE SPRING
C CONSTANT FOR A FLEXIBLE SUPPORT TO LINEAR DEFLECTION AT STATION (K), SPCR(K)
C SIMILAR FOR ROTATION AT STATION (K).  D1K(K) IS THE DISTANCE FROM STATION 1 TO
C STATION (K), STATION 1 AT LEFT END OF BEAM.  DELK(K) IS THE LENGTH OF BEAM
C ACTING AT STATION (K).  EIK(K) IS THE BEAM EI AT STATION (K).  QGIB(K) IS THE
C VALUE OF Q/GIB AT (K), WHERE  Q IS THE FIRST MOMENT OF AREA ABOVE NEUTRAL
C AXIS, B  IS THE WIDTH OF CROSS SECTION AT THE NEUTRAL AXIS, G  IS THE SHEAR
C MODULUS. BMASSK(K) IS THE MASS CONCENTRATED AT STATION (K).  RHO2K(K) IS THE
C RADIUS OF GYRATION SQUARED OF THE MASS AT (K).  IF THE BEAM HAS TWO OR MORE
C RESTRAINTS, VALUES OF BMASSK(K) OR RHO2K(K) DO NOT AFFECT THE RESULTS, BUT
C DUMMY VALUES MUST BE USED.  FOR THE DIMENSION STATEMENTS USED IN THE PROGRAMS,
C THE VALUE OF N MUST NOT EXCEED 30.  IF ANOTHER INPUT PROGRAM IS USED WITH THE
C FOLLOWING DECKS IT SHOULD TERMINATE WITH THE SAME WRITE TAPE STATEMENTS.
C IF BEAM IS CANTILEVER RIGIDLY FIXED AT STATION 1, PROGRAM CARD A55OUT1 OR
C OTHER OUTPUT PROGRAM CARD MAY FOLLOW PROGRAM CARD A55FMB1.  IF BEAM IS FREE OR
C HAS ONLY ONE SUPPORT, THE OUTPUT PROGRAM CARD MAY FOLLOW PROGRAM CARD A55FMB4
C IF DESIRED, AND PROGRAMS A55FMB5 THROUGH 7 OMITTED.  IF THE BEAM HAS TWO OR
C MORE RESTRAINTS, PROGRAMS A55FMB5 THROUGH 7 MAY FOLLOW A55FMB1, OMITTING
C A55FMB2 THROUGH 4.   THE COMPUTATION MAKES USE OF TAPES 1,2, AND 3.
    7     FORMAT(1H4,21HSTART PROGRAM A55INP1)
   20     FORMAT(I2)
   22     FORMAT(I1)
   30     FORMAT(E17.9)
   31     FORMAT(1H0,29HBEAM FIXITY INDICATORS KFP(K))
   33     FORMAT(1H0,29HBEAM FIXITY INDICATORS KFR(K))
   35     FORMAT(1H0,37HBEAM SUPPORT SPRING CONSTANTS SPCP(K))
   37     FORMAT(1H0,37HBEAM SUPPORT SPRING CONSTANTS SPCR(K))
   41     FORMAT(1H0,44HDISTANCE FROM STATION 1 TO STATION K, D1K(K))
   43     FORMAT(1H0,28HBEAM INCREMENT AT K, DELK(K))
   45     FORMAT(1H0,34HBEAM BENDING STIFFNESS AT K, EI(K))
```

```
47      FORMAT(1H0,34HBEAM SHEAR STIFFNESS AT K, QGIB(K))
49      FORMAT(1H0,33HMASS CONCENTRATED AT K, BMASSK(K))
52      FORMAT(1H0,49HRADIUS OF GYRATION SQUARED OF MASS AT K, RHO2K(K))
55      FORMAT(1H0,11HEND OF DATA)
        DIMENSION KFP(30),KFR(30),SPCP(30),SPCR(30),D1K(30),DELK(30)
        DIMENSION EIK(30),QGIB(30),BMASSK(30),RHO2K(30), Y(30,30)
        DIMENSION THETA(30,30),EPS(30,30),PHI(30,30)
        COMMON N,MC,Y
        PRINT 7
        READ INPUT TAPE 5,22,INTPRT
        READ INPUT TAPE 5,20,N
        READ INPUT TAPE 5,22,(KFP(K),K=1,N),(KFR(K),K=1,N)
        READ INPUT TAPE 5,30,(SPCP(K),K=1,N),(SPCR(K),K=1,N)
        READ INPUT TAPE 5,30,(D1K(K),K=1,N),(DELK(K),K=1,N)
        READ INPUT TAPE 5,30,(EIK(K),K=1,N),(QGIB(K),K=1,N)
        READ INPUT TAPE 5,30,(BMASSK(K),K=1,N),(RHO2K(K),K=1,N)
        MC=1
        PRINT 23
23      FORMAT(1H0,18HINPUT DATA FOLLOWS)
        PRINT 24,N,INTPRT
24      FORMAT(1H0,24HN, NUMBER OF STATIONS = I2,33H        INTPRT, PRINT IN
       1DICATOR =   I1)
        PRINT 31
        DO 32 J=1,N
32      Y(1,J)=KFP(J)
        CALL A37PM
        PRINT 33
        DO 34 J=1,N
34      Y(1,J)=KFR(J)
        CALL A37PM
        PRINT 35
        DO 36 J=1,N
36      Y(1,J)=SPCP(J)
        CALL A37PM
        PRINT 37
        DO 38 J=1,N
38      Y(1,J)=SPCR(J)
        CALL A37PM
        PRINT 41
        DO 42 J=1,N
42      Y(1,J)=D1K(J)
        CALL A37PM
        PRINT 43
        DO 44 J=1,N
44      Y(1,J)=DELK(J)
        CALL A37PM
        PRINT 45
        DO 46 J=1,N
46      Y(1,J)=EIK(J)
        CALL A37PM
        PRINT 47
        DO 48 J=1,N
48      Y(1,J)=QGIB(J)
        CALL A37PM
        PRINT 49
        DO 51 J=1,N
51      Y(1,J)=BMASSK(J)
        CALL A37PM
        PRINT 52
        DO 53 J=1,N
53      Y(1,J)=RHO2K(J)
        CALL A37PM
        REWIND 1
        WRITE TAPE 1,INTPRT,N,N,N,N,N,N,N
        WRITE TAPE 1, (KFP(K),K=1,N)
        WRITE TAPE 1, (KFR(K),K=1,N)
        WRITE TAPE 1, (SPCP(K),K=1,N)
        WRITE TAPE 1,(SPCR(K),K=1,N)
        WRITE TAPE 1, (D1K(K),K=1,N)
        WRITE TAPE 1, (DELK(K),K=1,N)
        WRITE TAPE 1, (EIK(K),K=1,N)
        WRITE TAPE 1, (QGIB(K),K=1,N)
        WRITE TAPE 1, (BMASSK(K),K=1,N)
        WRITE TAPE 1, (RHO2K(K),K=1,N)
```

```
         PRINT 55
         REWIND 2
         REWIND 3
         STOP
         END




    TITLEA55INP2        J.B.VERNON  0101
  C THIS PROGRAM COMPUTES THE INPUT QUANTITIES FOR A BEAM OF CONSTANT
  C CROSS SECTION DIVIDED INTO EQUAL SEGMENTS.  N IS THE NUMBER OF
  C STATIONS INCLUDING THE LEFT AND RIGHT ENDS.  IRHO IS AN INDICATOR
  C WHICH SHOULD BE SET EQUAL TO ZERO IF RHO SQUARED IS TO BE ASSUMED ZERO,,
  C AND 1 IF BEAM MASS IS ASSUMED TO BE DISTRIBUTED ALONG THE NEUTRAL
  C AXIS.  QGIB IS ASSUMED ZERO, AND THE BEAM IS ASSUMED TO BE FREE UNLESS
  C OTHERWISE SPECIFIED.  THE PROGRAM CAN ALSO BE USED TO ENTER ANY DATA OTHER
  C THAN THOSE ASSUMED BY DATA CARDS CONTAINING THE STATION NUMBER AND NUMERICAL
  C VALUE TO BE ENTERED, IN ACCORDANCE WITH FORMAT STATEMENT 185.  DATA FOR THE
  C VARIOUS QUANTITIES USED ARE SEPARATED BY DATA CARDS CONTAINING  -1  IN THE
  C FIRST TWO COLUMNS.  THEREFORE A DATA DECK SHOULD CONSIST OF IRHO, INTPRT, N,
  C AND TEN CARDS CONTAINING  -1  IN THE FIRST TWO COLUMNS.  IF ANY OTHER VALUES
  C ARE TO BE ENTERED, THE CARDS ARE INSERTED IN THE APPROPRIATE PLACES AMONG THE
  C TEN  -1  CARDS.
    7    FORMAT(1H4,21HSTART PROGRAM A55INP2)
    20   FORMAT(I2)
    22   FORMAT(I1)
    23   FORMAT(1H0,18HINPUT DATA FOLLOWS)
    24   FORMAT(1H0,24HN, NUMBER OF STATIONS = I2,33H        INTPRT, PRINT IN
        1DICATOR =  I1, 13H      IRHO  =   I1)
    30   FORMAT(E17.9)
    31   FORMAT(1H0,29HBEAM FIXITY INDICATORS KFP(K))
    33   FORMAT(1H0,29HBEAM FIXITY INDICATORS KFR(K),
    35   FORMAT(1H0,37HBEAM SUPPORT SPRING CONSTANTS SPCP(K))
    37   FORMAT(1H0,37HBEAM SUPPORT SPRING CONSTANTS SPCR(K))
    41   FORMAT(1H0,44HDISTANCE FROM STATION 1 TO STATION K, D1K(K))
    43   FORMAT(1H0,28HBEAM INCREMENT AT K, DELK(K))
    45   FORMAT(1H0,34HBEAM BENDING STIFFNESS AT K, EI(K))
    47   FORMAT(1H0,34HBEAM SHEAR STIFFNESS AT K, QGIB(K))
    49   FORMAT(1H0,33HMASS CONCENTRATED AT K, BMASSK(K))
    52   FORMAT(1H0,49HRADIUS OF GYRATION SQUARED OF MASS AT K, RHO2K(K))
    55   FORMAT(1H0,11HEND OF DATA)
    185  FORMAT(I2,E17.9)
         DIMENSION KFP(30),KFR(30),SPCP(30),SPCR(30),D1K(30),DELK(30)
         DIMENSION EIK(30),QGIB(30),BMASSK(30),RHO2K(30), Y(30,30)
         COMMON N,MC,Y
         PRINT 7
         READ INPUT TAPE 5,22,IRHO
         READ INPUT TAPE 5,22,INTPRT
         READ INPUT TAPE 5,20,N
         MC=1
         PRINT 23
         PRINT 24,N,INTPRT,IRHO
         FN = FLOATF(N)
         FNL2 = FN - 2.0
         NL1 = N-1
         D1K(1) = 0.0
         D1K(2) = 1.0/2.0/FNL2
         DO 110 J = 3,NL1
    110  D1K(J) = D1K(2) + 1.0/FNL2 * FLOATF(J-2)
         D1K(N) = 1.0
         BMASSK(1) = 0.0
         DELK(1) = 0.0
         DO 120 J=2,NL1
         BMASSK(J) = 1.0/FNL2
    120  DELK(J) = 1.0/FNL2
         BMASSK(N) = 0.0
         DELK(N) = 0.0
         DO 130 J=1,N
         EIK(J) = 1.0
    130  QGIB(J) = 0.0
         IF(IRHO)140,140,160
    140  DO 150 J=1,N
```

```
150    RHO2K(J) = 0.0
       GO TO 175
160    RHO2K(1) = 0.0
       RHO2K(N) = 0.0
       DO 170 J=2,NL1
170    RHO2K(J) = 1.0/12.0/FNL2/FNL2
175    DO 180 J=1,N
       KFP(J) = 0
       KFR(J) = 0
       SPCP(J) = 0.0
180    SPCR(J) = 0.0
       DO 310 I=1,10
       DO 300 J=1,N
       READ INPUT TAPE 5,185,JTEMP,ATEMP
       IF(JTEMP)310,310,190
190    GO TO (200,210,220,230,240,250,260,270,280,290),I
200    KFP(JTEMP) = 1
       GO TO 300
210    KFR(JTEMP) = 1
       GO TO 300
220    SPCP(JTEMP) = ATEMP
       GO TO 300
230    SPCR(JTEMP) = ATEMP
       GO TO 300
240    D1K(JTEMP) = ATEMP
       GO TO 300
250    DELK(JTEMP) = ATEMP
       GO TO 300
260    EIK(JTEMP) = ATEMP
       GO TO 300
270    QGIB(JTEMP) = ATEMP
       GO TO 300
280    BMASSK(JTEMP) = ATEMP
       GO TO 300
290    RHO2K(JTEMP) = ATEMP
300    CONTINUE
310    CONTINUE
       PRINT 31
       DO 32 J=1,N
32     Y(1,J)=KFP(J)
       CALL A37PM
       PRINT 33
       DO 34 J=1,N
34     Y(1,J)=KFR(J)
       CALL A37PM
       PRINT 35
       DO 36 J=1,N
36     Y(1,J)=SPCP(J)
       CALL A37PM
       PRINT 37
       DO 38 J=1,N
38     Y(1,J)=SPCR(J)
       CALL A37PM
       PRINT 41
       DO 42 J=1,N
42     Y(1,J)=D1K(J)
       CALL A37PM
       PRINT 43
       DO 44 J=1,N
44     Y(1,J)=DELK(J)
       CALL A37PM
       PRINT 45
       DO 46 J=1,N
46     Y(1,J)=EIK(J)
       CALL A37PM
       PRINT 47
       DO 48 J=1,N
48     Y(1,J)=QGIB(J)
       CALL A37PM
       PRINT 49
       DO 51 J=1,N
51     Y(1,J)=BMASSK(J)
       CALL A37PM
       PRINT 52
```

```
      DO 53 J=1,N
53    Y(1,J)=RHO2K(J)
      CALL A37PM
      REWIND 1
      REWIND 2
      REWIND 3
      WRITE TAPE 1,INTPRT,N,N,N,N,N,N,N
      WRITE TAPE 1, (KFP(K),K=1,N)
      WRITE TAPE 1, (KFR(K),K=1,N)
      WRITE TAPE 1, (SPCP(K),K=1,N)
      WRITE TAPE 1,(SPCR(K),K=1,N)
      WRITE TAPE 1, (D1K(K),K=1,N)
      WRITE TAPE 1, (DELK(K),K=1,N)
      WRITE TAPE 1, (EIK(K),K=1,N)
      WRITE TAPE 1, (QGIB(K),K=1,N)
      WRITE TAPE 1, (BMASSK(K),K=1,N)
      WRITE TAPE 1, (RHO2K(K),K=1,N)
      PRINT 55
      STOP
      END



TITLEA55FMB1        J.B.VERNON   0101
7     FORMAT(1H4,21HSTART PROGRAM A55FMB1)
74    FORMAT(1H0,34HCOEFFICIENTS Y(I,J) FOR CANTILEVER)
124   FORMAT(1H0,51HCOEFFICIENTS THETA(I,J) AND FPS(J,I) FOR CANTILEVER)
180   FORMAT(1H0,36HCOEFFICIENTS PHI(I,J) FOR CANTILEVER)
260   FORMAT(1H1,14HEND OF A55FMB1)
      DIMENSION KFP(30),KFR(30),SPCP(30),SPCR(30),D1K(30),DELK(30)
      DIMENSION EIK(30),QGIB(30),BMASSK(30),RHO2K(30), Y(30,30)
      DIMENSION THETA(30,30),EPS(30,30),PHI(30,30)
      COMMON N,MC,Y
      PRINT 7
      REWIND 1
      READ  TAPE 1,INTPRT,N,N,N,N,N,N,N
      READ TAPE 1,  (KFP(K),K=1,N)
      READ TAPE 1,  (KFR(K),K=1,N)
      READ TAPE 1,  (SPCP(K),K=1,N)
      READ TAPE 1,(SPCR(K),K=1,N)
      READ TAPE 1, (D1K(K),K=1,N)
      READ TAPE 1, (DELK(K),K=1,N)
      READ TAPE 1, (EIK(K),K=1,N)
      READ TAPE 1, (QGIB(K),K=1,N)
      READ TAPE 1, (BMASSK(K),K=1,N)
      READ TAPE 1, (RHO2K(K),K=1,N)
      REWIND 1
      WRITE TAPE 1,INTPRT,N,N,N,N,N,N,N
      WRITE TAPE 1, (KFP(K),K=1,N)
      WRI,TE TAPE 1, (KFR(K),K=1,N)
      WRITE TAPE 1, (SPCP(K),K=1,N)
      WRITE TAPE 1,(SPCR(K),K=1,N)
      WRITE TAPE 1, (D1K(K),K=1,N)
      WRITE TAPE 1, (DELK(K),K=1,N)
      WRITE TAPE 1, (EIK(K),K=1,N)
      WRITE TAPE 1, (QGIB(K),K=1,N)
      WRITE TAPE 1, (BMASSK(K),K=1,N)
      WRITE TAPE 1, (RHO2K(K),K=1,N)
      NL1=N-1
      DO 40 I=3,NL1
      DO 40 J=I,N
      Y(I,J)=(D1K(J)-D1K(I)+DELK(I)/3.0)*DELK(I)*DELK(I)/
     18.0/EIK(I)+DELK(I)*QGIB(I)/2.0
      IL1=I-1
      DO 40 K=2,IL1
40    Y(I,J)=Y(I,J)+((ABSF(D1K(K)-D1K(I))*ABSF(D1K(K)-D1K(J))
     1+DELK(K)*DELK(K)/12.0)/EIK(K)+QGIB(K))*DELK(K)
      DO 50 J=1,N
50    Y(1,J)=0.0
      DO 54 J=2,N
54    Y(2,J)=(D1K(J)-D1K(2)+DELK(2)/3.0)*DELK(2)*DELK(2)/
```

```
      1EIK(2)/8.0+QGIB(2)*DELK(2)/2.0
       Y(N,N)=0.0
       DO 60 K=2,NL1
60     Y(N,N)=Y(N,N)+(((D1K(N)-D1K(K))**2+DELK(K)*DELK(K)/
      112.0)/EIK(K)+QGIB(K))*DELK(K)
       DO 70 J=1,N
       DO 70 I=1,J
70     Y(J,I)=Y(I,J)
       MC=N
       IF(INTPRT)78,78,72
72     PRINT 74
       CALL A37PM
78     WRITE TAPE 1. ((Y(I,J),J=1,N),I=1,N)
       DO 80 I=3,NL1
       DO 80 J=I,N
       Y(I,J) = (D1K(J) - D1K(I) + DELK(I)/4.0)/EIK(I)/2.0*DELK(I)
       IL1=I-1
       DO 80 K=2,IL1
80     Y(I,J)=Y(I,J)+(ABSF(D1K(K)-D1K(J)))*DELK(K)/EIK(K)
       DO 84 J=2,N
84     Y(2,J)=(D1K(J)-D1K(2)+DELK(2)/4.0)*DELK(2)/EIK(2)/2.0
       DO 90 I=4,N
       IL1=I-1
       DO 90 J=3,IL1
       Y(I,J)=DELK(J)*DELK(J)/EIK(J)/8.0
       JL1=J-1
       DO 90 K=2,JL1
90     Y(I,J)=Y(I,J)+(ABSF(D1K(K)-D1K(J)))*DELK(K)/EIK(K)
       DUM6 = DELK(2)*DELK(2)/EIK(2)/8.0
       DO 94 I=3,N
94     Y(I,2) = DUM6
       DO 100 I=1,N
100    Y(I,1)=0.0
       DO 110 J=1,N
110    Y(1,J)=0.0
       Y(N,N)=0.0
       DO 120 K=2,NL1
120    Y(N,N) = Y(N,N) + (D1K(N) - D1K(K))*DELK(K)/EIK(K)
       IF(INTPRT)128,128,122
122    PRINT 124
       CALL A37PM
128    WRITE TAPE 1,((Y(I,J),I=1,N),J=1,N)
       WRITE TAPE 1, ((Y(I,J),J=1,N),I=1,N)
       DO 130 I=3,NL1
       DO 130 J=I,N
       Y(I,J)=DELK(I)/EIK(I)/2.0
       IL1=I-1
       DO 130 K=2,IL1
130    Y(I,J)=Y(I,J)+DELK(K)/EIK(K)
       Y(2,2)=DELK(2)/EIK(2)/2.0
       DO 140 J=3,N
140    Y(2,J)=Y(2,2)
       DO 150 J=1,N
150    Y(1,0)=0.0
       Y(N,N)=0.0
       DO 160 K=2,NL1
160    Y(N,N)=Y(N,N)+DELK(K)/EIK(K)
       DO 170 J=1,N
       DO 170 I=1,J
170    Y(J,I)=Y(I,J)
       IF(INTPRT)176,176,174
174    PRINT 180
       CALL A37PM
176    WRITE TAPE 1, ((Y(I,J),J=1,N),I=1,N)
       ITEST1=0
       DO 190 K=1,N
190    ITEST1=ITEST1+KFP(K)
       NKFP=ITEST1
       DO 194 K=1,N
194    ITEST1=ITEST1+KFR(K)
       NKFR=ITEST1-NKFP
       DO 198 K=1,N
       IF(ABSF(SPCP(K))-1.0E-30)198,198,196
196    ITEST1=ITEST1+1
```

```
198    CONTINUE
       NSPCP=ITEST1-NKFP-NKFR
       DO 202 K=1,N
       IF(ABSF(SPCR(K))-1.0E-30)202,202,200
200    ITEST1=ITEST1+1
202    CONTINUE
       NSPCR=ITEST1-NKFP-NKFR-NSPCP
       INDEX3 = 0
       IF(ITEST1 - 2)250,210,250
210    IF(KFP(1))250,250,220
220    IF(KFR(1))250,250,230
230    INDEX3 = 1
       REWIND 2
       ISING = 0
       WRITE TAPE 2,ISING,ITEST1,ITEST1,ITEST1,ITEST1,INDEX3
       STOP
250    PRINT 260
       REWIND 2
       WRITE TAPE 2, NKFP,NKFR,NSPCP,NSPCR,ITEST1,INDEX3
       STOP
       END




TITLEA55FMB2          J.B.VERNON   0101
7      FORMAT(1H4,21HSTART PROGRAM A55FMB2)
268    FORMAT(1H0,32HCANTILEVER BEAM--NO MORE CHANGES)
274    FORMAT(1H0,44HBEAM HAS TWO OR MORE SUPPORTS--GO TO A55FMB5)
373    FORMAT(1H0,24HCORRECTIONS-DELTA Y(I,J))
393    FORMAT(1H0,28HCORRECTIONS-DELTA THETA(I,J))
397    FORMAT(1H1,14HEND OF A55FMB2)
       DIMENSION KFP(30),KFR(30),SPCP(30),SPCR(30),D1K(30),DELK(30)
       DIMENSION EIK(30),QGIB(30),BMASSK(30),RHO2K(30), Y(30,30)
       DIMENSION THETA(30,30),EPS(30,30),PHI(30,30)
       COMMON N,MC,Y
       PRINT 7
       INDEX4 = 0
       INDEX5 = 0
       INDEX6 = 0
       INDEX7 = 0
       REWIND 1
       REWIND 2
       REWIND 3
       READ TAPE 2, NKFP,NKFR,NSPCP,NSPCR,ITEST1,INDEX3
       IF(INDEX3)270,270,264
264    PRINT 268
       STOP
270    IF(ITEST1-1)276,276,272
272    INDEX4 = 1
       PRINT 274
       STOP
276    READ   TAPE 1,INTPRT,N,N,N,N,N,N,N
       READ TAPE 1,   (KFP(K),K=1,N)
       READ TAPE 1,   (KFR(K),K=1,N)
       READ TAPE 1,   (SPCP(K),K=1,N)
       READ TAPE 1,(SPCR(K),K=1,N)
       READ TAPE 1,   (D1K(K),K=1,N)
       READ TAPE 1,   (DELK(K),K=1,N)
       READ TAPE 1,   (EIK(K),K=1,N)
       READ TAPE 1,   (QGIB(K),K=1,N)
       READ TAPE 1,   (BMASSK(K),K=1,N)
       READ TAPE 1,   (RHO2K(K),K=1,N)
       READ TAPE 1,((Y(I,J),J=1,N),I=1,N)
       READ TAPE 1,((THETA(I,J),I=1,N),J=1,N)
       READ TAPE 1,((THETA(I,J),J=1,N),I=1,N)
       READ TAPE 1,((PHI(I,J),J=1,N),I=1,N)
       MC=N
       REWIND 1
       REWIND 2
       WRITE TAPE 1, ((Y(I,J),J=1,N),I=1,N)
       WRITE TAPE 2,((THETA(I,J),J=1,N),I=1,N)
```

```
          WRITE TAPE 2,((PHI(I,J),J=1,N),I=1,N)
          IF(ITEST1)300,300,277
277   IF(NKFP + NSPCP)289,289,278
278   INDEX5 = 1
          IF(NKFP)282,282,279
279   INDEX6 = 1
          DO 281 K=1,N
          IF(KFP(K)) 281,281,280
280   KSTA = K
          GO TO 300
281   CONTINUE
282   DO 284 K=1,N
          IF(ABSF(SPCP(K))-1.0F-30)284,284,283
283   INDEX6 = -1
          KSTA = K
          GO TO 300
284   CONTINUE
289   INDEX5 = -1
          DO 292 K=1,N
          IF(KFR(K))292,292,291
291   KSTA = K
          INDEX7 = 1
          GO TO 300
292   CONTINUE
          DO 294 K=1,N
          IF(ABSF(SPCR(K))-1.0E-30)294,294,293
293   INDEX7 = -1
          KSTA = K
          GO TO 300
294   CONTINUE
300   TOTM=0.0
          DO 310 K=1,N
310   TOTM=TOTM+BMASSK(K)
314   QMASS = 0.0
          DO 320 K=1,N
320   QMASS=QMASS+BMASSK(K)*D1K(K)
          D1CG=QMASS/TOTM
          IF(INDEX5)336,322,321
321   TINER = (D1K(KSTA)*(D1K(KSTA)-2.0*D1CG))*TOTM
          D1CG = D1K(KSTA)
          GO TO 323
322   TINER=-D1CG*D1CG*TOTM
323   DO 330 K=1,N
330   TINER=TINER+(D1K(K)*D1K(K)+RHO2K(K))*BMASSK(K)
          IF(INDEX5)336,339,331
331   DO 332 K=1,N
          DO 332 J=1,N
332   PHI(K,J) = (D1K(J) - D1CG) * (D1K(K) - D1CG)/TINER * BMASSK(K)
          GO TO 342
336   DO 337 K=1,N
          DO 337 J=1,N
337   PHI(K,J) = 1.0/TOTM * BMASSK(K)
          GO TO 352
339   DO 340 K=1,N
          DO 340 J=1,N
340   PHI(K,J)=(1.0/TOTM+(D1K(J)-D1CG)*(D1K(K)-D1CG)/TINER)*
      1BMASSK(K)
342   DO 350 K=1,N
          DO 350 J=1,N
350   EPS(K,J) = (D1K(J) - D1CG) * BMASSK(K) * RHO2K(K)/TINER
352   REWIND 1
          READ TAPE 1, ((THETA(I,J),J=1,N),I=1,N)
          DO 360 I=1,N
          DO 360 J=1,N
          Y(I,J)=0.0
          DO 360 K=1,N
360   Y(I,J)=Y(I,J)+THETA(I,K)*PHI(K,J)
          IF(INDEX5)364,364,361
361   DO 363 I=1,N
          DO 363 J=1,N
          DUM = -1.0
          DO 362 K=1,N
362   DUM = DUM + (D1K(J) - D1K(KSTA))*(D1K(K) - D1K(KSTA)) * BMASSK(K)/
      1TINER
```

```
363   Y(I,J) = Y(I,J) - DUM * THETA(I,KSTA)
364   REWIND 2
      READ TAPE 2,((THETA(I,J),J=1,N),I=1,N)
      IF(INDEX5)3701,365,365
365   DO 370 I=1,N
      DO 370 J=1,N
      DO 370 K=1,N
370   Y(I,J) = Y(I,J) + THETA(K,I) * EPS(K,J)
      GO TO 371
3701  DO 3703 I=1,N
      DO 3703 J=1,N
      DUM = - D1K(J) + D1K(KSTA)
      DO 3702 K=1,N
3702  DUM = DUM + (D1K(K) - D1K(KSTA)) * BMASSK(K)/TOTM
3703  Y(I,J) = Y(I,J) - DUM * THETA(KSTA,I)
371   IF(INTPRT)376,376,372
372   PRINT 373
      CALL A37PM
376   WRITE TAPE 3,D1CG,TINER,KSTA,TOTM,INTPRT,ITEST1,INDEX3,INDEX4,
     1INDEX5,INDEX6,INDEX7,N
      WRITE TAPE 3,(KFP(K),K=1,N)
      WRITE TAPE 3, (KFR(K),K=1,N)
      WRITE TAPE 3, (SPCP(K),K=1,N)
      WRITE TAPE 3,(SPCR(K),K=1,N)
      WRITE TAPE 3, (D1K(K),K=1,N)
      WRITE TAPE 3, (DELK(K),K=1,N)
      WRITE TAPE 3, (EIK(K),K=1,N)
      WRITE TAPE 3, (QGIB(K),K=1,N)
      WRITE TAPE 3, (BMASSK(K),K=1,N)
      WRITE TAPE 3, (RHO2K(K),K=1,N)
      WRITE TAPE 3, ((Y(I,J),J=1,N),I=1,N)
      DO 380 I=1,N
      DO 380 J=1,N
      Y(I,J)=0.0
      DO 380 K=1,N
380   Y(I,J)=Y(I,J)+THETA(I,K)*PHI(K,J)
      IF(INDEX5)384,384,381
381   DO 383 I=1,N
      DO 383 J=1,N
      DUM = -1.0
      DO 382 K=1,N
382   DUM = DUM + (D1K(J) - D1K(KSTA))*(D1K(K) - D1K(KSTA)) * BMASSK(K)/
     1TINER
383   Y(I,J) = Y(I,J) - DUM * THETA(I,KSTA)
384   READ TAPE 2, ((THETA(I,J),J=1,N),I=1,N)
      IF(INDEX5)3901,385,385
385   DO 390 I=1,N
      DO 390 J=1,N
      DO 390 K=1,N
390   Y(I,J)=Y(I,J)+THETA(I,K)*EPS(K,J)
      IF(INDEX5)3901,391,391
3901  DO 3903 I=1,N
      DO 3903 J=1,N
      DUM = - D1K(J) + D1K(KSTA)
      DO 3902 K=1,N
3902  DUM = DUM + (D1K(K) - D1K(KSTA)) * BMASSK(K)/TOTM
3903  Y(I,J) = Y(I,J) - DUM * THETA(I,KSTA)
391   IF(INTPRT)396,396,392
392   PRINT 393
      CALL A37PM
396   WRITE TAPE 3, ((Y(I,J),J=1,N),I=1,N)
      PRINT 397
      STOP
      END


TITLEA55FMB3        J.B.VERNON   0101
7     FORMAT(1H4,21HSTART PROGRAM A55FMB3)
268   FORMAT(1H0,32HCANTILEVER BEAM--NO MORE CHANGES)
274   FORMAT(1H0,44HBEAM HAS TWO OR MORE SUPPORTS--GO TO A55FMB5)
```

```
433   FORMAT(1H0,26HCORRECTIONS-DELTA EPS(I,J))
453   FORMAT(1H0,26HCORRECTIONS-DELTA PHI(I,J))
473   FORMAT(1H0,28HY(I,J) WITH FIRST CORRECTION)
483   FORMAT(1H0,30HEPS(I,J) WITH FIRST CORRECTION)
493   FORMAT(1H0,32HTHETA(I,J) WITH FIRST CORRECTION)
503   FORMAT(1H0,30HPHI(I,J) WITH FIRST CORRECTION)
520   FORMAT(1H1,14HEND OF A55FMB3)
      DIMENSION KFP(30),KFR(30),SPCP(30),SPCR(30),D1K(30),DELK(30)
      DIMENSION EIK(30),QGIB(30),BMASSK(30),RHO2K(30), Y(30,30)
      DIMENSION THETA(30,30),EPS(30,30),PHI(30,30)
      COMMON N,MC,Y
      PRINT 7
      REWIND 3
      READ  TAPE 3,D1CG,TINER,KSTA,TOTM,IN,FRT,ITEST1,INDEX3,INDEX4,
     1INDEX5,INDEX6,INDEX7,N
      READ TAPE 3,   (KFP(K),K=1,N)
      READ TAPE 3,   (KFR(K),K=1,N)
      READ TAPE 3,   (SPCP(K),K=1,N)
      READ TAPE 3,   (SPCR(K),K=1,N)
      READ TAPE 3,   (D1K(K),K=1,N)
      READ TAPE 3,   (DELK(K),K=1,N)
      READ TAPE 3,   (EIK(K),K=1,N)
      READ TAPE 3,   (QGIB(K),K=1,N)
      READ TAPE 3,   (BMASSK(K),K=1,N)
      READ TAPE 3,   (RHO2K(K),K=1,N)
      READ  TAPE 3,((Y(I,J),J=1,N),I=1,N)
      READ  TAPE 3,((THETA(I,J),J=1,N),I=1,N)
      REWIND 3
      WRITE TAPE 3,((Y(I,J),J=1,N),I=1,N)
      WRITE TAPE 3,((THETA(I,J),J=1,N),I=1,N)
      MC=N
      IF(INDEX3)270,270,264
264   PRINT 268
      STOP
270   IF(ITEST1-1)276,276,272
272   PRINT 274
      STOP
276   IF(INDEX5)424,397,397
397   DO 400  K=1,N
400   PHI(K,1)= (D1K(K) -D1CG)*BMASSK(K)/TINER
      DO 404 J=1,N
      DO 404 K = 1,N
404   PHI(K,J) = PHI(K,1)
      DO 410 K= 1,N
410   EPS(K,1) = BMASSK(K) * RHO2K(K)/TINER
      DO 414 J=1,N
      DO 414 K=1,N
414   EPS(K,J) = EPS(K,1)
415   REWIND 1
      READ TAPE 1, ((THETA(I,J),J=1,N),I=1,N)
      DO 420 I=1,N
      DO 420 J=1,N
      Y(I,J)=0.0
      DO 420 K=1,N
420   Y(I,J)=Y(I,J)+THETA(I,K)*PHI(K,J)
      IF(INDEX5)424,424,421
421   DO 423 I=1,N
      DO 423 J=1,N
      DUM = 0.0
      DO 422 K=1,N
422   DUM = DUM + (D1K(K) - D1K(KSTA)) * BMASSK(K)/TINER
423   Y(I,J) = Y(I,J) - DUM * THETA(I,KSTA)
424   REWIND 2
      READ TAPE 2, ((THETA(I,J),J=1,N),I=1,N)
      IF(INDEX5)4300,425,425
425   DO 430 I=1,N
      DO 430 J=1,N
      DO 430 K=1,N
430   Y(I,J) = Y(I,J) + THETA(K,I) * EPS(K,J)
4300  IF(INDEX5)4301,431,431
4301  DO 4303 I=1,N
      DO 4303 J=1,N
4303  Y(I,J) = THETA(KSTA,I)
431   IF(INTPRT)436,436,432
```

```
432   PRINT 433
      CALL A37PM
436   READ TAPE 2, ((THETA(I,J),J=1,N),I=1,N)
      WRITE TAPE 3, ((Y(I,J),J=1,N),I=1,N)
      IF(INDEX5)4500,437,437
437   DO 440 I=1,N
      DO 440 J=1,N
      Y(I,J)=0.0
      DO 440 K=1,N
440   Y(I,J)=Y(I,J)+THETA(I,K)*EPS(K,J)
      IF(INDEX5)4500,444,441
441   REWIND 2
      READ TAPE 2,((THETA(I,J),J=1,N),I=1,N)
      DO 443 I=1,N
      DO 443 J=1,N
      DUM = 0.0
      DO 442 K=1,N
442   DUM = DUM + (D1K(K) - D1K(KSTA)) * BMASSK(K)/TINER
443   Y(I,J) = Y(I,J) - DUM * THETA(I,KSTA)
444   REWIND 2
      READ TAPE 2, ((THETA(I,J),J=1,N),I=1,N )
      DO 450 I=1,N
      DO 450 J=1,N
      DO 450 K=1,N
450   Y(I,J)=Y(I,J)+THETA(I,K)*PHI(K,J)
4500  IF(INDEX5)4501,451,451
4501  DO 4503 I=1,N
      DO 4503 J=1,N
      PHI(I,J) = THETA(I,J)
4503  Y(I,J) = THETA(I,KSTA)
451   IF(INTPRT)456,456,452
452   PRINT 453
      CALL A37PM
456   IF(INDEX5)458,457,457
457   READ TAPE 2, ((PHI(I,J),J=1,N),I=1,N)
458   DO 460 I=1,N
      DO 460 J=1,N
460   EPS(I,J)=PHI(I,J)-Y(I,J)
      REWIND 1
      READ TAPE 1, ((PHI(I,J),J=1,N),I=1,N)
      REWIND 3
      READ TAPE 3, ((THETA(I,J),J=1,N),I=1,N)
      DO 470 I=1,N
      DO 470 J=1,N
470   Y(I,J)=PHI(I,J)-THETA(I,J)
      IF(INTPRT)476,476,472
472   PRINT 473
      CALL A37PM
476   READ TAPE 3,((THETA(I,J),J=1,N),I=1,N)
      READ TAPE 3,((THETA(I,J),J=1,N),I=1,N)
      REWIND 2
      READ TAPE 2, ((PHI(I,J),J=1,N),I=1,N)
      REWIND 2
      WRITE TAPE 2,((Y(I,J),J=1,N),I=1,N)
      DO 480 I=1,N
      DO 480 J=1,N
480   Y(I,J)=PHI(J,I)-THETA(I,J)
      IF(INTPRT)486,486,482
482   PRINT 483
      CALL A37PM
486   WRITE TAPE 2, ((Y(I,J),J=1,N),I=1,N)
      BACKSPACE 3
      BACKSPACE 3
      READ TAPE 3, ((THETA(I,J),J=1,N),I=1,N)
      DO 490 I=1,N
      DO 490 J=1,N
490   Y(I,J) = PHI(I,J) - THETA(I,J)
      IF(INTPRT)496,496,492
492   PRINT 493
      CALL A37PM
496   REWIND 1
      REWIND 2
      READ TAPE 2, ((THETA(I,J),J=1,N),I=1,N)
      WRITE TAPE 1, ((Y(I,J),J=1,N),I=1,N)
```

```
       DO 500 I=1,N
       DO 500 J=1,N
500    Y(I,J)=EPS(I,J)
       IF(INTPRT)506,506,502
502    PRINT 503
       CALL A37PM
506    DO 510 I=1,N
       DO 510 J=1,N
       Y(I,J) = THETA(I,J)
510    PHI(I,J) = EPS(I,J)
       REWIND 1
       READ TAPE 1,((THETA(I,J),J=1,N),I=1,N)
       READ TAPE 2,((EPS(I,J),J=1,N),I=1,N)
       REWIND 1
       WRITE TAPE 1,INTPRT,N,N,N,N,N,N,N
       WRITE TAPE 1, (KFP(K),K=1,N)
       WRITE TAPE 1, (KFR(K),K=1,N)
       WRITE TAPE 1, (SPCP(K),K=1,N)
       WRITE TAPE 1,(SPCR(K),K=1,N)
       WRITE TAPE 1, (D1K(K),K=1,N)
       WRITE TAPE 1, (DELK(K),K=1,N)
       WRITE TAPE 1, (EIK(K),K=1,N)
       WRITE TAPE 1, (QGIB(K),K=1,N)
       WRITE TAPE 1, (BMASSK(K),K=1,N)
       WRITE TAPE 1, (RHO2K(K),K=1,N)
       WRITE TAPE 1, ((Y(I,J),J=1,N),I=1,N)
       WRITE TAPE 1,((EPS(I,J),J=1,N),I=1,N)
       WRITE TAPE 1,((THETA(I,J),J=1,N),I=1,N)
       WRITE TAPE 1,((PHI(I,J),J=1,N),I=1,N)
       REWIND 2
       WRITE TAPE 2, INDEX3,INDEX4,INDEX5,INDEX6,INDEX7,KSTA,ITEST1
       PRINT 520
       STOP
       END




TITLEA55FMB4        J.B.VERNON   0101
7      FORMAT(1H4,21HSTART PROGRAM A55FMB4)
268    FORMAT(1H0,32HCANTILEVER BEAM--NO MORE CHANGES)
274    FORMAT(1H0,44HBEAM HAS TWO OR MORE SUPPORTS--GO TO A55FMB5)
543    FORMAT(1H0,25HCORRECTIONS-DELTA2 Y(I,J) )
557    FORMAT(1H0,27HCORRECTIONS-DELTA2 EPS(I,J))
563    FORMAT(1H0,29HCORRECTIONS-DELTA2 THETA(I,J))
565    FORMAT(1H0,27HCORRECTIONS-DELTA2 PHI(I,J))
570    FORMAT(1H0,22HFINAL CORRECTED Y(I,J))
590    FORMAT(1H0,24HFINAL CORRECTED EPS(I,J))
610    FORMAT(1H0,26HFINAL CORRECTED THETA(I,J))
630    FORMAT(1H0,24HFINAL CORRECTED PHI(I,J))
762    FORMAT(1H1,14HEND OF FMB4)
       DIMENSION KFP(30),KFR(30),SPCP(30),SPCR(30),D1K(30),DELK(30)
       DIMENSION EIK(30),QGIB(30),BMASSK(30),RHO2K(30), Y(30,30)
       DIMENSION THETA(30,30),EPS(30,30),PHI(30,30)
       COMMON N,MC,Y
       PRINT 7
       REWIND 1
       REWIND 2
       REWIND 3
       READ TAPE 2, INDEX3,INDEX4,INDEX5,INDEX6,INDEX7,KSTA,ITEST1
       IF(INDEX3)270,270,264
264    PRINT 268
       STOP
270    IF(ITEST1-1)276,276,272
272    INDEX4 = 1
       PRINT 274
       STOP
276    READ  TAPE 1,INTPRT,N,N,N,N,N,N,N
       READ TAPE 1, (KFP(K),K=1,N)
       READ TAPE 1, (KFR(K),K=1,N)
       READ TAPE 1, (SPCP(K),K=1,N)
       READ TAPE 1,(SPCR(K),K=1,N)
```

```
      READ TAPE 1,   (D1K(K),K=1,N)
      READ TAPE 1,   (DELK(K),K=1,N)
      READ TAPE 1,   (EIK(K),K=1,N)
      READ TAPE 1,   (QGIB(K),K=1,N)
      READ TAPE 1,   (BMASSK(K),K=1,N)
      READ TAPE 1,   (RHO2K(K),K=1,N)
      READ TAPE 1,((Y(I,J),J=1,N),I=1,N)
      READ TAPE 1,((EPS(I,J),J=1,N),I=1,N)
      READ TAPE 1,((THETA(I,J),J=1,N),I=1,N)
      READ TAPE 1,((PHI(I,J),J=1,N),I=1,N)
      REWIND 2
      WRITE TAPE 2,((THETA(I,J),J=1,N),I=1,N)
      WRITE TAPE 2,((EPS(I,J),J=1,N),I=1,N)
      MC=N
      DO 510 I=1,N
      DO 510 J=1,N
      THETA(I,J) = Y(I,J)
510   EPS(I,J) = PHI(I,J)
      ITEST4=0
      TOTM = 0.0
      DO 512 K=1,N
512   TOTM = TOTM + BMASSK(K)
      QMASS = 0.0
      DO 514 K=1,N
514   QMASS = QMASS + BMASSK(K) * D1K(K)
      D1CG = QMASS/TOTM
      IF(INDEX5)5402,516,515
515   D1CG = D1K(KSTA)
516   DUM2=0.0
      DO 520 K=1,N
520   DUM2=DUM2+BMASSK(K)*(D1K(K)-D1CG)**2
508   DO 534 J=1,N
      DUM1=0.0
      DO 5101K=1,N
5101  DUM1=DUM1+BMASSK(K)*THETA(K,J)
      DUM1=DUM1/TOTM
      IF(INDEX5)5402,5103,5102
5102  DUM1 = THETA(KSTA,J)
5103  EIK(J) = DUM1
      DUM3=0.0
      DO 530 K=1,N
530   DUM3 = DUM3 + BMASSK(K) * (D1K(K) - D1CG) * (THETA(K,J) - DUM1)
534   RHO2K(J)=DUM3/DUM2
      DO 540 I=1,N
      DO 540 J=1,N
540   Y(I,J) = EIK(J) +(D1K(I)-D1CG) * RHO2K(J)
5401  IF(INDEX5)5402,5406,5406
5402  REWIND 2
      READ TAPE 2,((PHI(I,J),J=1,N),I=1,N)
5403  DO 5404 I=1,N
      DO 5404 J=1,N
      Y(I,J) = PHI(KSTA,J) * (D1K(I) - D1K(KSTA))
      DO 5404 K=1,N
5404  Y(I,J) = Y(I,J) + BMASSK(K)/TOTM * (THETA(K,J) - PHI(KSTA,J) *
     1 (D1K(K) - D1K(KSTA)))
5406  IF(ITEST4)541,541,555
541   IF(INTPRT)548,548,542
542   PRINT 543
      CALL A37PM
548   DO 550 I=1,N
      DO 550 J=1,N
550   PHI(I,J)=THETA(I,J)-Y(I,J)
      WRITE TAPE 3, ((PHI(I,J),J=1,N),I=1,N)
      REWIND 2
      READ TAPE 2,((THETA(I,J),J=1,N),I=1,N)
      READ TAPE 2, ((THETA(I,J),J=1,N),I=1,N)
      DO 554 J=1,N
554   DELK(J) = RHO2K(J)
      ITEST4=1
      IF(INDEX5)5541,508,508
5541  DO 5542 I=1,N
      DO 5542 J=1,N
5542  PHI(I,J) = EPS(I,J)
      GO TO 5403
```

```
 555   IF(INTPRT)558,558,556
 556   PRINT 557
       CALL A37PM
 558   DO 560 I=1,N
       DO 560 J=1,N
 560   PHI(I,J)=THETA(I,J)-Y(I,J)
       IF(INDEX5)5601,5603,5603
5601   REWIND 2
       READ TAPE 2,((Y(I,J),J=1,N),I=1,N)
       DO 5602 I=1,N
       DO 5602 J=1,N
       DELK(J) = Y(KSTA,J)
5602   Y(I,J) = Y(KSTA,J)
       GO TO 5621
5603   DO 562 I=1,N
       DO 562 J=1,N
 562   Y(I,J)=DELK(J)
5621   IF(INTPRT)5654,5654,5651
5651   PRINT 563
       CALL A37PM
5654   IF(INDEX5)5652,566,566
5652   DO 5653 I=1,N
       DO 5653 J=1,N
       RHO2K(J) = EPS(KSTA,J)
5653   Y(I,J) = EPS(KSTA,J)
       GO TO 5641
 566   DO 564 I=1,N
       DO 564 J=1,N
 564   Y(I,J)=RHO2K(J)
5641   IF(INTPRT)568,568,567
 567   PRINT 565
       CALL A37PM
 568   REWIND 3
       READ TAPE 3, ((Y(I,J),J=1,N),I=1,N)
       IF(ITEST1)571,571,5661
5661   IF(INDEX5)5691,571,5671
5671   IF(INDEX6)5681,571,571
5681   DO 569 I=1,N
       DO 569 J=1,N
 569   Y(I,J) = Y(I,J) + 1.0/SPCP(KSTA)
       GO TO 571
5691   IF(INDEX7)5692,571,571
5692   DO 5693 I=1,N
       DO 5693 J=1,N
5693   Y(I,J) = Y(I,J)+(D1K(I)-D1CG)   *(D1K(J)-D1CG)   /SPCR(KSTA)
 571   REWIND 3
       WRITE TAPE 3, ((Y(I,J),J=1,N),I=1,N)
       IF(INTPRT)576,576,572
 572   PRINT 570
       CALL A37PM
 576   DO 580 I=1,N
       DO 580 J=1,N
 580   Y(I,J)=PHI(I,J)
       IF(ITEST1)589,589,581
 581   IF(INDEX5)582,589,589
 582   IF(INDEX7)583,589,589
 583   DO 584 I=1,N
       DO 584 J=1,N
       Y(I,J) = Y(I,J) + (D1K(I) - D1CG)     /SPCR(KSTA)
 584   PHI(I,J) = Y(I,J)
 589   IF(INTPRT)596,596,592
 592   PRINT 590
       CALL A37PM
 596   REWIND 2
       READ TAPE 2, ((THETA(I,J),J=1,N),I=1,N)
       DO 600 I=1,N
       DO 600 J=1,N
 600   Y(I,J)=THETA(I,J)-DELK(J)
       IF(ITEST1)609,609,601
 601   IF(INDEX5)602,609,609
 602   IF(INDEX7)603,609,609
 603   DO 604 I=1,N
       DO 604 J=1,N
 604   Y(I,J) = Y(I,J) + (D1K(J) - D1CG)     /SPCR(KSTA)
 609   IF(INTPRT)611,611,608
```

```
608    PRINT 610
       CALL A37PM
611    DO 612 I=1,N
       DO 612 J=1,N
612    THETA(I,J) = Y(I,J)
       DO 620 I=1,N
       DO 620 J=1,N
620    Y(I,J)=EPS(I,J)-RHO2K(J)
       IF(ITEST1)629,629,621
621    IF(INDEX5)622,629,629
622    IF(INDEX7)623,629,629
623    DO 624 I=1,N
       DO 624 J=1,N
624    Y(I,J) = Y(I,J) + 1.0/SPCR(KSTA)
629    IF(INTPRT)650,650,631
631    PRINT 630
       CALL A37PM
650    DO 660 I=1,N
       DO 660 J=1,N
660    EPS(I,J) = PHI(I,J)
       DO 666 I=1,N
       DO 666 J=1,N
666    PHI(I,J) = Y(I,J)
       REWIND 3
       READ TAPE 3,((Y(I,J),J=1,N),I=1,N)
       REWIND 1
       READ  TAPE 1,INTPRT,N,N,N,N,N,N,N
       READ TAPE 1,   (KFP(K),K=1,N)
       READ TAPE 1,   (KFR(K),K=1,N)
       READ TAPE 1,   (SPCP(K),K=1,N)
       READ TAPE 1,(SPCR(K),K=1,N)
       READ TAPE 1,   (D1K(K),K=1,N)
       READ TAPE 1,   (DELK(K),K=1,N)
       READ TAPE 1,   (EIK(K),K=1,N)
       READ TAPE 1,   (QGIB(K),K=1,N)
       READ TAPE 1,   (BMASSK(K),K=1,N)
       READ TAPE 1,   (RHO2K(K),K=1,N)
       REWIND 1
       WRITE TAPE 1,INTPRT,N,N,N,N,N,N,N
       WRITE TAPE 1,   (KFP(K),K=1,N)
       WRITE TAPE 1,   (KFR(K),K=1,N)
       WRITE TAPE 1,   (SPCP(K),K=1,N)
       WRITE TAPE 1,(SPCR(K),K=1,N)
       WRITE TAPE 1,   (D1K(K),K=1,N)
       WRITE TAPE 1,   (DELK(K),K=1,N)
       WRITE TAPE 1,   (EIK(K),K=1,N)
       WRITE TAPE 1,   (QGIB(K),K=1,N)
       WRITE TAPE 1,   (BMASSK(K),K=1,N)
       WRITE TAPE 1,   (RHO2K(K),K=1,N)
       WRITE TAPE 1,   ((Y(I,J),J=1,N),I=1,N)
       WRITE TAPE 1,((EPS(I,J),J=1,N),I=1,N)
       WRITE TAPE 1,((THETA(I,J),J=1,N),I=1,N)
       WRITE TAPE 1,((PHI(I,J),J=1,N),I=1,N)
       IF(INDEX5)720,680,670
670    IF(INDEX6)680,680,690
680    ITEST1 = 0
       GO TO 760
690    TINER = 0.0
       DO 700 K=1,N
700    TINER = TINER + BMASSK(K) * (D1K(K) - D1K(KSTA))**2
       DO 710 J=1,N
       Y(KSTA,J) = -1.0
       DO 710 K=1,N
       Y(KSTA,J) = Y(KSTA,J) + (D1K(J) - D1K(KSTA))*(D1K(K) - D1K(KSTA))
      1* BMASSK(K)/TINER
710    EPS(KSTA,J) = (D1K(K) - D1K(KSTA)) * BMASSK(K)/TINER
       GO TO 755
720    IF(INDEX7)730,730,740
730    ITEST1 = 0
       GO TO 760
740    DO 750 J=1,N
       THETA(KSTA,J) = D1K(KSTA) - D1K(J)
       DO 750 K=1,N
       THETA(KSTA,J) = THETA(KSTA,J) + BMASSK(K) * (D1K(K) - D1K(KSTA))
```

```
     1/TOTM
750  PHI(KSTA,J) =-1.0
755  WRITE TAPE 1, ((Y(I,J),J=1,N),I=1,N)
     WRITE TAPE 1,((EPS(I,J),J=1,N),I=1,N)
     WRITE TAPE 1,((THETA(I,J),J=1,N),I=1,N)
     WRITE TAPE 1,((PHI(I,J),J=1,N),I=1,N)
760  REWIND 2
     ISING = 0
     WRITE TAPE 2,ISING,ITEST1,ITEST1,ITEST1,ITEST1,INDEX3
     PRINT 762
     STOP
     END




TITLEA55FMB5         J.B.VERNON   0101
7    FORMAT(1H4,21HSTART PROGRAM A55FMB5)
2003 FORMAT(1H0,73HFLEXIBILITY MATRIX HAS ALREADY BEEN COMPUTED--THIS P
    1ROGRAM NOT APPLICABLE)
2054 FORMAT(1H0,28HUPPER LEFT QUARTER OF LAMBDA)
2108 FORMAT(1H0,29HUPPER RIGHT QUARTER OF LAMBDA)
2148 FORMAT(1H0,28HLOWER LEFT QUARTER OF LAMBDA)
2198 FORMAT(1H0,29HLOWER RIGHT QUARTER OF LAMBDA)
2240 FORMAT(1H0,14HEND OF A55FMB5)
     DIMENSION A(60)
     DIMENSION KFP(30),KFR(30),SPCP(30),SPCR(30),D1K(30),DELK(30)
     DIMENSION EIK(30),QGIB(30),BMASSK(30),RHO2K(30), Y(30,30)
     DIMENSION THETA(30,30),EPS(30,30),PHI(30,30)
     COMMON N,MC,Y
     PRINT 7
     REWIND 1
     REWIND 2
     READ  TAPE 2,ITEST1,ITEST1,ITEST1,ITEST1,ITEST1,INDEX3
     IF(INDEX3)2001,2001,2002
2001 IF(ITEST1 - 1)2002,2002,2004
2002 PRINT 2003
     STOP
2004 READ  TAPE 1,INTPRT,N,N,N,N,N,N,N
     READ TAPE 1,  (KFP(K),K=1,N)
     READ TAPE 1,  (KFR(K),K=1,N)
     READ TAPE 1,  (SPCP(K),K=1,N)
     READ TAPE 1,(SPCR(K),K=1,N)
     READ TAPE 1,  (D1K(K),K=1,N)
     READ TAPE 1,  (DELK(K),K=1,N)
     READ TAPE 1,  (EIK(K),K=1,N)
     READ TAPE 1,  (QGIB(K),K=1,N)
     READ TAPE 1,  (BMASSK(K),K=1,N)
     READ TAPE 1,  (RHO2K(K),K=1,N)
     READ TAPE 1,((Y(I,J),J=1,N),I=1,N)
     READ TAPE 1,((EPS(I,J),J=1,N),I=1,N)
     READ TAPE 1,((THETA(I,J),J=1,N),I=1,N)
     READ TAPE 1,((PHI(I,J),J=1,N),I=1,N)
     MC=N
     REWIND 1
     REWIND 2
     WRITE TAPE 2,((THETA(I,J),J=1,N),I=1,N)
     WRITE TAPE 2,((PHI(I,J),J=1,N),I=1,N)
     WRITE TAPE 2, ((Y(I,J),J=1,N),I=1,N)
     DO 2006 I=1,N
     DO 2006 J=1,N
2006 EPS(I,J)=Y(I,J)
     DO 2010 J=1,N
2010 Y(1,J) = SPCP(J)
     DO 2020 I=2,N
     DO 2020 J=1,N
2020 Y(I,J)=Y(I,J)*SPCP(J)
     DO 2030 I=2,N
2030 Y(I,1)=Y(I,1)-1.0
     DO 2040 K=2,N
2040 Y(K,K)=Y(K,K)+1.0
     DO 2050 J=1,N
     IF(KFP(J))2050,2050,2044
```

```
2044 Y(1,J)=-1.0
     DO 2046 I=2,N
2046 Y(I,J)=-EPS(I,J)
2050 CONTINUE
     IF(INTPRT)2056,2056,2052
2052 PRINT 2054
     CALL A37PM
2056 WRITE TAPE 1,((Y(I,J),J=1,N),I=1,N)
     REWIND 2
     READ TAPE 2,((THETA(I,J),J=1,N),I=1,N)
     DO 2060 I=1,N
     DO 2060 J=1,N
2060 EPS(J,I)=THETA(I,J)
     DO 2070 J=1,N
2070 EPS(1,J)=0.0
     DO 2080 I=2,N
     DO 2080 J=1,N
2080 EPS(I,J)=EPS(I,J)*SPCR(J)
     DO 2090 I=2,N
2090 EPS(I,1)=EPS(I,1)-D1K(I)
     DO 2100 J=1,N
     IF(KFR(J))2100,2100,2094
2094 EPS(1,J)=0.0
     DO 2096 I=2,N
2096 EPS(I,J)=-THETA(J,I)
2100 CONTINUE
     DO 2104 I=1,N
     DO 2104 J=1,N
2104 Y(I,J)=EPS(I,J)
     IF(INTPRT)2109,2109,2106
2106 PRINT 2108
     CALL A37PM
2109 WRITE TAPE 1,((EPS(I,J),J=1,N),I=1,N)
     DO 2110 I=1,N
     DO 2110 J=1,N
2110 PHI(I,J)=THETA(I,J)
     DO 2120 J=1,N
2120 THETA(1,J)=SPCP(J)*D1K(J)
     DO 2130 I=2,N
     DO 2130 J=1,N
2130 THETA(I,J)=THETA(I,J)*SPCP(J)
     DO 2140 J=1,N
     IF(KFP(J)) 2140,2140,2134
2134 THETA(1,J)=-D1K(J)
     DO 2136 I=2,N
2136 THETA(I,J)=-PHI(I,J)
2140 CONTINUE
     DO 2144 I=1,N
     DO 2144 J=1,N
2144 Y(I,J)=THETA(I,J)
     IF(INTPRT)2149,2149,2146
2146 PRINT 2148
     CALL A37PM
2149 WRITE TAPE 1, ((Y(I,J),J=1,N),I=1,N)
     READ TAPE 2,((PHI(I,J),J=1,N),I=1,N)
     DO 2154 I=1,N
     DO 2154 J=1,N
2154 EPS(I,J)=PHI(I,J)
     DO 2150 J=1,N
2150 PHI(1,J) = SPCR(J)
     DO 2160 I=2,N
     DO 2160 J=1,N
2160 PHI(I,J)=PHI(I,J)*SPCR(J)
     DO 2170 I=2,N
2170 PHI(I,1)=PHI(I,1)-1.0
     DO 2180 K=2,N
2180 PHI(K,K)=PHI(K,K)+1.0
     DO 2190 J=1,N
     IF(KFR(J)) 2190,2190,2184
2184 PHI(1,J) = -1.0
     DO 2186 I=2,N
2186  PHI(I,J) = -EPS(I,J)
2190 CONTINUE
     DO 2194 I=1,N
```

```
      DO 2194 J=1,N
2194  Y(I,J)=PHI(I,J)
      IF(INTPRT)2199,2199,2196
2196  PRINT 2198
      CALL A37PM
2199  WRITE TAPE 1, ((Y(I,J),J=1,N),I=1,N)
      REWIND 2
      READ TAPE 2,((THETA(I,J),J=1,N),I=1,N)
      READ TAPE 2,((PHI(I,J),J=1,N),I=1,N)
      READ TAPE 2,((Y(I,J),J=1,N),I=1,N)
      REWIND 2
      WRITE TAPE 2,ITEST1,ITEST1,ITEST1,ITEST1,ITEST1,INDEX3
      WRITE TAPE 2,INTPRT,N
      WRITE TAPE 2, (KFP(K),K=1,N)
      WRITE TAPE 2, (KFR(K),K=1,N)
      WRITE TAPE 2, (D1K(K),K=1,N)
      WRITE TAPE 2, ((Y(I,J),J=1,N),I=1,N)
      WRITE TAPE 2,((THETA(I,J),J=1,N),I=1,N)
      WRITE TAPE 2,((PHI(I,J),J=1,N),I=1,N)
      REWIND 1
      READ TAPE 1,((Y(I,J),J=1,N),I=1,N)
      READ TAPE 1,((EPS(I,J),J=1,N),I=1,N)
      READ TAPE 1,((THETA(I,J),J=1,N),I=1,N)
      READ TAPE 1,((PHI(I,J),J=1,N),I=1,N)
      NT2 = N*2
      REWIND 1
      DO 2220 I=1,N
      DO 2210 J=1,N
2210  A(J) = Y(I,J)
      DO 2214 J=1,N
      JPN = J+N
2214  A(JPN) = EPS(I,J)
2220  WRITE TAPE 1,(A(J),J=1,NT2)
      DO 2230 I=1,N
      DO 2224 J=1,N
2224  A(J) = THETA(I,J)
      DO 2228 J=1,N
      JPN = J+N
2228  A(JPN) = PHI(I,J)
2230  WRITE TAPE 1,(A(J),J=1,NT2)
      PRINT 2240
      STOP
      END




TITLEA55FMB6        J.B.VERNON   0101
7     FORMAT(1H4,21HSTART PROGRAM A55FMB6)
140   FORMAT(1H0,21HMATRIX LAMBDA FOLLOWS)
250   FORMAT(1H0,18HLAMBDA IS SINGULAR)
580   FORMAT(1H0,25HINVERSE OF LAMBDA FOLLOWS)
640   FORMAT(1H0,80HMATRIX LAMBDA POSTMULTIPLIED BY ITS INVERSE HAS BEEN
     1 COMPUTED. THE MAX ERROR IS E17.9,14H FOR ELEMENT (I3,1H,I3,1H))
650   FORMAT(1H1,14HEND OF A55FMB6)
2003  FORMAT(1H0,73HFLEXIBILITY MATRIX HAS ALREADY BEEN COMPUTED--THIS P
     1ROGRAM NOT APPLICABLE)
      DIMENSION A(60,60),B(60), C(60),IXIMAX(60), JXJMAX(60),
     1ICHK(60),JCHK(60)
      COMMON N,MC,A
      PRINT 7
      ISING = 0
      REWIND 1
      REWIND 2
      REWIND 3
      READ  TAPE 2,ITEST1,ITEST1,ITEST1,ITEST1,ITEST1,INDEX3
      IF(INDEX3)2001,2001,2002
2001  IF(ITEST1 - 1)2002,2002,2004
2002  PRINT 2003
      WRITE TAPE 3,ISING,ISING,ISING,ISING,ISING,ISING,ISING,ISING
      STOP
2004  READ TAPE 2,INTPRT,N
```

```
        N = N*2
        DO 124 I=1,N
124     READ TAPE 1,(A(I,J),J=1,N)
        MC = N
        DO 132 J=1,N
        ICHK(J) = 0
132     JCHK(J) = 0
145     DO 420 IXA = 1,N
        AMAX = 0.0
        DO 160 I=1,N
        IF(ICHK(I))146,146,160
146     DO 158 J=1,N
        IF(JCHK(J))147,147,158
147     IF(AMAX - ABSF(A(I,J)))150,158,158
150     AMAX = ABSF(A(I,J))
        IMAX = I
        JMAX = J
158     CONTINUE
160     CONTINUE
        ICHK(IMAX) = 1
        JCHK(JMAX) = 1
        IXIMAX(IXA) = IMAX
        JXJMAX(IXA) = JMAX
        IF(AMAX - 1.0E-30)240,290,290
240     PRINT 250
        ISING = 1
        WRITE TAPE 3,ISING,ISING,ISING,ISING,ISING,ISING,ISING,ISING
        STOP
290     DUM = A(IMAX,JMAX)
        DO 310 J=1,N
        IF(JCHK(J))304,304,310
304     A(IMAX,J) = A(IMAX,J)/DUM
310     CONTINUE
        DO 380 I=1,N
        IF(I-IMAX)320,380,320
320     DO 340 J=1,N
        IF(JCHK(J))330,330,340
330     A(I,J) = A(I,J) - A(I,JMAX) * A(IMAX,J)
340     CONTINUE
380     CONTINUE
420     CONTINUE
        DO 430 J=1,N
        JT = JXJMAX(J)
430     WRITE TAPE 3,(A(I,JT),I=1,N)
        REWIND 3
        DO 440 I=1,N
        DO 440 J=1,N
440     A(I,J) = 0.0
        DO 450 I=1,N
450     A(I,I) = 1.0
        DO 560 IXA = 1,N
        READ TAPE 3, (B(I),I=1,N)
        IMAX = IXIMAX(IXA)
        JMAX= JXJMAX(IXA)
        DO 460 J=1,N
460     A(IMAX,J) = A(IMAX,J)/B(IMAX)
        DO 558 I=1,N
        IF(I-IMAX)470,558,470
470     DO 480 J=1,N
480     A(I,J) = A(I,J) - B(I) * A(IMAX,J)
558     CONTINUE
560     CONTINUE
        DO 570 IXA = 1,N
        IMAX = IXIMAX(IXA)
        JMAX = JXJMAX(IXA)
        IF(IMAX - JMAX)565,570,565
565     DO 566 J=1,N
        DUM = A(IMAX,J)
        A(IMAX,J) = A(JMAX,J)
566     A(JMAX,J) = DUM
        DO 569 I=IXA,N
        IF(IXIMAX(I) - JMAX)569,567,569
567     IXIMAX(I) = IMAX
        GO TO 570
```

```
569   CONTINUE
570   CONTINUE
      REWIND 3
      IF(INTPRT)576,576,572
572   PRINT 580
      CALL A37PM6
576   REWIND 1
      DO 620 I=1,N
      READ TAPE 1,(B(J),J=1,N)
      DO 610 J=1,N
      C(J) = 0.0
      DO 610 K=1,N
610   C(J) = C(J) + B(K) * A(K,J)
620   WRITE TAPE 3,(C(J),J=1,N)
      WRITE TAPE 3,((A(I,J),J=1,N),I=1,N)
      REWIND 3
      DO 630 I=1,N
630   READ TAPE 3,(A(I,J),J=1,N)
      DO 632 I=1,N
632   A(I,I) = A(I,I) - 1.0
      ERROR = -1.0
      DO 636 I=1,N
      DO 636 J=1,N
      IF(ABSF(A(I,J)) - ERROR)636,636,634
634   ERROR = ABSF(A(I,J))
      IMAXER = I
      JMAXER = J
636   CONTINUE
      PRINT 640,ERROR,IMAXER,JMAXER
      READ TAPE 3, ((A(I,J),J=1,N),I=1,N)
      REWIND 1
      ND2 = N/2
      N2P1 = ND2 + 1
      WRITE TAPE 1,((A(I,J),J=1,ND2),I=1,ND2)
      WRITE TAPE 1,((A(I,J),J=1,N2P1,N),I=1,ND2)
      WRITE TAPE 1,((A(I,J),J=1,ND2),I=N2P1,N)
      WRITE TAPE 1,((A(I,J),J=1,N2P1,N),I=N2P1,N)
      REWIND 3
      WRITE TAPE 3,ISING,ISING,ISING,ISING,ISING,ISING,ISING,ISING
      PRINT 650
      STOP
      END




TITLEA55FMB7         J.B.VERNON  0101
7     FORMAT(1H4,21HSTART PROGRAM A55FMB7)
2003 FORMAT(1H0,73HFLEXIBILITY MATRIX HAS ALREADY BEEN COMPUTED--THIS P
    1ROGRAM NOT APPLICABLE)
2359 FORMAT(1H0,19HLAMBDA WAS SINGULAR)
2430 FORMAT(1H0,41HFINAL Z(I,J), REACTIONS AT RIGID SUPPORTS)
2450 FORMAT(1H0,39HFINAL Z(I,J), DEFLECTIONS AT ALL POINTS)
2510 FORMAT(1H0,41HFINAL V(I,J), REACTIONS AT RIGID SUPPORTS)
2530 FORMAT(1H0,39HFINAL V(I,J), DEFLECTIONS AT ALL POINTS)
2540 FORMAT(1H1,14HEND OF A55FMB7)
      DIMENSION KFP(30),KFR(30),D1K(30)
      DIMENSION Y(30,30)
      DIMENSION THETA(30,30),EPS(30,30),PHI(30,30)
      COMMON N,MC,Y,EPS,THETA,PHI,KFP,KFR,ITEST1,INTPRT,ISING,INDEX3
      PRINT 7
      REWIND 3
      READ  TAPE 3,ISING,ISING,ISING,ISING,ISING,ISING,ISING,ISING
      REWIND 2
      READ  TAPE 2,ITEST1,ITEST1,ITEST1,ITEST1,ITEST1,INDEX3
      IF(INDEX3)2001,2001,2002
2001 IF(ITEST1 - 1)2002,2002,2004
2002 PRINT 2003
      STOP
2004 READ TAPE 2,INTPRT,N
      READ TAPE 2, (KFP(K),K=1,N)
      READ TAPE 2, (KFR(K),K=1,N)
      READ TAPE 2, (D1K(K),K=1,N)
```

```
      READ TAPE 2,((Y(I,J),J=1,N),I=1,N)
      MC=N
      IF(ISING)2362,2362,2357
2357  REWIND 2
      WRITE TAPE 2,ISING,ITEST1,ITEST1,ITEST1,ITEST1,INDEX3
      PRINT 2359
      STOP
2362  DO 2364 J=1,N
2364  Y(1,J)=1.0
      REWIND 1
      READ TAPE 1,((THETA(I,J),J=1,N),I=1,N)
      READ TAPE 1,((THETA(I,J),J=1,N),I=1,N)
      READ TAPE 1,((THETA(I,J),J=1,N),I=1,N)
      DO 2370 I=1,N
      DO 2370 J=1,N
      EPS(I,J)=0.0
      DO 2370 K=1,N
2370  EPS(I,J)=EPS(I,J)+THETA(I,K)*Y(K,J)
      READ TAPE 2,((Y(I,J),J=1,N),I=1,N)
      DO 2374 J=1,N
2374  Y(1,J) = D1K(J)
      READ TAPE 1,((PHI(I,J),J=1,N),I=1,N)
      DO 2380 I=1,N
      DO 2380 J=1,N
      DO 2380 K=1,N
2380  EPS(I,J)=EPS(I,J)+PHI(I,K)*Y(K,J)
      REWIND 3
      WRITE TAPE 3,((EPS(I,J),J=1,N),I=1,N)
      REWIND 2
      READ TAPE 2,I,I,I,I,I,I
      READ TAPE 2,I,I
      READ TAPE 2,(Y(1,J),J=1,N)
      READ TAPE 2,(Y(1,J),J=1,N)
      READ TAPE 2,(Y(1,J),J=1,N)
      READ TAPE 2,((Y(I,J),I=1,N),J=1,N)
      READ TAPE 2,((Y(I,J),I=1,N),J=1,N)
      DO 2384 J=1,N
2384  Y(1,J) = 0.0
      DO 2390 I=1,N
      DO 2390 J=1,N
      EPS(I,J)=0.0
      DO 2390 K=1,N
2390  EPS(I,J) = EPS(I,J) + THETA(I,K) * Y(K,J)
      READ TAPE 2,((Y(I,J),J=1,N),I=1,N)
      DO 2394 J=1,N
2394  Y(1,J) = 1.0
      DO 2400 I=1,N
      DO 2400 J=1,N
      DO 2400 K=1,N
2400  EPS(I,J)=EPS(I,J)+PHI(I,K)*Y(K,J)
      WRITE TAPE 3,((EPS(I,J),J=1,N),I=1,N)
      REWIND 1
      READ TAPE 1,((THETA(I,J),J=1,N),I=1,N)
      READ TAPE 1,((PHI(I,J),J=1,N),I=1,N)
      REWIND 2
      READ TAPE 2,I,I,I,I,I,I
      READ TAPE 2,I,I
      READ TAPE 2,(EPS(1,J),J=1,N)
      READ TAPE 2,(EPS(1,J),J=1,N)
      READ TAPE 2,(EPS(1,J),J=1,N)
      READ TAPE 2,((EPS(I,J),J=1,N),I=1,N)
      DO 2404 J=1,N
2404  EPS(1,J) = 1.0
      DO 2410 I=1,N
      DO 2410 J=1,N
      Y(I,J)=0.0
      DO 2410 K=1,N
2410  Y(I,J) = Y(I,J) + THETA(I,K) * EPS(K,J)
      READ TAPE 2,((EPS(I,J),J=1,N),I=1,N)
      DO 2414 J=1,N
2414  EPS(1,J) = D1K(J)
      DO 2420 I=1,N
      DO 2420 J=1,N
      DO 2420 K=1,N
```

```
2420 Y(I,J)=Y(I,J)+PHI(I,K)*EPS(K,J)
     IF(INTPRT)2426,2426,2422
2422 PRINT 2430
     CALL A37PM
2426 WRITE TAPE 3,((Y(I,J),J=1,N),I=1,N)
     ITEST1 = 0
     DO 2440 I=1,N
     IF(KFP(I)) 2440,2440,2434
2434 ITEST1 = ITEST1 + 1
     DO 2436 J=1,N
2436 Y(I,J)=0.0
2440 CONTINUE
     IF(INTPRT)2446,2446,2442
2442 PRINT 2450
     CALL A37PM
2446 WRITE TAPE 3,((Y(I,J),J=1,N),I=1,N)
     REWIND 2
     READ TAPE 2,I,I,I,I,I,I
     READ TAPE 2,I,I
     READ TAPE 2,(EPS(1,J),J=1,N)
     READ TAPE 2,(EPS(1,J),J=1,N)
     READ TAPE 2,(EPS(1,J),J=1,N)
     READ TAPE 2,((EPS(I,J),I=1,N),J=1,N)
     READ TAPE 2,((EPS(I,J),I=1,N),J=1,N)
     DO 2456 J=1,N
2456 EPS(1,J) = 0.0
     DO 2460 I=1,N
     DO 2460 J=1,N
     Y(I,J)=0.0
     DO 2460 K=1,N
2460 Y(I,J) = Y(I,J) + THETA(I,K) * EPS(K,J)
     READ TAPE 2,((EPS(I,J),J=1,N),I=1,N)
     DO 2466 J=1,N
2466 EPS(1,J) = 1.0
     DO 2470 I=1,N
     DO 2470 J=1,N
     DO 2470 K=1,N
2470 Y(I,J)=Y(I,J)+PHI(I,K)*EPS(K,J)
     IF(INTPRT)2476,2476,2472
2472 PRINT 2510
     CALL A37PM
2476 WRITE TAPE 3,((Y(I,J),J=1,N),I=1,N)
     DO 2482 I=1,N
     DO 2482 J=1,N
2482 EPS(I,J)=Y(I,J)
     DO 2490 I=1,N
     IF(KFP(I))2490,2490,2484
2484 DO 2486 J=1,N
2486 Y(I,J)=0.0
2490 CONTINUE
     IF(INTPRT)2496,2496,2492
2492 PRINT 2530
     CALL A37PM
2496 WRITE TAPE 3, ((Y(I,J),J=1,N),I=1,N)
     CALL A55B7S
     PRINT 2540
     STOP
     END



     SUBROUTINE A55B7S
     DIMENSION KFP(30),KFR(30),Y(30,30),EPS(30,30),THETA(30,30),PHI(30,
     130)
2480 FORMAT(1H0,45HFINAL ALPHA(I,J), REACTIONS AT RIGID SUPPORTS)
2500 FORMAT(1H0,43HFINAL ALPHA(I,J), DEFLECTIONS AT ALL POINTS)
2540 FORMAT(1H0,44HFINAL BETA(I,J), REACTIONS AT RIGID SUPPORTS)
2560 FORMAT(1H0,42HFINAL BETA(I,J), DEFLECTIONS AT ALL POINTS)
     COMMON N,MC,Y,EPS,THETA,PHI,KFP,KFR,ITEST1,INTPRT,ISING,INDEX3
     REWIND 3
     READ TAPE 3,((Y(I,J),J=1,N),I=1,N)
```

```
      REWIND 2
      WRITE TAPE 2, ((Y(I,J),J=1,N),I=1,N)
      IF(INTPRT)2506,2506,2505
 2505 PRINT 2480
      CALL A37PM
 2506 DO 2520 I=1,N
      IF(KFR(I))2520,2520,2514
 2514 ITEST1 = ITEST1 + 1
      DO 2516 J=1,N
 2516 Y(I,J)=0.0
 2520 CONTINUE
      IF(INTPRT)2524,2524,2522
 2522 PRINT 2500
      CALL A37PM
 2524 DO 2526 I=1,N
      DO 2526 J=1,N
 2526 THETA(I,J) = Y(I,J)
      READ TAPE 3,((Y(I,J),J=1,N),I=1,N)
      WRITE TAPE 2, ((Y(I,J),J=1,N),I=1,N)
      IF(INTPRT)2538,2538,2536
 2536 PRINT 2540
      CALL A37PM
 2538 DO 2550 I=1,N
      IF(KFR(I))2550,2550,2544
 2544 DO 2546 J=1,N
 2546 Y(I,J)=0.0
 2550 CONTINUE
      IF(INTPRT)2556,2556,2552
 2552 PRINT 2560
      CALL A37PM
 2556 DO 2558 I=1,N
      DO 2558 J=1,N
 2558 PHI(I,J) = Y(I,J)
      READ TAPE 3,((Y(I,J),J=1,N),I=1,N)
      WRITE TAPE 2, ((Y(I,J),J=1,N),I=1,N)
      READ TAPE 3,((Y(I,J),J=1,N),I=1,N)
      READ TAPE 3,((EPS(I,J),J=1,N),I=1,N)
      WRITE TAPE 2,((EPS(I,J),J=1,N),I=1,N)
      READ TAPE 3,((EPS(I,J),J=1,N),I=1,N)
      REWIND 1
      WRITE TAPE 1,INTPRT,N,N,N,N,N,N,N
      DO 2570 I=1,10
 2570 WRITE TAPE 1, (KFP(K),K=1,N)
      WRITE TAPE 1, ((Y(I,J),J=1,N),I=1,N)
      WRITE TAPE 1,((EPS(I,J),J=1,N),I=1,N)
      WRITE TAPE 1,((THETA(I,J),J=1,N),I=1,N)
      WRITE TAPE 1,((PHI(I,J),J=1,N),I=1,N)
      REWIND 2
      READ TAPE 2,((THETA(I,J),J=1,N),I=1,N)
      READ TAPE 2,((PHI(I,J),J=1,N),I=1,N)
      READ TAPE 2,((Y(I,J),J=1,N),I=1,N)
      READ TAPE 2,((EPS(I,J),J=1,N),I=1,N)
      WRITE TAPE 1, ((Y(I,J),J=1,N),I=1,N)
      WRITE TAPE 1,((EPS(I,J),J=1,N),I=1,N)
      WRITE TAPE 1,((THETA(I,J),J=1,N),I=1,N)
      WRITE TAPE 1,((PHI(I,J),J=1,N),I=1,N)
      REWIND 2
      WRITE TAPE 2,ISING,ITEST1,ITEST1,ITEST1,ITEST1,INDEX3
      RETURN
      END


TITLEA55OUT1       J.B.VERNON  0101
C THIS PROGRAM CAUSES THE RESULTS OF THE FLEXIBILITY MATRIX COMPUTATION OF
C PROGRAMS A55FMB1 THROUGH A55FMB6 TO BE PRINTED.  Z(I,J) IS THE LINEAR
C DEFLECTION AT I CAUSED BY A UNIT FORCE AT J.  V(I,J) IS LINEAR DEFLECTION AT
C I CAUSED BY UNIT MOMENT AT J.  ALPHA(I,J) IS ANGULAR DEFLECTION AT I CAUSED
C BY UNIT FORCE AT J.  BETA(I,J) IS ANGULAR DEFLECTION AT I CAUSED BY UNIT
C MOMENT AT J.  IF SOME OTHER FORM OF OUTPUT IS DESIRED A DIFFERENT OUTPUT
C PROGRAM CAN BE WRITTEN. TO OBTAIN THE NECESSARY RESULTS FROM TAPE USE THE
C READ TAPE STATEMENTS IN THIS PROGRAM.
```

```
  22    FORMAT(1H0,19HLAMBDA WAS SINGULAR)
 640    FORMAT(1H0,40HEND OF COMPUTATION OF FLEXIBILITY MATRIX)
 680    FORMAT(E17.9)
2430    FORMAT(1H0,41HFINAL Z(I,J), REACTIONS AT RIGID SUPPORTS)
2450    FORMAT(1H0,39HFINAL Z(I,J), DEFLECTIONS AT ALL POINTS)
2480    FORMAT(1H0,45HFINAL ALPHA(I,J), REACTIONS AT RIGID SUPPORTS)
2500    FORMAT(1H0,43HFINAL ALPHA(I,J), DEFLECTIONS AT ALL POINTS)
2510    FORMAT(1H0,41HFINAL V(I,J), REACTIONS AT RIGID SUPPORTS)
2530    FORMAT(1H0,39HFINAL V(I,J), DEFLECTIONS AT ALL POINTS)
2540    FORMAT(1H0,44HFINAL BETA(I,J), REACTIONS AT RIGID SUPPORTS)
2560    FORMAT(1H0,42HFINAL BETA(I,J), DEFLECTIONS AT ALL POINTS)
        DIMENSION KFP(30)
        DIMENSION Y(30,30)
        DIMENSION THETA(30,30),EPS(30,30),PHI(30,30)
        COMMON N,MC,Y
        REWIND 1
        REWIND 2
        READ TAPE 2,ISING,ITEST1,ITEST1,ITEST1,ITEST1,INDEX3
        IF(ISING)30,30,20
  20    PRINT 22
        STOP
  30    READ   TAPE 1,INTPRT,N,N,N,N,N,N,N
        MC=N
        DO 40 I=1,10
  40    READ TAPE 1,   (KFP(K),K=1,N)
        PRINT 2450
        READ TAPE 1,((Y(I,J),J=1,N),I=1,N)
        CALL A37PM
        PRINT 2530
        READ TAPE 1,((Y(I,J),J=1,N),I=1,N)
        CALL A37PM
        PRINT 2500
        READ TAPE 1,((Y(I,J),J=1,N),I=1,N)
        CALL A37PM
        PRINT 2560
        READ TAPE 1,((Y(I,J),J=1,N),I=1,N)
        CALL A37PM
        IF(INDEX3)60,60,648
  60    IF(ITEST1)648,648,2428
2428    PRINT 2430
        READ TAPE 1,((Y(I,J),J=1,N),I=1,N)
        CALL A37PM
        PRINT 2510
        READ TAPE 1,((Y(I,J),J=1,N),I=1,N)
        CALL A37PM
        PRINT 2480
        READ TAPE 1,((Y(I,J),J=1,N),I=1,N)
        CALL A37PM
        PRINT 2540
        READ TAPE 1,((Y(I,J),J=1,N),I=1,N)
        CALL A37PM
        PRINT 640
 648    STOP
        END
```

```
TITLEA74INP1        J.B.VERNON  0101
C THIS PROGRAM PREPARES TAPE 1 FOR USE BY PROGRAM A74PFD.   INPUT FOR THIS
C PROGRAM IS A DATA DECK CONSISTING OF VARIABLES IN THE FOLLOWING ORDER, EACH
C VARIABLE ON A SEPARATE CARD.   IPRDTA, WHICH SHOULD BE 1 IF THE ORIGINAL
C MATRICES ARE TO BE PRINTED, ZERO OTHERWISE, N, THE ORDER OF THE MATRICES,
C AND THEN THE ELEMENTS OF MATRICES A, B, C, BY ROWS.   FOR THE DIMENSION
C STATEMENT USED, N CANNOT EXCEED 30.   IF SOME OTHER PROGRAM IS USED TO
C GENERATE THE MATRICES A, B, C, IT SHOULD LEAVE TAPE 1 IN THE SAME CONDITION
C AS THE WRITE TAPE 1 STATEMENTS AT THE END OF THIS PROGRAM.   MATRICES A, B,
C AND C ARE DEFINED IN PROGRAM A74PFD.   THE FORMAT STATEMENTS FOR IPRDTA, N,
C AND EACH OF THE ELEMENTS OF THE MATRICES ARE (I1), (I2), AND (E17.9)
C RESPECTIVELY.   ONLY TAPE 1 IS USED IN THIS COMPUTATION.
  10    FORMAT(I1)
  20    FORMAT(I2)
  26    FORMAT(E17.9)
```

```
      DIMENSION A(30,30), B(30,30), C(30,30)
      READ INPUT TAPE 5,10,IPRDTA
      READ INPUT TAPE 5, 20, N
      READ INPUT TAPE 5, 26, ((A(I,J),J=1,N),I=1,N)
      READ INPUT TAPE 5,26,((B(I,J),J=1,N),I=1,N)
      READ INPUT TAPE 5,26,((C(I,J),J=1,N),I=1,N)
      REWIND 1
      WRITE TAPE 1,N,IPRDTA
      WRITE TAPE 1,((A(I,J), J=1,N), I=1,N)
      WRITE TAPE 1, ((B(I, J), J=1,N), I=1,N)
      WRITE TAPE 1,((C(I,J),J=1,N),I=1,N)
      STOP
      END
```

```
 TITLEA74PFD        101   J.B.VERNON
C THIS PROGRAM WILL COMPUTE THE CHARACTERISTIC POLYNOMIAL FROM A DETERMINANT.
C EACH ELEMENT OF THE DETERMINANT IS A QUADRATIC IN THE VARIABLE S OF THE
C FORM A + B*S + C*S**2 WHERE OF COURSE ANY OF THE COEFFICIENTS, A, B,
C OR C COULD BE ZERO AS A SPECIAL CASE.  A MATRIX IS FORMED OF THE CONSTANT
C TERMS AND DESIGNATED AS THE MATRIX A.  SIMILAR MATRICES B AND C ARE
C FORMED FROM THE B AND C COEFFICIENTS.  THE INPUT TO THIS PROGRAM CONSISTS
C OF N, IPRDTA, AND THE ELEMENTS OF MATRICES A, B, AND C, AS INDICATED IN
C PROGRAM A74INP1.              THE RESULT OF THE CALCULATION IS THE
C POLYNOMIAL E(0) + E(1)*S + E(2)*S**2 + ... + E(N*2)*S**(N*2) WHERE THE
C NUMBERS IN PARENTHESES FOLLOWING E ARE SUBSCRIPTS.  THIS POLYNOMIAL IS
C PRINTED AND ALSO STORED ON TAPE 1 IN CASE IT IS DESIRED TO USE THESE RESULTS
C IN A FOLLOWING CALCULATION.  AN OUTPUT PROGRAM MUST BE CONSISTENT WITH THE
C WRITE TAPE 1 STATEMENTS 600 THROUGH 610 OF  THIS PROGRAM.  NT2P1 IS THE
C NUMBER OF TERMS IN THE POLYNOMIAL, EQUAL TO TWICE THE ORDER, N, PLUS ONE.
C MATRICES A, B, AND C, ARE ALSO STORED ON THETAPE AFTER THE POLYNOMIAL.
      DIMENSION A(30,30), B(30,30), C(30,30), H(31,61), E(61)
      DIMENSION ASN(30), JU(30), IU(30)
      COMMON NP,MP,C
      PRINT 40
40    FORMAT(1H1,1H )
      PRINT 50
50    FORMAT(1H0,12HSTART A74PFD)
100   FORMAT(I2,I3)
110   FORMAT(E17.9)
      REWIND 1
      READ TAPE 1,N,IPRDTA
      MP = N
      NP = N
      READ TAPE 1, ((C(I,J), J=1,N), I=1,N)
      IF(IPRDTA)102,102,101
101   CALL A37PM
102   DO 103 I=1,N
      DO 103 J=1,N
103   A(I,J) = C(I,J)
      READ TAPE 1, ((C(I,J), J=1,N), I=1,N)
      IF(IPRDTA)105,105,104
104   CALL A37PM
105   DO 106 I = 1,N
      DO 106 J = 1,N
106   B(I,J) = C(I,J)
      READ TAPE 1, ((C(I,J), J=1,N), I=1,N)
      REWIND 1
      WRITE TAPE 1, ((A(I,J), J=1,N), I=1,N)
      WRITE TAPE 1, ((B(I,J), J=1,N), I=1,N)
      WRITE TAPE 1, ((C(I,J), J=1,N), I=1,N)
      REWIND 1
      IF(IPRDTA)108,108,107
107   CALL A37PM
108   NT2 = N*2
      NT2P1 = N*2 + 1
      NP1 = N + 1
      DO 210 I = 1,NP1
      DO 210 J = 1,NT2P1
210   H(I,J) = 0.0
```

```
         H(1,1) = 1.0
         DO 230 I = 1,N
         E(I) = 0.0
         ASN(I) = 1.0
         JU(I) = 0
230      IU(I) = 0
         DO 254 I=1,N
         DO 254 J=1,N
         IF(ABSF(A(I,J)) - 1.0E-30)251,251,254
251      IF(ABSF(B(I,J)) - 1.0E-30)252,252,254
252      IF(ABSF(C(I,J)) - 1.0E-30)253,253,254
253      IU(I) = IU(I) + 1
254      CONTINUE
         NL1 = N-1
         DO 273   J=1,NL1
         IT = IU(J)
         JP1 = J+1
         DO 263   I=JP1,N
         IF(IU(I) - IT)263,263,262
262      IT = IU(I)
         ITR = I
263      CONTINUE
         IF(IT - IU(J))273,273,271
271      DO 272 K=1,N
         SV = A(J,K)
         A(J,K) = A(ITR,K)
         A(ITR,K) = -SV
         SV = B(J,K)
         B(J,K) = B(ITR,K)
         B(ITR,K) = -SV
         SV = C(J,K)
         C(J,K) = C(ITR,K)
272      C(ITR,K) = -SV
         IU(ITR) = IU(J)
273      CONTINUE
         DO 275 I=1,N
         IU(I) = 0
275      JU(I) = 0
         I = 1
300      IUP1 = IU(I) + 1
         DO 500 J = IUP1,N
         IF(JU(J))500,310,500
310      IF(ABSF(A(I,J)) - 1.0E-30)320,320,340
320      IF(ABSF(B(I,J)) - 1.0E-30)330,330,340
330      IF(ABSF(C(I,J)) - 1.0E-30)490,490,340
340      IT2 = I*2
         IT2L1 = IT2 - 1
         IT2P1 = IT2 + 1
         IP1 = I + 1
         DO 350 K = 1,IT2L1
350      H(IP1,K) = H(I,K) * A(I,J) * ASN(I)
         DO 360 K = 2,IT2
         KL1 = K - 1
360      H(IP1,K) = H(IP1,K) + H(I,KL1) * B(I,J) * ASN(I)
         DO 370 K = 3,IT2P1
         KL2 = K - 2
370      H(IP1,K) = H(IP1,K) + H(I,KL2) * C(I,J) * ASN(I)
         ASN(I) = -1.0 * ASN(I)
         JU(J) = 1
         IU(I) = J
         IF(N-I)380,380,400
380      DO 390 K =1,NT2P1
390      E(K) = E(K) + H(NP1,K)
         GO TO 510
400      I = I + 1
         GO TO 300
490      ASN(I) = -1.0 * ASN(I)
500      CONTINUE
510      IU(I) = N
520      IF(IU(I) - N)540,530,530
530      I = I - 1
         IF(I)560,560,520
540      IP1 = I + 1
         IL1 = I - 1
```

```
      DO 545 IT = 1,N
545   JU(IT) = 0
      IF(IL1)548,548,546
546   DO 547 IT = 1,IL1
      ITEMP = IU(IT)
547   JU(ITEMP) = 1
548   DO 550 IT = IP1,N
      ASN(IT) = 1.0
550   IU(IT) = 0
      DO 555 IT = IP1,NP1
      DO 555 J=1,NT2P1
555   H(IT,J) = 0.0
      GO TO 300
560   DO 570 K=1,NT2P1
      KL1 = K - 1
570   PRINT 580, KL1, E(K)
580   FORMAT(1H0, 19HCOEFFICIENT OF S** I2,  3H = E17.9)
      READ  TAPE 1, ((A(I,J), J=1,N), I=1,N)
      READ  TAPE 1, ((B(I,J), J=1,N), I=1,N)
      READ  TAPE 1, ((C(I,J), J=1,N), I=1,N)
      REWIND 1
600   WRITE TAPE 1,N,NT2P1
      WRITE TAPE 1, (E(J), J=1,NT2P1)
      WRITE TAPE 1, ((A(I,J), J=1,N), I=1,N)
      WRITE TAPE 1, ((B(I,J), J=1,N), I=1,N)
610   WRITE TAPE 1, ((C(I,J), J=1,N), I=1,N)
      PRINT 620
620   FORMAT(1H1,13HEND OF A74PFD)
      STOP
      END



      TITLEA74A86A        J.B.VERNON  0101
C THIS PROGRAM CONNECTS PROGRAM A74PFD  AND PROGRAM A86FP
100   FORMAT(I3)
120   FORMAT(E17.9)
130   FORMAT(I1)
214   FORMAT(1H0,44HFIRST POWER OF S WITHOUT ZERO COEFFICIENT IS  I4)
230   FORMAT(1H2,48HVALUE OF LOWEST NON-ZERO TERM BEFORE DIVISION =
     1E17.9)
250   FORMAT(1H ,2HE( I2, 4H) =  E17.9)
      DIMENSION E(51)
      REWIND 1
      READ TAPE 1, N, N2P1
      READ TAPE 1, (E(J),J=1,N2P1)
      DO 200 J=1,N2P1
      N2P2LJ = N2P1 + 1 - J
      IF(ABSF(E(N2P2LJ)) - 1.0E-30)200,200,210
200   CONTINUE
210   DO 212 J=1,N2P2LJ
      IF(ABSF(E(J))-1.0E-30)212,212,213
212   CONTINUE
      J=N2P2LJ
213   LOWEXP = J-1
      PRINT 214,LOWEXP
      JP = LOWEXP + 1
      DUM = E(JP)
      JPP1 = JP + 1
      PRINT 230, DUM
      DO 220 J=1,N2P2LJ
      E(J) = E(J)/DUM
220   CONTINUE
      N = N2P2LJ - JP
      READ INPUT TAPE 5,100,ITER
      READ INPUT TAPE 5,120,ACC
      READ INPUT TAPE 5,130,INTPRT
      READ INPUT TAPE 5,100,IDIVLT
      READ INPUT TAPE 5,120,ASSUM1
      READ INPUT TAPE 5,120,ASSUM2
      READ INPUT TAPE 5,120,ASSUM3
```

```
      READ INPUT TAPE 5,120,ASSUM4
      READ INPUT TAPE 5,120,ASSUM5
      READ INPUT TAPE 5,120,ASSUM6
      REWIND 1
      WRITE TAPE 1,N,ITER,ACC,INTPRT,IDIVLI,ASSUM1,ASSUM2,ASSUM3,
     1ASSUM4,ASSUM5,ASSUM6
      WRITE TAPE 1,(E(J),J=JPP1,N2P2LJ)
      DO 240 J=1,N2P2LJ
  240 PRINT 250, J , E(J)
      STOP
      END
```

```
TITLEA86INP1        J.B.VERNON  0101
C SEE PROGRAM A86FP FOR COMMENTS.
  100 FORMAT(I3)
  120 FORMAT(E17.9)
  130 FORMAT(I1)
      DIMENSION C(100)
      READ INPUT TAPE 5,100,N
      READ INPUT TAPE 5,100,ITER
      READ INPUT TAPE 5,120,ACC
      READ INPUT TAPE 5,130,INTPRT
      READ INPUT TAPE 5,100,IDIVLT
      READ INPUT TAPE 5,120,ASSUM1
      READ INPUT TAPE 5,120,ASSUM2
      READ INPUT TAPE 5,120,ASSUM3
      READ INPUT TAPE 5,120,ASSUM4
      READ INPUT TAPE 5,120,ASSUM5
      READ INPUT TAPE 5,120,ASSUM6
      READ INPUT TAPE 5,120,(C(J),J=1,N)
      REWIND 1
  145 WRITE TAPE 1,N,ITER,ACC,INTPRT,IDIVLT,ASSUM1,ASSUM2,ASSUM3,
     1ASSUM4,ASSUM5,ASSUM6
      WRITE TAPE 1,(C(J),J=1,N)
      STOP
      END
```

```
TITLEA86FP          J.B.VERNON  0101
C THIS PROGRAM FACTORS A POLYNOMIAL UP TO THE 100TH ORDER.  RESULTS ARE THE
C QUADRATIC FACTORS OF THE POLYNOMIAL, WHICH ARE PRINTED IN THIS PROGRAM AND
C ALSO STORED ON TAPE 1.  INPUT TO THIS PROGRAM IS READ FROM TAPE 1 BY
C STATEMENTS 130 AND 132.  TAPE 1 MUST BE PREPARED BY ANOTHER PROGRAM TO AGREE
C WITH THESE STATEMENTS.  N IS THE DEGREE OF THE POLYNOMIAL, ITER THE NUMBER
C OF ITERATIONS ALLOWED, ACC THE DESIRED ACCURACY,INTPRT AN INDEX WHICH SHOULD
C BE   1  IF IT IS DESIRED THAT INTERMEDIATE RESULTS BE PRINTED AND ZERO
C OTHERWISE.  IDIVLT IS THE LIMITING NUMBER OF TIMES THAT DIFFERENCES BETWEEN
C SUCCESSIVE APPROXIMATIONS MAY BE INCREASING INSTEAD OF DECREASING.  WHEN THIS
C LIMIT IS REACHED, IT IS ASSUMED THAT THE CALCULATION IS DIVERGING AND A
C DIFFERENT ASSUMPTION IS TRIED.    ASSUM1, ASSUM2, ETC., ARE THREE SETS OF
C INITIAL ASSUMPTIONS FOR THE COEFFICIENTS OF THE QUADRATIC FACTORS, A1 AND A2.
C POSSIBLE VALUES ARE 0.0, 0.0, 1.0, 1.0, 1.0, -1.0.  THE ORIGINAL POLYNOMIAL
C IS OF THE FORM 1 + C(1)*S + C(2)*S**2 +...+ C(N)*S**N AND THE FACTORS ARE OF
C THE FORM   1 + A(1)*S + A(2)*S**2    AS A CHECK, THE FACTORS ARE MULTIPLIED
C TOGETHER AND THE RESULTING POLYNOMIAL PRINTED FOR COMPARISON WITH THE ORIGINAL
C POLYNOMIAL.  THE ORIGINAL DATA, POLYNOMIAL, AND ALL THE FACTORS ARE STORED ON
C TAPE 1 BY STATEMENTS 145,146,455,655,665, FOR POSSIBLE USE IN A LATER
C PROGRAM.  TAPE 1 IS THE ONLY TAPE USED IN THIS PROGRAM.
  150 FORMAT(1H2,12HDATA-- N = I3, 8H/ITER = I3, 7H/ACC = E14.7,
     110H/INTPRT = I1, 10H/IDIVLT = I3, 10H/ASSUM1 = E14.7, 10H/ASSUM2 =
     2 E14.7)
  151 FORMAT(1H2, 9HASSUM3 = E16.9,10H/ASSUM4 = E16.9,10H/ASSUM5 = E16.9
     1,10H/ASSUM6 = E16.9)
  152 FORMAT(1H ,16HCONSTANT TERM = E16.9)
  153 FORMAT(1H ,25HCOOEFFICIENT OF S TO THE I3, 9HPOWER IS E16.9
  154 FORMAT(1H1,11HEND OF DATA)
```

```
155   FORMAT(1H2,22HRESULTS OF COMPUTATION)
358   FORMAT(1H0,91HPOLYNOMIAL CANNOT BE FACTORED BEYOND THIS POINT WITH
      1 THESE ASSUMPTIONS. FACTOR REMAINING IS
410   FORMAT(1H ,9HITERNO = I3,6H/A1 = E16.9,6H/A2 = E16.9,9H/ACCUR =
      1E16.9,8H/IDIV = I3,8H/IFLIP = I2,9H/IASSUM = I2)
450   FORMAT(1H ,29HQUADRATIC FACTOR   = 1.0  + E16.9,8H(S)  + E16.9,
      119H(S**2)/ ACCURACY =   E16.9,13H/ITERATIONS, I3)
660   FORMAT(1H2,26HLINEAR FACTOR  = 1.0  + E16.9,3H(S))
1080  FORMAT(1H0,13HEND OF A86FP)
      DIMENSION  B(100), C(100), PBA1(100), PBA2(100),D(100)
      REWIND 1
130   READ TAPE 1,N,ITER,ACC,INTPRT,IDIVLT,ASSUM1,ASSUM2,ASSUM3,
      1ASSUM4,ASSUM5,ASSUM6
132   READ TAPE 1,(C(J),J=1,N)
      REWIND 1
      NORIG = N
145   WRITE TAPE 1,N,ITER,ACC,INTPRT,IDIVLT,ASSUM1,ASSUM2,ASSUM3,
      1ASSUM4,ASSUM5,ASSUM6
146   WRITE TAPE 1, (C(J),J=1,N)
170   PRINT 150,N,ITER,ACC,INTPRT,IDIVLT,ASSUM1,ASSUM2
      PRINT 151,ASSUM3,ASSUM4,ASSUM5,ASSUM6
      CO = 1.0
      PRINT 152,CO
      PRINT 153, (J,C(J) ,J=1,N)
      IF(NORIG-N)174,174,246
174   PRINT 154
      PRINT 155
246   IFLIP = 0
      IASSUM = -1
      IDIV = 0
250   IF(IASSUM)260,270,280
260   A1 = ASSUM1
      A2 = ASSUM2
      GO TO 290
270   A1 = ASSUM3
      A2 = ASSUM4
      GO TO 290
280   A1 = ASSUM5
      A2 = ASSUM6
290   DF1LST = 1.0E+30
      DF2LST = 1.0E+30
      IF(N-3)510,520,292
292   DO 425 ITERNO = 1,ITER
      B(1) = C(1) - A1
      B(2) = C(2) - A2 - A1*B(1)
      NL1 = N-1
      NL2 = N-2
      NL3 = N-3
      DO 310 K=3,NL1
      KL1 = K-1
      KL2 = K-2
310   B(K) = C(K) - A2*B(KL2) - A1*B(KL1)
      PBA1(1) = -1.0
      PBA1(2) = -B(1) + A1
      PBA2(1) = 0.0
      PBA2(2) = -1.0
      DO 320 K=3,NL1
      KL1 = K-1
      KL2 = K-2
      PBA1(K) = -A2*PBA1(KL2) - A1*PBA1(KL1) - B(KL1)
320   PBA2(K) = -A2*PBA2(KL2) - A1*PBA2(KL1) - B(KL2)
      PF1A1 = PBA1(NL1)
      PF1A2 = PBA2(NL1)
      PF2A1 = -A2 * PBA1(NL2)
      PF2A2 = -B(NL2) - A2*PBA2(NL2)
      P1 = PF1A1 * PF2A2
      P2 = PF2A1 * PF1A2
      DENOM = P1 - P2
      IF(ABSF(P1)-1.0E-30)330,340,340
330   IF(ABSF(P2)-1.0E-30)352,350,350
340   IF(ABSF(DENOM/P1)-1.0E-07)352,360,360
350   IF(ABSF(DENOM/P2) -1.0E-07)352,360,360
352   IASSUM = IASSUM +1
      IDIV = 0
```

```
        IF(IASSUM - 1)250,250,353
353    IF(IFLIP)354,354,357
354    DO 355 J=1,NL1
        NLJ = N-J
355    B(NLJ) = C(J)/C(N)
        B(N) = 1.0/C(N)
        DO 356 J=1,N
356    C(J) = B(J)
        IFLIP = 1
        IASSUM = -1
        IDIV = 0
        GO TO 250
357    PRINT 358
        DO 359 J=1,NL1
        NLJ = N-J
359    B(NLJ) = C(J)/C(N)
        B(N) = 1.0/C(N)
        BO = 1.0
        PRINT 152, BO
        PRINT 153, (J,B(J) ,J=1,N)
        STOP
360    F1 = B(NL1)
        F2 = C(N) - A2*B(NL2)
        DELA1 =(-F1*PF2A2 + F2*PF1A2)/DENOM
        DELA2 =(-F2*PF1A1 + F1*PF2A1)/DENOM
        A1LST = A1
        A2LST = A2
        A1 = A1 + DELA1
        A2 = A2 + DELA2
        DIFFA1 = ABSF(A1-A1LST)
        DIFFA2 = ABSF(A2 - A2LST)
        TEST1 =(DIFFA1 - DF1LST)/(DIFFA1 + DF1LST)
        TEST2 = DIFFA2 - DF2LST
        IF(TEST1-1.0E-07)370,362,362
362    IDIV = IDIV + 1
        GO TO 373
370    IF(TEST2 - 1.0E-07)380,372,372
372    IDIV = IDIV + 1
373    IF(IDIV - IDIVLT)380,380,374
374    IASSUM = IASSUM + 1
        IF(IASSUM - 1)375,375,376
375    IDIV = 0
        GO TO 250
376    IF(IFLIP)377,377,357
377    IFLIP = 1
        IDIV = 0
        IASSUM = -1
        DO 378 J = 1,NL1
        NLJ = N-J
378    B(NLJ) = C(J)/C(N)
        B(N) = 1.0/C(N)
        DO 379 J=1,N
379    C(J) = B(J)
        GO TO 250
380    ACCUR = (DIFFA1 + DIFFA2)/(ABSF(A1) + ABSF(A2))
385    IF(ACCUR - ACC)430,390,390
390    IF(INTPRT)420,420,400
400    PRINT 410,ITERNO,A1,A2,ACCUR,IDIV,IFLIP,IASSUM
420    DF1LST = DIFFA1
        DF2LST = DIFFA2
425    CONTINUE
        ITERNO = ITER
430    IF(IFLIP)440,440,460
440    PRINT 450,A1,A2,ACCUR,ITERNO
455    WRITE TAPE 1,A1,A2
        GO TO 480
460    A1 = A1/A2
        A2 = 1.0/A2
        PRINT 450,A1,A2,ACCUR,ITERNO
465    WRITE TAPE 1,A1,A2
        DO 470 J=1,NL3
        NL2LJ = NL2 - J
470    C(NL2LJ) = B(J)/B(NL2)
        C(NL2) = 1.0/B(NL2)
```

```
            GO TO 492
    480     DO 490 J=1,NL2
    490     C(J) = B(J)
    492     N = N-2
            IF(INTPRT)246,246,170
    510     PRINT 450,C(1),C(2)
    515     WRITE TAPE 1,C(1),C(2)
            GO TO 666
    520     IF(C(3))521,522,522
    521     ISIGN1 = -1
            GO TO 523
    522     ISIGN1 = 1
    523     A1 = 10.0
    524     B(1) = C(1) - A1
            B(2) = C(2) - A1 * B(1)
            F = C(3) - A1 * B(2)
            I=0
            IF(F)525,650,526
    525     ISIGN2 = -1
            GO TO 527
    526     ISIGN2 = 1
    527     IF(ISIGN1 + ISIGN2)528,532,528
    528     IF(A1-1.0E+30)529,531,531
    529     A1 = A1 * 10.0
            IF(A1+1.0E+30)5311,5311,524
    531     A1 = -10.0
            GO TO 524
   5311     PRINT 358
            PRINT 152,BO
            PRINT 153, (J,C(J) ,J=1,3)
    532     A1ST = 0.0
            A2ND = A1
   5321     A3RD = (A1ST + A2ND)/2.0
            B(1) = C(1) - A3RD
            B(2) = C(2) - A3RD*B(1)
            F = C(3) - A3RD*B(2)
            IF(INTPRT)5324,5324,5322
   5322     PRINT 5323,A3RD,F
   5323     FORMAT(1H ,22HASSUMED VALUE OF A1 =   E16.9, 19HYIELDS REMAINDER =
          1 E16.9)
   5324     IF(ABSF(F/C(3))-ACC)538,538,5326
   5326     IF(ITER-I)538,5327,5327
   5327     I=I+1
            IF(F)533,538,534
    533     ISIGN3= -1
            GO TO 535
    534     ISIGN3 = 1
    535     IF(ISIGN1 + ISIGN3)537,536,537
    536     A2ND = A3RD
            ISIGN2 = ISIGN3
            GO TO 5321
    537     A1ST = A3RD
            ISIGN1 = ISIGN3
            GO TO 5321
    538     A1 = A3RD
    650     PRINT 450,B(1),B(2)
    655     WRITE TAPE 1, B(1), B(2)
            PRINT 660, A1
    665     WRITE TAPE 1, A1,A1
    666     REWIND 1
            READ TAPE 1,N,ITER,ACC,INTPRT,IDIVLT,ASSUM1,ASSUM2,ASSUM3,
          1ASSUM4,ASSUM5,ASSUM6
            READ TAPE 1,(C(J),J=1,N)
            READ TAPE 1,B(1),B(2)
            ILIM = NORIG/2-1
            N=4
            DO 1030 I=1,ILIM
            READ TAPE 1,A1,A2
            C(1) = B(1) + A1
            C(2) = B(2) + A2 + A1*B(1)
            NL1 = N-1
            NL2 = N-2
            NL3 = N-3
            IF(N-4)1020,1020,1000
   1000     DO 1010 K=3,NL2
```

```
       KL1 = K-1
       KL2 = K-2
 1010 C(K) = B(K) + A1*B(KL1) + A2*B(KL2)
 1020 C(NL1) = A1*B(NL2) + A2*B(NL3)
       C(N) = A2*B(NL2)
       DO 1025 J=1,N
 1025 B(J) = C(J)
       N = N+2
 1030 CONTINUE
       IF(NORIG + 2 - N)1060,1060,1040
 1040 READ TAPE 1,A1
       N=NORIG
       NL1 = N-1
       C(1) = A1 + B(1)
       DO 1050 K=2,NL1
       KL1 = K-1
 1050 C(K) = B(K) + A1*B(KL1)
       C(N) = A1*B(NL1)
 1060 N=NORIG
       PRINT 1070
 1070 FORMAT(1H0,31HCHECK MULTIPLICATION OF FACTORS)
       PRINT 152,CO
       PRINT 153, (J,C(J) ,J=1,N)
       PRINT 1080
       STOP
       END




       SUBROUTINE  A86FPS
C       THIS SUBROUTINE WILL FACTOR A POLYNOMIAL OF ORDER  N.   BEFORE CALLING
C THIS SUBROUTINE IT IS NECESSARY TO HAVE ESTABLISHED THE VALUES OF THE
C VARIABLES INDICATED IN THE COMMON STATEMENT, EXCEPT  B, PBA1, PBA2, GKS,
C CSAVE, A1SAVE, A2SAVE.   THE OTHER VARIABLES ARE DEFINED IN MAIN PROGRAM
C A86FP.  THE RESULTS OF THE FACTORING PROGRAM WILL BE STORED IN A1SAVE AND
C A2SAVE WHERE QUADRATIC FACTORS ARE  1 + A1SAVE(K) * S + A2SAVE(K. * S**2.  IF
C THE ORDER IS ODD THE FINAL LINEAR FACTOR IS  1 + A1SAVE(K) * S       NO TAPE IS
C USED IN THIS SUBROUTINE.
 152  FORMAT(1H ,16HCONSTANT TERM = E16.9)
 153  FORMAT(1H ,25HCOEFFICIENT OF S TO THE    I3, 9HPOWER IS  E17.9)
 358  FORMAT(1H0,91HPOLYNOMIAL CANNOT BE FACTORED BEYOND THIS POINT WITH
      1 THESE ASSUMPTIONS. FACTOR REMAINING IS)
 410  FORMAT(1H ,9HITERNO = I3,6H/A1 = E16.9,6H/A2 = E16.9,9H/ACCUR =
      1E16.9,8H/IDIV = I3,8H/IFLIP = I2,9H/IASSUM = I2)
 450  FORMAT(1H ,29HQUADRATIC FACTOR  =  1.0  +  E16.9,8H(S)  +  E16.9,
      119H(S**2)/ ACCURACY =   E16.9,13H/ITERATIONS, I3)
 660  FORMAT(1H2,26HLINEAR FACTOR  =  1.0  +  E16.9,3H(S))
       DIMENSION  B(100), C(100), PBA1(100), PBA2(100)
       DIMENSION CSAVE(100),A1SAVE(100),A2SAVE(100)
       COMMON N,ITER,ACC,INTPRT,IDIVLT,ASSUM1,ASSUM2,ASSUM3,ASSUM4,
      1ASSUM5,ASSUM6,GKS,B,C,PBA1,PBA2,CSAVE,A1SAVE,A2SAVE
       NORIG = N
       IFACTR = 0
       CO = 1.0
       DO 245 J=1,N
 245  CSAVE(J) = C(J)
 246  IFLIP = 0
       IASSUM = -1
       IDIV = 0
 250  IF(IASSUM)260,270,280
 260  A1 = ASSUM1
       A2 = ASSUM2
       GO TO 290
 270  A1 = ASSUM3
       A2 = ASSUM4
       GO TO 290
 280  A1 = ASSUM5
       A2 = ASSUM6
 290  DF1LST = 1.0E+30
       DF2LST = 1.0E+30
       IF(N-3)510,520,292
```

```
292   DO 425 ITERNO = 1,ITER
      B(1) = C(1) - A1
      B(2) = C(2) - A2 - A1*B(1)
      NL1 = N-1
      NL2 = N-2
      NL3 = N-3
      DO 310 K=3,NL1
      KL1 = K-1
      KL2 = K-2
310   B(K) = C(K) - A2*B(KL2) - A1*B(KL1)
      PBA1(1) = -1.0
      PBA1(2) = -B(1) + A1
      PBA2(1) = 0.0
      PBA2(2) = -1.0
      DO 320 K=3,NL1
      KL1 = K-1
      KL2 = K-2
      PBA1(K) = -A2*PBA1(KL2) - A1*PBA1(KL1) - B(KL1)
320   PBA2(K) = -A2*PBA2(KL2) - A1*PBA2(KL1) - B(KL2)
      PF1A1 = PBA1(NL1)
      PF1A2 = PBA2(NL1)
      PF2A1 = -A2 * PBA1(NL2)
      PF2A2 = -B(NL2) - A2*PBA2(NL2)
      P1 = PF1A1 * PF2A2
      P2 = PF2A1 * PF1A2
      DENOM = P1 - P2
      IF(ABSF(P1)-1.0E-30)330,340,340
330   IF(ABSF(P2)-1.0E-30)352,350,350
340   IF(ABSF(DENOM/P1)-1.0E-07)352,360,360
350   IF(ABSF(DENOM/P2) -1.0E-07)352,360,360
352   IASSUM = IASSUM +1
      IDIV = 0
      IF(IASSUM - 1)250,250,353
353   IF(IFLIP)354,354,357
354   DO 355 J=1,NL1
      NLJ = N-J
355   B(NLJ) = C(J)/C(N)
      B(N) = 1.0/C(N)
      DO 356 J=1,N
356   C(J) = B(J)
      IFLIP = 1
      IASSUM = -1
      IDIV = 0
      GO TO 250
357   PRINT 358
      DO 359 J=1,NL1
      NLJ = N-J
359   B(NLJ) = C(J)/C(N)
      B(N) = 1.0/C(N)
      BO = 1.0
      PRINT 152, BO
      PRINT 153, (J,B(J) ,J=1,N)
      RETURN
360   F1 = B(NL1)
      F2 = C(N) - A2*B(NL2)
      DELA1 =(-F1*PF2A2 + F2*PF1A2)/DENOM
      DELA2 =(-F2*PF1A1 + F1*PF2A1)/DENOM
      A1LST = A1
      A2LST = A2
      A1 = A1 + DELA1
      A2 = A2 + DELA2
      DIFFA1 = ABSF(A1-A1LST)
      DIFFA2 = ABSF(A2 - A2LST)
      TEST1 =(DIFFA1 - DF1LST)/(DIFFA1 + DF1LST)
      TEST2 = DIFFA2 - DF2LST
      IF(TEST1-1.0E-07)370,362,362
362   IDIV = IDIV + 1
      GO TO 373
370   IF(TEST2 - 1.0E-07)380,372,372
372   IDIV = IDIV + 1
373   IF(IDIV - IDIVLT)380,380,374
374   IASSUM = IASSUM + 1
      IF(IASSUM - 1)375,375,376
375   IDIV = 0
```

```
           GO TO 250
376    IF(IFLIP)377,377,357
377    IFLIP = 1
           IDIV = 0
           IASSUM = -1
           DO 378 J = 1,NL1
           NLJ = N-J
378    B(NLJ) = C(J)/C(N)
           B(N) = 1.0/C(N)
           DO 379 J=1,N
379    C(J) = B(J)
           GO TO 250
380    ACCUR = (DIFFA1 + DIFFA2)/(ABSF(A1) + ABSF(A2))
385    IF(ACCUR - ACC)430,390,390
390    IF(INTPRT)420,420,400
400    PRINT 410,ITERNO,A1,A2,ACCUR,IDIV,IFLIP,IASSUM
420    DF1LST = DIFFA1
           DF2LST = DIFFA2
425    CONTINUE
           ITERNO = ITER
430    IF(IFLIP)440,440,460
440    IFACTR = IFACTR + 1
           A1SAVE(IFACTR) = A1
           A2SAVE(IFACTR) = A2
           IF(INTPRT)480,480,442
442    PRINT 450,A1SAVE(IFACTR),A2SAVE(IFACTR),ACCUR,ITERNO
           GO TO 480
460    A1 = A1/A2
           A2 = 1.0/A2
           IFACTR = IFACTR + 1
           A1SAVE(IFACTR) = A1
           A2SAVE(IFACTR) = A2
           DO 470 J=1,NL3
           NL2LJ = NL2 - J
470    C(NL2LJ) = B(J)/B(NL2)
           C(NL2) = 1.0/B(NL2)
           IF(INTPRT)492,492,472
472    PRINT 450,A1SAVE(IFACTR),A2SAVE(IFACTR),ACCUR,ITERNO
           GO TO 492
480    DO 490 J=1,NL2
490    C(J) = B(J)
492    N = N-2
           GO TO 246
510    IFACTR = IFACTR + 1
           A1SAVE(IFACTR) = C(1)
           A2SAVE(IFACTR) = C(2)
           IF(INTPRT)666,666,512
512    PRINT 450,A1SAVE(IFACTR),A2SAVE(IFACTR),ACCUR,ITERNO
           GO TO 666
520    IF(C(3))521,522,522
521    ISIGN1 = -1
           GO TO 523
522    ISIGN1 = 1
523    A1 = 10.0
524    B(1) = C(1) - A1
           B(2) = C(2) - A1 * B(1)
           F = C(3) - A1 * B(2)
           I=0
           IF(F)525,650,526
525    ISIGN2 = -1
           GO TO 527
526    ISIGN2 = 1
527    IF(ISIGN1 + ISIGN2)528,532,528
528    IF(A1-1.0E+30)529,531,531
529    A1 = A1 * 10.0
           IF(A1+1.0E+30)5311,5311,524
531    A1 = -10.0
           GO TO 524
5311   PRINT 358
           PRINT 152,BO
           PRINT 153, (J,C(J) ,J=1,3)
532    A1ST = 0.0
           A2ND = A1
5321   A3RD = (A1ST + A2ND)/2.0
```

```
          B(1) = C(1) - A3RD
          B(2) = C(2) - A3RD*B(1)
          F = C(3) - A3RD*B(2)
          IF(INTPRT)5324,5324,5322
 5322     PRINT 5323,A3RD,F
 5323     FORMAT(1H ,22HASSUMED VALUE OF A1 =    E16.9, 19HYIELDS REMAINDER =
      1   E16.9)
 5324     IF(ABSF(F/C(3))-ACC)538,538,5326
 5326     IF(ITER-I)538,5327,5327
 5327     I=I+1
          IF(F)533,538,534
  533     ISIGN3= -1
          GO TO 535
  534     ISIGN3 = 1
  535     IF(ISIGN1 + ISIGN3)537,536,537
  536     A2ND = A3RD
          ISIGN2 = ISIGN3
          GO TO 5321
  537     A1ST = A3RD
          ISIGN1 = ISIGN3
          GO TO 5321
  538     A1 = A3RD
          ACCUR = ABSF(F/C(3))
          ITERNO = I
  650     IFACTR = IFACTR + 1
          A1SAVE(IFACTR) = B(1)
          A2SAVE(IFACTR) = B(2)
          ALAST = A1
          IF(INTPRT)654,654,652
  652     PRINT 450,A1SAVE(IFACTR),A2SAVE(IFACTR),ACCUR,ITERNO
          PRINT 660, A1
  654     IFACTR = IFACTR + 1
          A1SAVE(IFACTR) = A1
          A2SAVE(IFACTR) = 0.0
  666     ILIM = NORIG/2-1
          B(1) = A1SAVE(1)
          B(2) = A2SAVE(1)
          IF(NORIG-3)670,670,690
  670     A1 = A1SAVE(2)
          C(1) = A1 + B(1)
          C(2) = A1*B(1) + B(2)
          C(3) = A1*B(2)
          GO TO 1060
  690     N=4
          DO 1030 I=1,ILIM
          IP1 = I+1
          A1 = A1SAVE(IP1)
          A2 = A2SAVE(IP1)
          C(1) = B(1) + A1
          C(2) = B(2) + A2 + A1*B(1)
          NL1 = N-1
          NL2 = N-2
          NL3 = N-3
          IF(N-4)1020,1020,1000
 1000     DO 1010 K=3,NL2
          KL1 = K-1
          KL2 = K-2
 1010     C(K) = B(K) + A1*B(KL1) + A2*B(KL2)
 1020     C(NL1) = A1*B(NL2) + A2*B(NL3)
          C(N) = A2*B(NL2)
          DO 1025 J=1,N
 1025     B(J) = C(J)
          N = N+2
 1030     CONTINUE
          IF(NORIG + 2 - N)1060,1060,1040
 1040     A1 = ALAST
          N=NORIG
          NL1 = N-1
          C(1) = A1 + B(1)
          DO 1050 K=2,NL1
          KL1 = K-1
 1050     C(K) = B(K) + A1*B(KL1)
          C(N) = A1*B(NL1)
 1060     N=NORIG
```

```
      TESCO = 0.0
      DO 1080 J=1,N
      IF(ABSF(CSAVE(J))-1.0E-30)1080,1080,1062
 1062 TEST = ABSF((C(J) - CSAVE(J))/CSAVE(J))
      IF(TEST - TESCO)1080,1080,1064
 1064 TESCO = TEST
 1080 CONTINUE
      PRINT 1066, TESCO
 1066 FORMAT(1H0, 111HTHE FACTORS WERE MULTIPLIED TOGETHER AND THE COEFF
     1ICIENTS COMPARED WITH THE ORIGINAL POLYNOMIAL.  MAX. ERROR =
     2  E9.2)
      RETURN
      END




      SUBROUTINE A86RTS
      DIMENSION  B(100), C(100), PBA1(100), PBA2(100)
      DIMENSION CSAVE(100),A1SAVE(100),A2SAVE(100),SR(100),SI(100)
      DIMENSION GN(100),GD(100),HN(100),HD(100),GHN(100),GHD(100),GK(22)
      COMMON N,ITER,ACC,INTPRT,IDIVLT,ASSUM1,ASSUM2,ASSUM3,ASSUM4,
     1ASSUM5,ASSUM6,GKS,B,C,PBA1,PBA2,CSAVE,A1SAVE,A2SAVE
      IC=0
      NP=N/2
      PRINT 100,GKS
  100 FORMAT(1H0,35HCLOSED LOOP POLES FOR GAIN OF GH =  E17.9)
      PRINT 110
  110 FORMAT(1H0,51HREAL PART OF THE ROOT     POS.IMAG. PART OF THE ROOT)
      IF(N-1)120,130,140
  120 PRINT 121
  121 FORMAT(1H0,18HTHERE ARE NO ROOTS)
      RETURN
  130 IC = 1
      SR(1) = 1.0/A1SAVE(1)
      SI(1) = 0.0
      GO TO 205
  140 DO 200 I=1,NP
      BA= A1SAVE(I)/A2SAVE(I)
      CA= 1.0/A2SAVE(I)
      BC = BA*BA - 4.0*CA
      IF(ABSF(0.25*BC/CA) - 1.0E-07)160,160,145
  145 IF(BC)150,160,170
  150 IC = IC+1
      SR(IC) = -0.5 * BA
      SI(IC) = 0.5 * SQRTF(-BC)
      GO TO 200
  160 IC = IC +1
      SR(IC) = -0.5 * BA
      SI(IC) = 0.0
      IC = IC+1
      SR(IC) = -0.5 * BA
      SI(IC) = 0.0
      GO TO 200
  170 IC = IC+1
      BCSR = SQRTF(BC)
      SR(IC) = 0.5 * (-BA + BCSR)
      SI(IC) = 0.0
      IC = IC+1
      SR(IC) = 0.5 * (-BA - BCSR)
      SI(IC) = 0.0
  200 CONTINUE
      IF(NP*2-N)201,205,205
  201 IC = IC+1
      I = NP + 1
      SR(IC) =-1.0/A1SAVE(I)
      SI(IC) = 0.0
  205 DO 210 I=1,IC
  210 PRINT 220, SR(I), SI(I)
  220 FORMAT(1H , 2E21.9)
      RETURN
      END
```

```
TITLEA87SHK        101  J.B.VERNON
C PROGRAM A87SHK COMPUTES THE SHOCK SPECTRUM FOR A SHOCK OF THE FORM INDICATED
C IN FIG. 1-16(B). OUTPUT IS PEAK VALUE OF ACCELERATION EXPRESSED AS A FACTOR
C TIMES THE PEAK IMPUT ACCELERATION AND THE TIME AT WHICH THE PEAK ACCELERATION
C OCCURS EXPRESSED AS A FACTOR TIMES THE PULSE RISE TIME.  THESE ARE INDICATED
C FOR VARIOUS VALUES OF B*TA WHERE B IS THE NATURAL FREQUENCY IN CYCLES PER
C SECOND AND TA THE PULSE RISE TIME IN SECONDS.  INPUT IS INDICATED BY THE READ
C INPUT TAPE STATEMENTS AND THEIR FORMAT STATEMENTS, WHERE N = NUMBER OF VALUES
C OF B*TA AT WHICH THE COMPUTATION IS TO BE MADE, NT = NUMBER OF TIME INTERVALS
C INTO WHICH EACH PORTION OF THE SHOCK IS TO BE DIVIDED FOR THE PURPOSE OF
C COMPUTING THE RESPONSE IN ORDER TO DETERMINE THE MAXIMUM RESPONSE, (NT = 500
C IS SUFFICIENT FOR THE LARGEST VALUES OF B*TA LIKELY TO BE OF INTEREST.)  TB =
C DWELL TIME AS A FACTOR TIMES RISE TIME. TC = DECAY TIME AS A FACTOR TIMES RISE
C TIME.  Z = DAMPING FACTOR, FRACTION OF
C CRITICAL, MUST BE LESS THAN 1.0  B(I) ARE THE N VALUES OF B*TA FOR WHICH THE
C PEAK ACCELERATION IS TO BE COMPUTED.  THE RISE TIME CANNOT BE ZERO FOR THIS
C CALCULATION.  TO SIMULATE ZERO RISE TIME LET TB BE LARGE.  A VALUE OF 10.0 IS
C SATISFACTORY.
      PRINT 10
10    FORMAT(1H1,1H )
      DIMENSION  B(100), X(100)
      READ INPUT TAPE 5, 100, N
      READ INPUT TAPE 5, 100, NT
      READ INPUT TAPE 5, 110, TB
      READ INPUT TAPE 5, 110, TC
      READ INPUT TAPE 5, 110, Z
      READ INPUT TAPE 5, 110, (B(I),I=1,N)
      PRINT 21
21    FORMAT(1H0,18HINPUT DATA FOLLOWS)
      PRINT 22,N,NT,TB,TC,Z
22    FORMAT(1H0,4HN =  I4,9H,    NT =  I4,9H,    TB =  F6.2,9H,    TC =
     1 F6.2,8H,    Z =  F6.2)
      PRINT 23
23    FORMAT(1H0,51HVALUES OF BETA*TA ARE LISTED AS B*TA IN THE RESULTS)
      PRINT 20
20    FORMAT(1H0,35HBEGIN COMPUTATION OF SHOCK SPECTRUM)
      PRINT 30
30    FORMAT(1H ,98HB*TA    TIME FOR PEAK   PEAK ACCEL.   TIME FOR PEAK
     1 PEAK ACCELER.  TIME FOR PEAK   PEAK ACCELER.       )
      PRINT 31
31    FORMAT(1H0,98H            PRIMARY SHOCK  PRIMARY SHOCK   RESIDUAL POS.
     1 PESIDUAL POS.  RESIDUAL NEG.  RESIDUAL NEG.       )
100   FORMAT(I4)
110   FORMAT(F6.2)
      ZS = SQRTF(1.0 - Z*Z)
      FNT = FLOATF(NT)
      DTB = TB/FNT
      DTC = TC/FNT
      SXPF(TS) = EXPF(-Z*BT*TS) * SINF(ZS*BT*TS)
      CXPF(TS) = EXPF(-Z*BT*TS) * COSF(ZS*BT*TS)
      DO 240 I=1,N
      T = 1.0
      X(I) = 0.0
      BT = B(I) * 6.2832
      CONST = 1.0/BT/ZS
      X(I) = T - 1.0/BT/ZS*SXPF(T)
      XT = X(I)
      TX = 1.0
      IF(TB - 1.0E-07)165,165,145
145   T = 1.0 + DTB
      DO 160 J=1,NT
      TLTA = T - 1.0
      XT = (1.0 +   CONST   * (SXPF(TLTA) - SXPF(T)))
      T = T + DTB
      IF(XT - X(I))160,160,150
150   X(I) = XT
      TX = T - DTB
160   CONTINUE
165   IF(TC - 1.0E-07)225,225,200
200   T = 1.0 + TB + DTC
      DO 220 J=1,NT
      TLTAB = T - 1.0 - TB
      TLTA  = T - 1.0
      XT =  1.0 +   CONST   * (SXPF(TLTA) - SXPF(T))
```

```
      1 - 1.0/TC * (TLTAB - 1.0/BT/ZS * SXPF(TLTAB))
      T = T + DTC
      IF(XT - X(I))220,220,210
 210  X(I) = XT
      TX = T - DTC
 220  CONTINUE
 225  XP = XT
      XN = XT
      DT = 0.1/BT
      T = 1.0 + TB + TC + DT
      TLTC = T-1.0-TB-TC
      TLTB = T-1.0-TB
      TLTA = T-1.0
      IF(TC-1.0E-07)2251,2251,2252
 2251 XT = CONST*(SXPF(TLTA)-SXPF(T)) + CXPF(TLTB) -Z/ZS*SXPF(TLTB)
      GO TO 2253
 2252 XT =    CONST  *(SXPF(TLTA)-SXPF(T)-1.0/TC*(SXPF(TLTC)-SXPF(TLTB)))
 2253 IF(XT-XP)232,2391,226
 226  DO 228 J=1,NT
      TLTC = T-1.0-TB-TC
      TLTB = T-1.0-TB
      TLTA = T-1.0
      IF(TC-1.0E-07)2261,2261,2262
 2261 XT = CONST*(SXPF(TLTA)-SXPF(T)) + CXPF(TLTB) -Z/ZS*SXPF(TLTB)
      GO TO 2263
 2262 XT =    CONST  *(SXPF(TLTA)-SXPF(T)-1.0/TC*(SXPF(TLTC)-SXPF(TLTB)))
 2263 IF(XT-XP)229,227,227
 227  XP = XT
      TP = T
      T = T + DT
 228  CONTINUE
 229  T = T + DT
      XN = XP
      DO 231 J=1,NT
      TLTC = T-1.0-TB-TC
      TLTB = T-1.0-TB
      TLTA = T-1.0
      IF(TC-1.0E-07)2291,2291,2292
 2291 XT = CONST*(SXPF(TLTA)-SXPF(T)) + CXPF(TLTB) -Z/ZS*SXPF(TLTB)
      GO TO 2293
 2292 XT =    CONST  *(SXPF(TLTA)-SXPF(T)-1.0/TC*(SXPF(TLTC)-SXPF(TLTB)))
 2293 IF(XT-XN)230,230,238
 230  XN = XT
      TN = T
      T = T + DT
 231  CONTINUE
      GO TO 238
 232  DO 234 J=1,NT
      TLTC = T-1.0-TB-TC
      TLTB = T-1.0-TB
      TLTA = T-1.0
      IF(TC-1.0E-07)2321,2321,2322
 2321 XT = CONST*(SXPF(TLTA)-SXPF(T)) + CXPF(TLTB) -Z/ZS*SXPF(TLTB)
      GO TO 2323
 2322 XT =    CONST  *(SXPF(TLTA)-SXPF(T)-1.0/TC*(SXPF(TLTC)-SXPF(TLTB)))
 2323 IF(XT-XN)233,233,235
 233  XN = XT
      TN = T
      T = T + DT
 234  CONTINUE
 235  T = T + DT
      XP = XN
      DO 237 J=1,NT
      TLTC = T-1.0-TB-TC
      TLTB = T-1.0-TB
      TLTA = T-1.0
      IF(TC - 1.0E-07)2351,2351,2352
 2351 XT = CONST*(SXPF(TLTA)-SXPF(T)) + CXPF(TLTB) -Z/ZS*SXPF(TLTB)
      GO TO 2353
 2352 XT =    CONST     *(SXPF(TLTA)-SXPF(T)-1.0/TC*(SXPF(TLTC)-SXPF(TLTB)))
 2353 IF(XT-XP)238,236,236
 236  XP = XT
      TP = T
      T = T + DT
```

```
237   CONTINUE
238   PRINT 239,B(I),TX,X(I),TP,XP,TN,XN
239   FORMAT(1H ,F6.3,F12.3,5F15.3)
      GO TO 240
2391  PRINT 2392
2392  FORMAT(1H ,22HRESIDUAL SHOCK IS ZERO)
240   CONTINUE
      PRINT 250
250   FORMAT(1H1,33HEND OF SHOCK SPECTRUM CALCULATION)
      STOP
      END
```

```
TITLED52FR            101   J. B. VERNON
C THIS PROGRAM COMPUTES THE FREQUENCY RESPONSE FOR THE TRANSFER FUNCTIONS
C G, H, 1/H, GH, AND G/(1+GH).  OUTPUT IS THE VALUE OF EACH OF THESE AT VARIOUS
C FREQUENCIES IN THE REGION FOR WHICH THE ABSOLUTE VALUE OF G OR 1/H (WHICHEVER
C IS LOWER) IS WITHIN THE RANGE OF PLUS OR MINUS 80 DECIBELS.  EACH LINE OF
C OUTPUT SPECIFIES A COMPLEX NUMBER IN THE FORM OF ITS REAL AND IMAGINARY PARTS,
C ITS ABSOLUTE VALUE (NUMERIC AND DECIBEL), AND ITS ANGLE.  INPUT DATA IS READ
C FROM TAPE 1 IN ACCORDANCE WITH THE READ TAPE 1 STATEMENTS BELOW.  SEE PROGRAM
C D91PRE FOR DEFINITIONS OF THE VARIABLES.
      DIMENSION F(28),TNG(20),QGNS(20),QGNSS(20),TDG(20),QGDS(20)
      DIMENSION QGDSS(20),TNH(20),QHNS(20),QHNSS(20),TDH(20),QHDS(20)
      DIMENSION QHDSS(20)
      COMMON    TNG,QGNS,QGNSS,TDG,QGDS,QGDSS,TNH,QHNS,QHNSS,TDH,QHDS,
     1QHDSS,NEXPG,NEXPH,NLNG,NQNG,NLDG,NQDG,NLNH,NQNH,NLDH,NQDH,GAING,
     2GAINH,F,NG,NH,LF,GR,GI,GAB,GDB,GANG,HR,HI,HAB,HDB,HANG,HINR,HINI,
     3HINAB,HINDB,HINANG,CRR,CRI,CRAB,CRDB,CRANG,B,GHR,GHI,GHAB,GHDB,
     4GHANG
      REWIND 1
      F(1) = 1.1
      DO 10 I = 2,6
      IL1 = I - 1
10    F(I) = F(IL1) + 0.1
      DO 20 I = 7,18
      IL1 = I - 1
20    F(I) = F(IL1) + 0.2
      DO 30 I = 19,26
      IL1 = I - 1
30    F(I) = F(IL1) + 0.5
      F(27) = 9.0
      F(28) = 10.0
      READ TAPE 1,GAING,NEXPG
      READ TAPE 1,GAINH,NEXPH
      READ TAPE 1,NLNG,NQNG
      IF(NLNG)125,125,120
120   READ  TAPE 1, (TNG(I),I=1,NLNG)
125   IF(NQNG)135,135,130
130   READ   TAPE 1, (QGNS(I),QGNSS(I)  ,I=1,NQNG)
135   READ TAPE 1,NLDG,NQDG
      IF(NLDG)145,145,140
140   READ   TAPE 1,(TDG(I),I=1,NLDG)
145   IF(NQDG)155,155,150
150   READ   TAPE 1,  (QGDS(I),QGDSS(I)  ,I=1,NQDG)
155   READ   TAPE 1,NLNH,NQNH
      IF(NLNH)165,165,160
160   READ   TAPE 1,(TNH(I),I=1,NLNH)
165   IF(NQNH)175,175,170
170   READ   TAPE 1,  (QHNS(I),QHNSS(I)  ,I=1,NQNH)
175   READ   TAPE 1,NLDH,NQDH
      IF(NLDH)185,185,180
180   READ   TAPE 1, (TDH(I),I=1,NLDH)
185   IF(NQDH)191,191,190
190   READ   TAPE 1,  (QHDS(I),QHDSS(I)  ,I=1,NQDH)
191   PRINT 192
192   FORMAT(1H1,1H )
      PRINT 193
193   FORMAT(1H0,11HSTART D52FR)
      IF(NLNG-NQNG)1951,1951,1952
```

```
1951 NG=NQNG
     GO TO 1953
1952 NG=NLNG
1953 IF(NG-NLDG)1954,1955,1955
1954 NG=NLDG
1955 IF(NG-NQDG)1956,196,196
1956 NG = NQDG
196  IF(NLNH-NQNH)1961,1961,1962
1961 NH = NQNH
     GO TO 1963
1962 NH = NLNH
1963 IF(NH-NLDH)1964,1965,1965
1964 NH=NLDH
1965 IF(NH-NQDH)1966,197,197
1966 NH=NQDH
197  IF(XABSF(NEXPG)-XABSF(NEXPH))200,200,210
200  LS = -30/XABSF(NEXPH)
     GO TO 220
210  LS = -30/XABSF(NEXPG)
220  MG = NLNG + 2* NQNG - NLDG - 2*NQDG
     MH =-NLNH - 2* NQNH + NLDH + 2*NQDH
     IF(XABSF(MG)-XABSF(MH))230,230,240
230  LE = 30/(XABSF(MH) + 3)
     GO TO 245
240  LE = 30/(XABSF(MG) + 3)
245  L = LS
250  B = 1.0 * 10.0**L
260  IF(1.0 * 10.0**LE - B)340,270,270
270  CALL D52CN
     IF(GDB - HINDB)280,280,290
280  TEST = GDB
     GO TO 300
290  TEST = HINDB
300  IF(ABSF(TEST) - 80.0)320,320,310
310  L = L+1
     GO TO 250
320  LF = L-1
     PRINT 311
311  FORMAT(1H1,1H )
     PRINT 312
312  FORMAT(1H ,87HFUNCTION    FREQUENCY    REAL PART    IMAG. PART  ABS
    1.VAL,NUM   ABS.VAL,DB    ANGLE   DEG  )
     DO 330 I=1,28
     B = F(I) * 10.0**LF
     CALL D52CN
     PRINT 322,B,GR,GI,GAB,GDB,GANG
322  FORMAT(1H ,8HG          4E13.3,2F13.2
     PRINT 323,B,HR,HI,HAB,HDB,HANG
323  FORMAT(1H ,8HH          4E13.3,2F13.2)
     PRINT 324,B,HINR,HINI,HINAB,HINDB,HINANG
324  FORMAT(1H ,8H1/H        4E13.3,2F13.2
     PRINT 325,B,GHR,GHI,GHAB,GHDB,GHANG
325  FORMAT(1H ,8HGH         4E13.3,2F13.2)
     PRINT 326,B,CRR,CRI,CRAB,CRDB,CRANG
326  FORMAT(1H0,8HG/(1+GH) 4E13.3,2F13.2)
330  CONTINUE
     L=L+1
     GO TO 250
340  PRINT 350
350  FORMAT(1H1,18HEND OF COMPUTATION)
     STOP
     END



     SUBROUTINE D52CN
     DIMENSION F(28),TNG(20),QGNS(20),QGNSS(20),TDG(20),QGDS(20)
     DIMENSION QGDSS(20),TNH(20),QHNS(20),QHNSS(20),TDH(20),QHDS(20)
     DIMENSION QHDSS(20)
     COMMON    TNG,QGNS,QGNSS,TDG,QGDS,QGDSS,TNH,QHNS,QHNSS,TDH,QHDS,
    1QHDSS,NEXPG,NEXPH,NLNG,NQNG,NLDG,NQDG,NLNH,NQNH,NLDH,NQDH,GAING,
    2GAINH,F,NG,NH,LF,GR,GI,GAB,GDB,GANG,HR,HI,HAB,HDB,HANG,HINR,HINI,
```

```
     3HINAB,HINDB,HINANG,CRR,CRI,CRAB,CRDB,CRANG,B,GHR,GHI,GHAB,GHDB,
     4GHANG
       TWL = 20.0/LOGF(10.0)
       NEOG = NEXPG/2 * 2
       IF(NEXPG - NEOG)510,520,510
510    GR = 0.0
       NEOG=(NEXPG-1)/2
       GI = GAING * B**NEXPG * (-1.0)**NEOG
       GO TO 530
520    GI = 0.0
       NEOG = NEXPG/2
       GR = GAING * B**NEXPG * (-1.0)**NEOG
530    NEOH = NEXPH/2*2
       IF(NEXPH - NEOH)540,550,540
540    HR = 0.0
       NEOH =(NEXPH-1)/2
       HI = GAINH * B**NEXPH * (-1.0)**NEOH
       GO TO 560
550    HI = 0.0
       NEOH= NEXPH/2
       HR = GAINH * B**NEXPH * (-1.0)**NEOH
560    DO 640 J=1,NG
       IF(NLNG-J+1)580,580,570
570    AR = GR - GI*TNG(J)*B
       GI = GI + GR*TNG(J)*B
       GR = AR
580    IF(NLDG-J+1)600,600,590
590    DE = 1.0+B*B*TDG(J)*TDG(J)
       AR =(GR + GI*TDG(J)*B)/DE
       GI =(GI- GR*TDG(J)*B)/DE
       GR=AR
600    IF(NQNG-J+1)620,620,610
610    C = 1.0 - QGNSS(J)*B*B
       AR = GR*C - GI*QGNS(J)*B
       GI = GI*C + GR*QGNS(J)*B
       GR = AR
620    IF(NQDG-J+1)640,640,630
630    C = 1.0 - QGDSS(J)*B*B
       DE = C*C + QGDS(J)*QGDS(J)*B*B
       AR =(GR*C + GI*QGDS(J)*B)/DE
       GI =(GI*C - GR*QGDS(J)*B)/DE
       GR = AR
640    CONTINUE
       DO 720 J=1,NH
       IF(NLNH-J+1)660,660,650
650    AR = HR - HI*TNH(J)*B
       HI = HI + HR*TNH(J)*B
       HR = AR
660    IF(NLDH-J+1)680,680,670
670    DE = 1.0 + B*B*TDH*TDH
       AR =(HR + HI*TDH(J)*B)/DE
       HI =(HI - HR*TDH(J)*B)/DE
       HR = AR
680    IF(NQNH-J+1)700,700,690
690    C = 1.0 -QHNSS(J)*B*B
       AR = HR*C - HI*QHNS(J)*B
       HI = HI*C + HR*QHNS(J)*B
       HR = AR
700    IF(NQDH-J+1)720,720,710
710    C = 1.0 - QHDSS(J)*B*B
       DE = C*C + QHDS(J)*QHDS(J)*B*B
       AR =(HR*C + HI*QHDS(J)*B)/DE
       HI =(HI*C - HR*QHDS(J)*B)/DE
       HR = AR
720    CONTINUE
       HINR = HR/(HR*HR + HI*HI)
       HINI = -HI/(HR*HR + HI*HI)
       GHR = GR*HR - GI*HI
       GHI = GR*HI + GI*HR
       GHRP1 = GHR + 1.0
       DE = GHRP1*GHRP1 + GHI*GHI
       CRR = (GR*GHRP1 + GI*GHI)/DE
       CRI = (GI*GHRP1 - GR*GHI)/DE
       IX = 0
```

```
725    IX = IX+1
       GO TO (730,740,750,760,770,890),IX
730    AR = GR
       AI = GI
       GO TO 780
740    AR = HR
       AI = HI
       GO TO 780
750    AR = HINR
       AI = HINI
       GO TO 780
760    AR = GHR
       AI = GHI
       GO TO 780
770    AR = CRR
       AI = CRI
780    AB = SQRTF(AR*AR + AI*AI)
       DB = TWL * LOGF(AB)
       ANG = ATANF(AI/AR) * 360.0/2.0/3.1416
       IF(AI)790,810,810
790    IF(AR)800,830,830
800    ANG = ANG - 180.0
       GO TO 830
810    IF(AR)820,830,830
820    ANG = ANG+ 180.0
830    GO TO (840,850,860,870,880),IX
840    GAB = AB
       GDB = DB
       GANG = ANG
       GO TO 725
850    HAB = AB
       HDB = DB
       HANG = ANG
       GO TO 725
860    HINAB = AB
       HINDB = DB
       HINANG = ANG
       GO TO 725
870    GHAB = AB
       GHDB = DB
       GHANG = ANG
       GO TO 725
880    CRAB = AB
       CRDB = DB
       CRANG = ANG
       GO TO 725
890    RETURN
       END
```

```
TITLED86FT        101  J.B.VERNON
C     THIS PROGRAM COMPUTES EITHER THE FOURIER TRANSFORM FOR A PULSE OR THE
C COEFFICIENTS OF THE FOURIER SERIES FOR A REPEATING PULSE.  INPUT DATA SHOULD
C BE IN ACCORDANCE WITH THE READ INPUT TAPE STATEMENTS.  IFT  IS AN INDICATOR
C TELLING WHETHER THE COMPUTATION IS FOR THE TRANSFORM OR THE SERIES.  IFT
C SHOULD BE ZEROIF THE TRANSFORM IS COMPUTED AND A POSITIVE NUMBER IF THE SERIES
C IS TO BE COMPUTED.  WS  AND  WE  ARE THE LOWER AND UPPER LIMITS FOR THE
C FREQUENCY VARIABLE IN THE TRANSFORM CALCULATION, BOTH POSITIVE NUMBERS.  (THE
C NEGATIVE RANGE WILL BE CALCULATED AUTOMATICALLY FOR THE SAME LIMITS.)   NW   IS
C THE NUMBER OF INTERVALS INTO WHICH THE FREQUENCY RANGE SHOULD BE DIVIDED IF
C THE CALCULATION IS FOR THE TRANSFORM, OR IT IS THE NUMBER OF HARMONICS
C DESIRED IF THE SERIES IS BEING COMPUTED.  DATA FOR THE PULSE ARE SPECIFIED BY
C T() AND F(), WHERE T IS THE INDEPENDENT VARIABLE AND F THE VALUE OF THE
C FUNCTION AT VALUES OF T.  STRAIGHT LINE INTERPOLATION IS ASSUMED.  AFTER THE
C LAST DATA CARD USE A CARD WITH  1  PUNCHED IN COLUMN 36 TO SIGNAL THE END OF
C DATA.  OUTPUT FOR THE FOURIER TRANSFORM IS THE REAL AND IMAGINARY PARTS OF
C G(W) = INTEGRAL FROM - INFINITY TO + INFINITY OF
C F(T) * EXP(-W*T*SQRTF(-1))*DT, W IS IN RADIANS/UNIT OF T.  OUTPUT FOR THE
C FOURIER SERIES IS THE COEFFICIENTS OF THE SERIES
C A(0) + A(K)*COS(K*2*PI*T/PERIOD) + B(K)*SIN(K*2*PI*T/PERIOD).
       REWIND 1
```

```
      DIMENSION T(1000),F(1000)
      READ INPUT TAPE 5, 80, IFT
      WRITE TAPE 1,IFT
 80   FORMAT(I4)
      READ INPUT TAPE 5,80,IDTA
      IF(IFT)82,82,85
 82   READ INPUT TAPE 5,100,WS,WE
      WRITE TAPE 1,WS,WE
 85   READ INPUT TAPE 5,80,NW
      WRITE TAPE 1,NW
      IF(IDTA)99,99,92
 92   PRINT 93
 93   FORMAT(1H0,18HINPUT DATA FOLLOWS)
      IF(IFT)94,94,95
 94   PRINT 941,WS,WE,NW
 941  FORMAT(1H0, 5HWS =  E17.9, 7H  WE =  E17.9, 8H   NW = I4)
      GO TO 97
 95   PRINT 96, NW
 96   FORMAT(1H0,38HFOURIER SERIES,NUMBER OF HARMONICS =      I4)
 97   PRINT 98
 98   FORMAT(1H0,34H        TIME, T        FUNCTION, F(T) )
 99   DO 110 I=1,1000
      READ INPUT TAPE 5,100,T(I),F(I),IEXIT
 100  FORMAT(2E17.9,I4)
      IF(IEXIT)104,104,120
 104  IF(IDTA)110,110,105
 105  PRINT 107,T(I),F(I)
 107  FORMAT(1H ,2E17.5)
 110  CONTINUE
 120  N = I - 1
      PRINT 130
 130  FORMAT(1H1,1H )
      PRINT 140
 140  FORMAT(1H0,14HRESULTS FOLLOW)
      IF(IFT)142,142,152
 142  PRINT 150
 150  FORMAT(1H0,50H       (OMEGA, W)       (G(W),REAL) (G(W),IMAGINARY))
      GO TO 155
 152  PRINT 153
 153  FORMAT(1H0,50HHARMONIC   COEFF. OF COS. TERM  COEFF. OF SIN TERM )
 155  GR = 0.0
      NL1 = N - 1
      DO 160 I=1,NL1
      IP1 = I+1
 160  GR = GR + 0.5 * (F(I) + F(IP1))*(T(IP1) - T(I))
      W = 0.0
      GI = 0.0
      IF(IFT)162,162,166
 162  PRINT 164,W,GR,GI
      WRITE TAPE 1,W,GR,GI
 164  FORMAT(1H , 3E17.4)
      W = WS
      ISN = 1
      FNW = FLOATF(NW)
      DW = (WE - WS)/FNW
      GO TO 171
 166  GR = GR/(T(N) - T(1))
      PRINT 168,GR
 168  FORMAT(1H ,11HCONSTANT =  E17.4)
      TPI = 2.0*3.14159265
      TNLT1 = T(N) - T(1)
 171  DO 200 I=1,NW
      FI = FLOATF(I)
      IF(IFT)173,173,172
 172  W = TPI*FI/TNLT1
      GO TO 174
 173  W = W + DW
 174  WIN = 1.0/W
      GR = 0.0
      GI = 0.0
      DO 180 J=1,NL1
      JP1 = J+1
      IF(ABSF((T(JP1)-T(J)))/(ABSF(T(JP1))+ABSF(T(J)))-1.0E-07)180,180,
     1175
```

```
175   SN1 = SINF(W*T(J))
      SN2 = SINF(W*T(JP1))
      CN1 = COSF(W*T(J))
      CN2 = COSF(W*T(JP1))
      TSN1 = T(J) * SN1
      TSN2 = T(JP1) * SN2
      TCN1 = T(J) * CN1
      TCN2 = T(JP1) * CN2
      FT = (F(JP1) - F(J))/(T(JP1) - T(J))
      TFT = (T(JP1) * F(J) - T(J) * F(JP1))/(T(JP1) - T(J))
      SN = SN2 - SN1
      CN = CN2 - CN1
      TSN = TSN2 - TSN1
      TCN = TCN2 - TCN1
      GR = GR + TFT * SN + FT * (TSN + WIN   * CN)
      GI = GI + TFT * CN + FT * (TCN - WIN   * SN)
180   CONTINUE
      IF(IFT)186,186,181
181   GR = 2.0*GR/TNLT1/W
      GI = 2.0*GI/TNLT1/W
      PRINT 184,I,GR,GI
184   FORMAT(1H ,I5,2E21.4)
      WRITE TAPE 1,I,GR,GI
      GO TO 200
186   GR = GR/W
      GI = GI/W
      PRINT 164,W,GR,GI
      WRITE TAPE 1,W,GR,GI
200   CONTINUE
      IF(IFT)202,202,220
202   IF(ISN)220,210,210
210   ISN = -1
      DW = -DW
      W = -WS
      GO TO 171
220   PRINT 230
230   FORMAT(1H1,26HEND OF FOURIER COMPUTATION)
      STOP
      END
```

```
TITLED87IFT        101   J.B.VERNON
C     THIS PROGRAM WILL COMPUTE THE FUNCTION OF  T  WHICH IS THE INVERSE FOURIER
C TRANSFORM OF A FUNCTION OF OMEGA.  INPUT DATA MUST BE STORED ON TAPE 1 BY
C ANOTHER PROGRAM IN ACCORDANCE WITH THE READ TAPE 1 STATEMENTS.  IDTA SHOULD BE
C 1 IF INPUT DATA IS TO BE PRINTED,ZERO OTHERWISE.  TS AND TE ARE LOWER AND UPPER
C LIMITS OF THE RANGE OF T FOR WHICH THE COMPUTATION IS TO BE MADE, POSITIVE
C NUMBERS.  (THE NEGATIVE RANGE IS ACCOUNTED FOR AUTOMATICALLY.)  NT  IS THE
C NUMBER OF INTERVALS INTO WHICH THE RANGE OF  T  IS DIVIDED.  W  IS THE VALUE
C OF OMEGA FOR WHICH THE FUNCTIONS  GR  AND  GI  ARE THE REAL AND IMAGINARY
C PARTS OF THE FOURIER TRANSFORM.  STRAIGHT LINE INTERPOLATION IS ASSUMED
C BETWEEN VALUES OF  W  AT WHICH  GR  AND  GI  ARE GIVEN.  AFTER THE LAST DATA
C CARD USE A CARD WITH  1  PUNCHED IN COLUMN 54 TO SIGNAL THE END OF DATA.
C OUTPUT OF THE COMPUTATION IS PRINTED AS REAL AND IMAGINARY PARTS OF THE
C FUNCTION OF  T.  (THE IMAGINARY PART SHOULD BE ZERO IF THE TRANSFORM WAS OF A
C REAL VARIABLE.)  DEFINITION OF THE INVERSE TRANSFORM IS
C F(T) = INTEGRAL FROM -INFINITY TO +INFINITY OF
C G(W) * EXP(T*W*SQRTF(-1)) * DW, W IN RADIANS/UNIT OF T.
      DIMENSION W(1000),GR(1000),GI(1000)
      REWIND 1
      PRINT 100
100   FORMAT(1H1,1H )
      PRINT 110
110   FORMAT(1H0,33HSTART FOURIER INVERSE CALCULATION)
      READ TAPE 1,IDTA
      IF(IDTA)160,160,130
130   PRINT 140
140   FORMAT(1H0,19HINPUT DATA FOLLOWS.)
      PRINT 150
150   FORMAT(1H0,49H   (OMEGA, W)        (G, REAL)        (G,IMAGINARY)   )
```

```
160   READ TAPE 1, TS,TE
      READ TAPE 1,NT
      DO 173 I=1,1000
      READ TAPE 1,W(I),GR(I),GI(I),IEND
      IF(IEND)171,171,174
171   IF(IDTA)173,173,172
172   PRINT 190,W(I),GR(I),GI(I)
173   CONTINUE
174   N = I - 1
      NL1 = N-1
      FR = 0.0
      FI = 0.0
      TPIN = 1.0/2.0/3.14159265
      DO 176 J = 1,NL1
      JP1 = J+1
      DELW = W(JP1) - W(J)
      FR = FR + DELW *(GR(J) + GR(JP1))
176   FI = FI + DELW *(GI(J) + GI(JP1))
      FR = FR*TPIN*0.5
      FI = FI*TPIN*0.5
      PRINT 178
178   FORMAT(1H0,29HRESULTS OF CALCULATION FOLLOW)
      PRINT 180
180   FORMAT(1H0,48H     (TIME, T)        (F(T),REAL)   (F(T),IMAGINARY)   )
      T = 0.0
      PRINT 190,T,FR,FI
190   FORMAT(1H ,E12.4,E16.4,E17.4)
      ISN = 1
      FNT = FLOATF(NT)
      DT = (TE - TS)/FNT
195   T = TS + DT
      DO 210 I=1,NT
      T = T + DT
      TIN = 1.0/T
      FR = 0.0
      FI = 0.0
      DO 200  J=1,NL1
      JP1 = J+1
      IF(ABSF((W(JP1)-W(J)))/(ABSF(W(JP1))+ABSF(W(J)))-1.0E-07)200,200,
     1198
198   SN1 = SINF(T*W(J))
      SN2 = SINF(T*W(JP1))
      CN1 = COSF(T*W(J))
      CN2 = COSF(T*W(JP1))
      SN = SN2 - SN1
      CN = CN2 - CN1
      DELW = W(JP1) - W(J)
      WGR = (W(JP1)*GR(J) - W(J)*GR(JP1))/DELW
      GWR = (GR(JP1) - GR(J))/DELW
      WGI = (W(JP1)*GI(J) - W(J)*GI(JP1))/DELW
      GWI = (GI(JP1) - GI(J))/DELW
      WSN1 = W(J)*SN1
      WSN2 = W(JP1) * SN2
      WCN1 = W(J) * CN1
      WCN2 = W(JP1) * CN2
      WSN = WSN2 - WSN1
      WCN = WCN2 - WCN1
      FR = WGR*SN+GWR*(WSN+TIN*CN)+WGI*CN+GWI*(WCN-TIN*SN) + FR
      FI = WGI*SN+GWI*(WSN+TIN*CN)-WGR*CN-GWR*(WCN-TIN*SN) + FI
200   CONTINUE
      TPIT = TPIN*TIN
      FR = FR*TPIT
      FI = FI*TPIT
      PRINT 190,T,FR,FI
210   CONTINUE
      IF(ISN)230,230,220
220   DT = -DT
      TS = - TS
      ISN = -1
      GO TO 195
230   PRINT 240
240   FORMAT(1H1,44HEND OF FOURIER INVERSE TRANSFORM COMPUTATION)
      STOP
      END
```

```
TITLED91PRE        101 J.B.VERNON
C     THIS PROGRAM PREPARES DATA FOR PROGRAMS E11TRN, D52FR, AND D91RTL.  SEE
C THESE PROGRAMS FOR ADDITIONAL COMMENTS.  PROGRAM D91RTL REQUIRES THE TRANSFER
C FUNCTION IN POLYNOMIAL FORM, D52FR IN FACTORED FORM, AND E11TRN MIXED FACTORED
C AND POLYNOMIAL.  DATA MAY BE SUPPLIED TO THIS PROGRAM (D91PRE) IN EITHER ALL-
C FACTORED OR ALL-POLYNOMIAL FORM, AND THIS PROGRAM CONVERTS IT TO THE APPRO-
C PRIATE FORM.   DATA MUST BE SPECIFIED IN ACCORDANCE WITH THE READ
C INPUT TAPE STATEMENTS AND THEIR FORMATS, WHERE THE VARIABLES ARE NOW DEFINED.
C INPUT IS AN INDEX TELLING WHETHER THE FUNCTIONS OF S ARE IN FACTORED OR
C POLYNOMIAL FORM.  INPUT SHOULD BE ZERO IF G AND H ARE IN FACTORED FORM AND A
C POSITIVE NUMBER IF IN POLYNOMIAL FORM.  IOUTPT IS AN INDEX SPECIFYING HOW THE
C OUTPUT IS TO BE PREPARED FOR THE FOLLOWING PROGRAM..  IF IOUTPT IS A POSITIVE
C NUMBER, THE DATA WILL BE PREPARED FOR D91RTL, IF ZERO FOR D52FR, AND IF
C NEGATIVE FOR E11TRN.  THE VARIABLES ITER, ACC, ETC. THROUGH ASSUM6 ARE DEFINED
C IN PROGRAM A86FP.  ENTER REALISTIC VALUES FOR THESE VARIABLES EVEN IF INPUT IS
C ALREADY FACTORED.  THE REST OF THE READ INPUT TAPE STATEMENTS SPECIFY THE
C TRANSFER FUNCTIONS  G  AND  H, IF THE FOLLOWING PROGRAMS ARE D52FR OR D91RTL,
C OR JUST  G  IF THE FOLLOWING PROGRAM IS E11TRN.  (NO  H  IS USED FOR E11TRN,
C AND  G  ITSELF IS THE OVERALL  CLOSED LOOP TRANSFER FUNCTION.  FOR D52FR OR
C D91RTL,  G  IS ONLY THE FORWARD FUNCTION AND  H  IS THE FEEDBACK FUNCTION.)
C     IF THE INPUT IS IN FACTORED FORM, THE READ INPUT TAPE STATEMENTS STARTING
C WITH STATEMENT  40  AND ENDING WITH  190  APPLY, AND THE DATA MUST BE IN THE
C FORM INDICATED BELOW.  G  OR  H  IS SPECIFIED AS
C GAIN CONSTANT * (S**N) * PRODUCT OF NUMERATOR FACTORS/PRODUCT OF DENOMINATORS
C FACTORS , WHERE THE FACTORS ARE OF THE FORM (1+TS) FOR LINEAR FACTORS AND
C (1+AS+BS**2) FOR QUADRACTIC FACTORS.  DATA SHOULD BE SUPPLIED IN ACCORDANCE
C WITH FORMAT STATEMENTS 100,110, OR 115 AS INDICATED BY THE READ INPUT TAPE
C STATEMENTS.  THE VARIABLES ARE DEFINED BELOW.
C     GAING = GAIN CONSTANT FOR G
C     NEXPG = EXPONENT OF S IN G
C     GAINH = GAIN CONSTANT FOR H
C     NEXPH = EXPONENT OF S IN H
C     NLNG = NUMBER OF LINEAR FACTORS IN THE NUMERATOR OF G
C     NQNG = NUMBER OF QUADRATIC FACTORS IN THE NUMERATOR OF G
C     ETC.
C     TNG(I) = COEFFICIENT OF S IN ITH LINEAR FACTOR OF NUMERATOR OF G
C     QGNS(I) = COEFFICIENT OF S IN ITH QUADRATIC FACTOR OF NUMERATOR OF G
C     QGNSS(I) = COEFF. OF S SQUARED IN ITH QUADRATIC FACTOR OF NUMERATOR OF G
C     ETC.
C IF ANY OF THE ABOVE FACTORS ARE REPEATED (LINEAR OR QUADRATIC) THEY SHOULD BE
C ENTERED AS SEPARATE FACTORS AS MANY TIMES AS THE EXPONENT OF THE REPEATED
C FACTOR.
CIN ACCORDANCE WITH THESE CONVENTIONS THE FOLLOWING SAMPLE DATA DECK WOULD BE
C REQUIRED FOR THE SYSTEM FOR WHICH
C     G = 10.*(1.+.1*S)*(1.+1.*S+1.*S**2)/S**2*(1.+2.*S)(1.+4.*S)
C     H = S/1.+.01*S)
C
C 0                                      (INPUT)
C 1                                      (IOUTPT)
C90                                      (ITER)
C          1.0E-07                       (ACC)
C 1                                      (INTPRT
C 25                                     (IDIVLT)
C          1.0E+00                       (ASSUM1)
C          1.0E+00                       (ASSUM2)
C          1.0E+00                       (ASSUM3)
C         -1.0E+00                       (ASSUM4)
C          1.0E+00                       (ASSUM5)
C         10.0E+00                       (ASSUM6)
C         10.0E+00                       (GAING)
C-2                                      (NEXPG)
C          1.0E+00                       (GAINH)
C 1                                      (NEXPH)
C 1                                      (NLNG)
C 1                                      (NQNG)
C 2                                      (NLDG)
C 1                                      (NQDG)
C 0                                      (NLNH)
C 0                                      (NQNH)
C 1                                      (NLDH)
C 0                                      (NQDH)
C          0.1E+00                       (TNG(1))
C          1.0E+00       1.0E+00         (QGNS(1) AND QGNSS(1))
C          2.0E+00                       (TDG(1))
```

```
C              4.0E+00                           (TDG(2))
C              1.0E-02                           (TDH(1))
C
C       IF  G  AND  H  ARE IN POLYNOMIAL FORM, THE PORTION OF THE PROGRAM
C BEGINNING WITH STATEMENT 210 AND ENDING WITH 390 IS APPLICABLE.
C G  AND  H  ARE OF THE FORM   G ' NUMERATOR/DENOMINATOR, WHERE NUMERATOR OF  G
C IS OF THE FORM
C GAING *(S**NEXPG)*(1+GN(1)*S + GN(2)*S**2+...+GN(NORNG)*S**NORNG)
C AND THE DENOMINATOR OF THE FORM
C (1+GD(1)*S+GD(2)*S**2+...+GD(NORDG)*S**NORDG)
C SIMILAR EXPRESSIONS APPLY FOR H, BUT USING THE VARIABLES GAINH, NEXPH, HN, HD,
C NORNH, NORDH.  IN ACCORDANCE WITH THESE CONVENTIONS, THE FOLLOWING SAMPLE DATA
C DECK WOULD BE REQUIRED FOR THE SYSTEM FOR WHICH
C G = 10(1.0 + 1.1S + 1.1S**2 + 0.1S**3)/S**2(1.0 + 6.0S + 8.0S**2)
C H = S/(1+.01S)
C 1                                    (INPUT)
C 0                                    (IOUTPT)
C90                                    (ITER)
C              1.0E-07                 (ACC)
C 0                                    (INTPRT)
C 25                                   (IDIVLT)
C              1.0E+00                 (ASSUM1)
C              1.0E+00                 (ASSUM2)
C              1.0E+00                 (ASSUM3)
C             -1.0E+00                 (ASSUM4)
C              1.0E+00                 (ASSUM5)
C             10.0E+00                 (ASSUM6)
C             10.0E+00                 (GAING)
C-2                                    (NEXPG)
C              1.0E+00                 (GAINH)
C 1                                    (NEXPH)
C 3                                    (NORNG)
C 2                                    (NORDG)
C              1.1E+00                 (GN(1))
C              1.1E+00                 (GN(2))
C              0.1E+00                 (GN(3))
C              6.0E+00                 (GD(1))
C              8.0E+00                 (GD(2))
C 0                                    (NORNH)
C 1                                    (NORDH)
C              1.0E-02                 (HD(1))
      DIMENSION        TNG(20),QGNS(20),QGNSS(20),TDG(20),QGDS(20)
      DIMENSION QGDSS(20),TNH(20),QHNS(20),QHNSS(20),TDH(20),QHDS(20)
      DIMENSION QHDSS(20)
      DIMENSION  B(100), C(100), PBA1(100), PBA2(100)
      DIMENSION CSAVE(100),A1SAVE(100),A2SAVE(100)
      DIMENSION GN(100),GD(100),HN(100),HD(100),GHN(100),GHD(100),GK(22)
      COMMON N,ITER,ACC,INTPRT,IDIVLT,ASSUM1,ASSUM2,ASSUM3,ASSUM4,
     1ASSUM5,ASSUM6,GKS,B,C,PBA1,PBA2,CSAVE,A1SAVE,A2SAVE
      REWIND 1
      READ INPUT TAPE 5,100,INPUT
      READ INPUT TAPE 5, 100, IOUTPT
      READ INPUT TAPE 5,100,ITER
      READ INPUT TAPE 5,115,ACC
      READ INPUT TAPE 5,100,INTPRT
      READ INPUT TAPE 5,100,IDIVLT
      READ INPUT TAPE 5,115,ASSUM1
      READ INPUT TAPE 5,115,ASSUM2
      READ INPUT TAPE 5,115,ASSUM3
      READ INPUT TAPE 5,115,ASSUM4
      READ INPUT TAPE 5,115,ASSUM5
      READ INPUT TAPE 5,115,ASSUM6
      IF(IOUTPT)28,28,23
23    WRITE TAPE 1,ITER,ACC,INTPRT,IDIVLT,ASSUM1,ASSUM2,ASSUM3,ASSUM4,
     1ASSUM5,ASSUM6
28    READ INPUT TAPE 5, 115, GAING
      READ INPUT TAPE 5,100, NEXPG
      WRITE TAPE 1,GAING,NEXPG
      IF(IOUTPT)35,30,30
30    READ INPUT TAPE 5,115, GAINH
      READ INPUT TAPE 5, 100, NEXPH
      WRITE TAPE 1,GAINH,NEXPH
35    IF(INPUT)40,40,210
40    READ INPUT TAPE 5,100, NLNG
```

```
            READ INPUT TAPE 5,100, NQNG
            READ INPUT TAPE 5,100, NLDG
            READ INPUT TAPE 5,100, NQDG
            PRINT 211,GAING
            PRINT 212,NEXPG
            IF(IOUTPT)44,43,44
  43        WRITE TAPE 1,NLNG,NQNG
  44        IF(IOUTPT)50,45,45
  45        READ INPUT TAPE 5,100, NLNH
            READ INPUT TAPE 5,100, NQNH
            READ INPUT TAPE 5,100, NLDH
            READ INPUT TAPE 5,100, NQDH
 100        FORMAT(I3)
 110        FORMAT(2E17.9)
 115        FORMAT(E17.9)
  50        IF(NLNG)125,125,120
 120        READ INPUT TAPE 5,115,(TNG(I),I=1,NLNG)
            PRINT 121
 121        FORMAT(1H ,39HLINEAR FACTORS IN NUMERATOR OF G FOLLOW)
            DO 122 I=1,NLNG
 122        PRINT 123,TNG(I)
 123        FORMAT(1H ,7H(1.0 + E17.9,5H * S))
            IF(IOUTPT)125,124,125
 124        WRITE TAPE 1, (TNG(I),I=1,NLNG)
 125        IF(NQNG)135,135,130
 130        READ INPUT TAPE 5,110, (QGNS(I),QGNSS(I) ,I=1,NQNG)
            PRINT 131
 131        FORMAT(1H ,42HQUADRATIC FACTORS IN NUMERATOR OF G FOLLOW)
            DO 132 I=1,NQNG
 132        PRINT 133,QGNS(I),QGNSS(I)
 133        FORMAT(1H ,7H(1.0 + E17.9,7H * S + E17.9,8H * S**2))
            IF(IOUTPT)135,134,137
 134        WRITE TAPE 1, (QGNS(I),QGNSS(I) ,I=1,NQNG)
 135        IF(IOUTPT)136,136,137
 136        WRITE TAPE 1,NLDG,NQDG
 137        IF(NLDG)145,145,140
 140        READ INPUT TAPE 5,115,(TDG(I),I=1,NLDG)
            PRINT 141
 141        FORMAT(1H ,41HLINEAR FACTORS IN DENOMINATOR OF G FOLLOW)
            DO 142 I=1,NLDG
 142        PRINT 123,TDG(I)
            IF(IOUTPT)144,144,145
 144        WRITE TAPE 1,(TDG(I),I=1,NLDG)
 145        IF(NQDG)154,154,150
 150        READ INPUT TAPE 5,110, (QGDS(I),QGDSS(I) ,I=1,NQDG)
            PRINT 151
 151        FORMAT(1H ,44HQUADRATIC FACTORS IN DENOMINATOR OF G FOLLOW)
            DO 152 I=1,NQDG
 152        PRINT 133,QGDS(I),QGDSS(I)
            IF(IOUTPT)153,153,154
 153        WRITE TAPE 1, (QGDS(I),QGDSS(I) ,I=1,NQDG)
 154        IF(IOUTPT)511,156,156
 156        PRINT 287,GAINH
            PRINT 288,NEXPH
            IF(IOUTPT)157,157,158
 157        WRITE TAPE 1,NLNH,NQNH
 158        IF(NLNH)165,165,160
 160        READ INPUT TAPE 5,115,(TNH(I),I=1,NLNH)
            PRINT 161
 161        FORMAT(1H ,39HLINEAR FACTORS IN NUMERATOR OF H FOLLOW)
            DO 162 I=1,NLNH
 162        PRINT 123,TNH(I)
            IF(IOUTPT)163,163,165
 163        WRITE TAPE 1,(TNH(I),I=1,NLNH)
 165        IF(NQNH)175,175,170
 170        READ INPUT TAPE 5,110, (QHNS(I),QHNSS(I) ,I=1,NQNH)
            PRINT 171
 171        FORMAT(1H ,42HQUADRATIC FACTORS IN NUMERATOR OF H FOLLOW)
            DO 172 I=1,NQNH
 172        PRINT 133,QHNS(I),QHNSS(I)
            IF(IOUTPT)173,173,177
 173        WRITE TAPE 1, (QHNS(I),QHNSS(I) ,I=1,NQNH)
 175        IF(IOUTPT)176,176,177
 176        WRITE TAPE 1,NLDH,NQDH
```

```
177    IF(NLDH)185,185,180
180    READ INPUT TAPE 5,115,(TDH(I),I=1,NLDH)
       PRINT 181
181    FORMAT(1H ,41HLINEAR FACTORS IN DENOMINATOR OF H FOLLOW)
       DO 182 I=1,NLDH
182    PRINT 123,TDH(I)
       IF(IOUTPT)183,183,185
183    WRITE TAPE 1, (TDH(I),I=1,NLDH)
185    IF(NQDH)195,195,190
190    READ INPUT TAPE 5,110, (QHDS(I),QHDSS(I) ,I=1,NQDH)
       PRINT 191
191    FORMAT(1H ,44HQUADRATIC FACTORS IN DENOMINATOR OF H FOLLOW)
       DO 192 I=1,NQDH
192    PRINT 133,QHDS(I),QHDSS(I)
       IF(IOUTPT)193,193,195
193    WRITE TAPE 1,   (QHDS(I),QHDSS(I)  ,I=1,NQDH)
195    IF(IOUTPT)196,196,512
196    STOP
210    READ INPUT TAPE 5, 100, NORNG
       READ INPUT TAPE 5, 100, NORDG
       GN(1) = 1.0
       GD(1) = 1.0
       NGN = NORNG + 1
       NGD = NORDG + 1
       PRINT 211, GAING
211    FORMAT(1H ,22HGAIN CONSTANT FOR G = E17.9)
       PRINT 212,NEXPG
212    FORMAT(1H ,21HEXPONENT OF S IN G = I2)
       PRINT 215
215    FORMAT(1H ,34HNUMERATOR POLYNOMIAL FOR G FOLLOWS)
       IF(NORNG)220,220,230
220    PRINT 225
225    FORMAT(1H ,49HNUMERATOR POLYNOMIAL FOR G IS 1.0, EXCLUDING GAIN)
       GO TO 247
230    READ INPUT TAPE 5, 115,(GN(I),I=2,NGN)
       DO 240 I= 1,NGN
       IL1 = I-1
240    PRINT 245, IL1, GN(I)
245    FORMAT(1H ,19HCOEFFICIENT OF S** I2,  3H = E17.9)
247    PRINT 250
250    FORMAT(1H ,36HDENOMINATOR POLYNOMIAL FOR G FOLLOWS)
       IF(NORDG)260,260,270
260    PRINT 265
265    FORMAT(1H ,22HDENOMINATOR OF G = 1.0)
       GO TO 281
270    READ INPUT TAPE 5, 115,(GD(I),I=2,NGD)
       DO 280 I=1,NGD
       IL1 = I-1
280    PRINT 245, IL1, GD(I)
281    IF(IOUTPT)282,286,286
282    DO 283 I=1,NGN
283    GHN(I) = GN(I)
       DO 284 I=1,NGD
284    GHD(I) = GD(I)
       NN = NGN
       ND = NGD
       GO TO 613
286    READ INPUT TAPE 5, 100, NORNH
       READ INPUT TAPE 5, 100, NORDH
       HN(1) = 1.0
       HD(1) = 1.0
       NHN = NORNH + 1
       NHD = NORDH + 1
       PRINT 287,GAINH
287    FORMAT(1H ,22HGAIN CONSTANT FOR H = E17.9)
       PRINT 288,NEXPH
288    FORMAT(1H ,21HEXPONENT OF S IN H = I2)
       PRINT 300
300    FORMAT(1H ,34HNUMERATOR POLYNOMIAL FOR H FOLLOWS)
       IF(NORNH)310,310,330
310    PRINT 320
320    FORMAT(1H ,49HNUMERATOR POLYNOMIAL FOR H IS 1.0, EXCLUDING GAIN)
       GO TO 350
330    READ INPUT TAPE 5, 115,(HN(I),I=2,NHN)
```

```
          DO 340 I=1,NHN
          IL1 = I-1
340       PRINT 245, IL1, HN(I)
350       PRINT 360
360       FORMAT(1H ,36HDENOMINATOR POLYNOMIAL FOR H FOLLOWS)
          IF(NORDH)370,370,390
370       PRINT 380
380       FORMAT(1H ,22HDENOMINATOR OF H = 1.0)
          GO TO 405
390       READ INPUT TAPE 5, 115,(HD(I),I=2,NHD)
          DO 400 I=1,NHD
          IL1 = I-1
400       PRINT 245, IL1, HD(I)
405       IF(IOUTPT)612,612,410
410       NN = NORNG + NORNH + 1
          ND = NORDG + NORDH + 1
          DO 420 J=1,NN
420       GHN(J) = 0.0
          DO 430 I=1,NGN
          DO 430 J=1,NHN
          K = I + J - 1
430       GHN(K) = GHN(K) + GN(I) * HN(J)
          DO 440 J=1,ND
440       GHD(J) = 0.0
          DO 450 I=1,NGD
          DO 450 J=1,NHD
          K = I + J - 1
450       GHD(K) = GHD(K) + GD(I) * HD(J)
510       IF(IOUTPT)612,612,690
511       IF(IOUTPT)5111,512,512
5111      NN = 1 + NLNG + 2*NQNG
          ND = 1 + NLDG + 2*NQDG
          GO TO 5121
512       NN = 1 + NLNG + NLNH + 2*(NQNG + NQNH)
          ND = 1 + NLDG + NLDH + 2*(NQDG + NQDH)
5121      DO 513 I=1,NN
513       GHN(I) = 0.0
          DO 514 I =1,ND
514       GHD(I) = 0.0
          GHN(1) = 1.0
          GHD(1) = 1.0
          IF(NLNG)522,522,515
515       DO 520 I=1,NLNG
          IP1 = I+1
          DO 520 K=2,IP1
          IP = IP1 - K+2
          IPL1 = IP-1
520       GHN(IP) = GHN(IP) +GHN(IPL1) * TNG(I)
522       IF(NLDG)529,529,523
523       DO 525 I=1,NLDG
          IP1 = I+1
          DO 525 K=2,IP1
          IP = IP1-K+2
          IPL1 = IP-1
525       GHD(IP) = GHD(IP) + GHD(IPL1) * TDG(I)
529       IF(IOUTPT)560,530,530
530       IF(NLNH)545,545,535
535       DO 540 I=1,NLNH
          IP1 = I+1+NLNG
          DO 540 K=2,IP1
          IP = IP1 - K+2
          IPL1 = IP-1
540       GHN(IP) = GHN(IP) + GHN(IPL1) * TNH(I)
545       IF(NLDH)560,560,550
550       DO 555 I=1,NLDH
          IP1 = I+1+NLDG
          DO 555 K=2,IP1
          IP = IP1-K+2
          IPL1 = IP-1
555       GHD(IP) = GHD(IP) + GHD(IPL1) * TDH(I)
560       IF(NQNG)575,575,565
565       DO 574 I=1,NQNG
          IF(IOUTPT)566,567,567
566       IP = I*2 - 1 + NLNG
```

```
           GO TO 568
567    IP = I*2-1 + NLNG + NLNH
568    DO 570 K=1,NN
570    C(K) = GHN(K)
           DO 571 K=1,IP
           KP1 = K + 1
571    C(KP1) = C(KP1) + GHN(K) * QGNS(I)
           DO 572 K=1,IP
           KP2 = K + 2
572    C(KP2) = C(KP2) + GHN(K) * QGNSS(I)
           IPN = IP +2
           DO 573 K=1,IPN
573    GHN(K) = C(K)
574    CONTINUE
575    IF(NQDG)586,586,580
580    DO 585 I=1,NQDG
           IF(IOUTPT)5801,5802,5802
5801   IP = I*2 - 1 + NLDG
           GO TO 5803
5802   IP = I*2-1+NLDG+NLDH
5803   DO 581 K=1,ND
581    C(K) = GHD(K)
           DO 582 K=1,IP
           KP1 = K + 1
582    C(KP1) = C(KP1) + GHD(K) * QGDS(I)
           DO 583 K=1,IP
           KP2 = K + 2
583    C(KP2) = C(KP2) + GHD(K) * QGDSS(I)
           IPN= IP+2
           DO 584 K=1,IPN
584    GHD(K) = C(K)
585    CONTINUE
586    IF(IOUTPT)587,590,590
587    DO 588 I=1,NN
588    GN(I) = GHN(I)
           DO 589 I=1,ND
589    GD(I) = GHD(I)
           NGN = NN
           NGD = ND
           GO TO 690
590    IF(NQNH)605,605,595
595    DO 600 I=1,NQNH
           IP = I*2-1 + NLNG+ NLNH+NQNG*2
           DO 596 K=1,NN
596    C(K) = GHN(K)
           DO 597 K=1,IP
           KP1 = K + 1
597    C(KP1) = C(KP1) + GHN(K) * QHNS(I)
           DO 598 K=1,IP
           KP2 = K + 2
598    C(KP2) = C(KP2) + GHN(K) * QHNSS(I)
           IPN= IP+2
           DO 599 K=1,IPN
599    GHN(K) = C(K)
600    CONTINUE
605    IF(NQDH)615,690,606
606    DO 611 I=1,NQDH
           IP = I*2-1 + NLDG+NLDH+NQDG*2
           DO 607 K=1,ND
607    C(K) = GHD(K)
           DO 608 K=1,IP
           KP1 = K + 1
608    C(KP1) = C(KP1) + GHD(K) * QHDS(I)
           DO 609 K=1,IP
           KP2 = K + 2
609    C(KP2) = C(KP2) + GHD(K) * QHDSS(I)
           IPN= IP+2
           DO 610 K=1,IPN
610    GHD(K) = C(K)
611    CONTINUE
612    IF(IOUTPT)613,613,690
613    IGGH = 0
614    IGGH = IGGH + 1
           IF(IOUTPT)615,616,616
```

```
615    GO TO (614,616,690),IGGH
616    GO TO (623,617,619,621,196),IGGH
617    NGN = NGD
       DO 618 K=1,NGN
618    GN(K) = GD(K)
       GO TO 623
619    NGN = NHN
       DO 620 K=1,NHN
620    GN(K) = HN(K)
       GO TO 623
621    NGN = NHD
       DO 622 K=1,NHD
622    GN(K) = HD(K)
623    N = NGN - 1
       IF(N-1)624,625,626
624    NLNG = 0
       NQNG = 0
       GO TO 650
625    NLNG = 1
       NQNG = 0
       TNG(1) = GN(2)
       GO TO 650
626    IF(N-2)630,630,628
628    DO 629 K=1,N
       KP1 = K + 1
629    C(K) = GN(KP1)
       CALL A86FPS
630    NP = N/2
       NLNG = 0
       NQNG = 0
       IF(N-2)631,631,6311
631    A1SAVE(1) = GN(2)
       A2SAVE(1) = GN(3)
6311   DO 640 K=1,NP
       SQR = A1SAVE(K) * A1SAVE(K) * 0.25
       BC = SQR - A2SAVE(K)
       IF(ABSF(BC/A2SAVE(K))-1.0E-07)638,638,632
632    IF(BC)634,638,636
634    NQNG = NQNG + 1
       QGNS(NQNG) = A1SAVE(K)
       QGNSS(NQNG) = A2SAVE(K)
       GO TO 640
636    NLNG = NLNG + 1
       SQR = SQRTF(BC)
       TNG(NLNG) = 0.5 * A1SAVE(K) + SQR
       NLNG = NLNG + 1
       TNG(NLNG) = 0.5 * A1SAVF(K) - SQR
       GO TO 640
638    NLNG = NLNG + 1
       TNG(NLNG) = 0.5 * A1SAVE(K)
       NLNG = NLNG + 1
       TNG(NLNG) = 0.5 * A1SAVE(K)
640    CONTINUE
       IF(NP*2 - N)645,650,650
645    NLNG = NLNG + 1
       NPP1 = NP + 1
       TNG(NLNG) = A1SAVE(NPP1)
650    WRITE TAPE 1,NLNG,NQNG
       IF(NLNG)660,660,655
655    WRITE TAPE 1, (TNG(I),I=1,NLNG)
660    IF(NQNG)614,614,665
665    WRITE TAPE 1, (QGNS(I),QGNSS(I)  ,I=1,NQNG
670    GO TO 614
690    WRITE TAPE 1,NN,ND
       WRITE TAPE 1, (GHN(K),K=1,NN)
       WRITE TAPE 1, (GHD(K),K=1,ND)
       WRITE TAPE 1,ACC
       STOP
       END
```

```
TITLED91RTL        101   J.B.VERNON
C THIS PROGRAM WILL COMPUTE THE ROOT LOCUS FOR A FUNCTION OF THE FORM GH = -1.
C INPUT TO THIS PROGRAM IS SUPPLIED BY PROGRAM D91PRE AND ALSO BY INPUT TAPE.
C PROGRAM D91PRE PREPARES THE TRANSFER FUNCTION AND STORES THE INFORMATION ON
C TAPE 1, WHERE IT IS READ BY THIS PROGRAM ACCORDING TO THE READ TAPE 1
C STATEMENTS OF THIS PROGRAM.  VARIABLES ITER, ACC, INTPRT, ETC., OF THE FIRST
C READ TAPE STATEMENT ARE DEFINED IN PROGRAM A86FP.  THE VARIABLES GAING,
C GAINH, NEXPG, AND NEXPH ARE DEFINED IN PROGRAM D91PRE.  THE VARIABLES, GHN( ),
C ARE COEFFICIENTS OF THE VARIOUS POWERS OF THE NUMERATOR POLYNOMIAL.  GHN(1) =
C 1.0, GHN(2) IS THE COEFFICIENT OF S, GHN(3) OF S**2, ETC.  NN IS ONE MORE THAN
C THE ORDER OF THE NUMERATOR POLYNOMIAL.   SIMILAR DEFINITIONS APPLY FOR GHD( )
C AND ND FOR THE DENOMINATOR POLYNOMIAL.
C THE LOCUS IS CALCULATED FOR VARIABLE VALUES OF THE PRODUCT
C OF THE GAIN OF G*GAIN OF H.  THE ROOTS OF THE CLOSED LOOP CHARACTERISTIC
C EQUATION ARE COMPUTED AT VALUES OF GAIN DETERMINED BY THE TWO INPUT VARIABLES,
C STRTK AND FACTK, AS WELL AS FOR ZERO, INFINITY, AND THE NOMINAL VALUE.  IF
C STRTK AND FACTK ARE BOTH UNITY, GAINS WILL VARY FROM 1.0 TO 100.  IF STRTK
C WERE 2.0, THEN GAINS WOULD VARY FROM 2.0 TO 200.  IF STRTK WERE 1.0 AND FACTK
C WERE 2.0,GAINS WOULD VARY FROM 1.0 TO 10000.  THE RANGE IS EXPANDED OR
C CONTRACTED BY SPECIFYING FACTK GREATER OR LESS THAN 1.0, THE UPPER LIMIT BEING
C RAISED TO THE POWER, FACTK, THE VARIABLE STRTK INDICATES THE LOWER LIMIT FOR
C GAIN.  THERE WILL BE 21 CALCULATIONS BETWEEN AND INCLUDING THESE LIMITS, AS
C WELL AS THE CALCULATION FOR ZERO AND INFINITE GAIN AND THE CALCULATION AT
C NOMINAL GAIN, WHICH WILL BE THE LAST CALCULATION.  NOTE THAT  STRTK  AND
C FACTK ARE READ FROM INPUT TAPE RATHER THAN TAPE 1.
        DIMENSION  B(100), C(100), PBA1(100), PBA2(100)
        DIMENSION CSAVE(100),A1SAVE(100),A2SAVE(100)
        DIMENSION GN(100),GD(100),HN(100),HD(100),GHN(100),GHD(100),GK(22)
        COMMON N,ITER,ACC,INTPRT,IDIVLT,ASSUM1,ASSUM2,ASSUM3,ASSUM4,
       1ASSUM5,ASSUM6,GKS,B,C,PBA1,PBA2,CSAVE,A1SAVE,A2SAVE
        REWIND 1
        READ   TAPE 1,ITER,ACC,INTPRT,IDIVLT,ASSUM1,ASSUM2,ASSUM3,ASSUM4,
       1ASSUM5,ASSUM
        READ TAPE 1,GAING,NEXPG
        READ TAPE 1,GAINH,NEXPH
        READ TAPE 1,NN,ND
        READ TAPE 1, (GHN(K),K=1,NN)
        READ TAPE 1, (GHD(K),K=1,ND)
        GK(22) = GAING * GAINH
        NEXP = NEXPG + NEXPH
        PRINT 10
10      FORMAT(1H1,1H )
        PRINT 11
11      FORMAT(1H0,10HINPUT DATA)
        PRINT 12,GK(22),NEXP
12      FORMAT(1H0,6HGAIN =  E17.9,  10H    NEXP =  I2)
        PRINT 13
13      FORMAT(1H0,23HPOLYNOMIAL COEFFICIENTS  )
        DO 14 I = 1,NN
14      PRINT 15, I, GHN(I)
15      FORMAT(1H ,4HGHN(  I2,  4H) =  E17.9)
        DO 16 I=1,ND
16      PRINT 17, I, GHD(I)
17      FORMAT(1H ,4HGHD(  I2, 4H) =  E17.9)
        GK(1) = 1.0
        GK(2) = 1.4
        GK(3) = 2.0
        DO 20 I=4,11
        IL1 = I-1
20      GK(I) = GK(IL1) + 1.0
        GK(12) = 14.0
        GK(13) = 20.0
        DO 22 I=14,21
        IL1 = I-1
22      GK(I) = GK(IL1) + 10.0
100     FORMAT(I3)
110     FORMAT(2E17.9)
        READ INPUT TAPE 5,115,STRTK
        READ INPUT TAPE 5,115,FACTK
        DO 25 I=1,21
25      GK(I) = STRTK * GK(I)**FACTK
115     FORMAT(E17.9)
        IF(NEXP)620,680,650
620     DO 630 I=1,ND
```

```
       NDLIP = ND-I+1
       NDLEX = NDLIP-NEXP
  630  GHD(NDLEX) = GHD(NDLIP)
       ND = ND-NEXP
       NT = -NEXP
       DO 640 I=1,NT
  640  GHD(I) = 0.0
       GO TO 680
  650  DO 660 I=1,NN
       NNLIP = NN-I+1
       NNLEX = NNLIP+NEXP
  660  GHN(NNLEX) = GHN(NNLIP
       NN = NN+NEXP
       DO 670 I=1,NEXP
  670  GHN(I) = 0.0
  680  PRINT 690
  690  FORMAT(1H0,22HOPEN LOOP ROOTS FOLLOW)
       IF(ND-1)692,692,694
  692  PRINT 693
  693  FORMAT(1H0,28HTHERE ARE NO OPEN LOOP POLES)
       GO TO 770
  694  IF(NEXP)695,696,696
  695  N = ND-NT-1
       GO TO 697
  696  N = ND - 1
       NT = 0
  697  IF(NEXP)700,718,718
  700  PRINT 710,NT
  710  FORMAT(1H0,40HORDER OF OPEN LOOP POLES AT S = 0.0 IS    I2)
       IF(N)713,713,718
  713  PRINT 716
  716  FORMAT(1H0,34HTHERE ARE NO OTHER OPEN LOOP POLES)
       GO TO 770
  718  NTP2 = NT+2
       DO 720 I=NTP2,ND
       ILNT = I-NT-1
  720  C(ILNT) = GHD(I)
       A1SAVE(1) = C(1)
       A2SAVE(1) = C(2)
       IF(N-2)760,760,750
  750  CALL A86FPS
  760  GKS = 0.0
       CALL A86RTS
  770  PRINT 780
  780  FORMAT(1H0,22HOPEN LOOP ZEROS FOLLOW)
       IF(NEXP)790,790,810
  790  N = NN-1
       NXP2 = 2
       IF(N) 800,800,810
  800  PRINT 805
  805  FORMAT(1H0 28HTHERE ARE NO OPEN LOOP ZEROS)
       GO TO 860
  810  IF(NEXP)811,811,812
  811  NTT = 0
       GO TO 813
  812  NTT = NEXP
  813  PRINT 815, NTT
  815  FORMAT(1H0 39HORDER OF OPEN LOOP ZEROS AT S = 0.0 IS I2)
       IF(NEXP)8152,8152,8151
 8151  NXP2 = NEXP+2
       N = NN-NEXP-1
 8152  IF(N) 816,816,818
  816  PRINT 817
  817  FORMAT(1H0,34HTHERE ARE NO OTHER OPEN LOOP ZEROS)
       GO TO 860
  818  DO 820 I=NXP2,NN
       ILNX = I - NTT - 1
  820  C(ILNX) = GHN(I)
       A1SAVE(1) = C(1)
       A2SAVE(1) = C(2)
       IF (N-2)830,830,825
  825  CALL A86FPS
  830  GKS = 1.0 E+30
       CALL A86RTS
```

```
860     PRINT 870
870     FORMAT(1H0,51HCLOSED LOOP POLES FOR VARIABLE GAIN CONSTANT FOLLOW)
        IF(ND-NN)871,874,874
871     N = NN-1
        DO 872 I = ND,N
        IP1 = I+1
872     GHD(IP1)= 0.0
        GO TO 877
874     N = ND-1
        DO 875 I=NN,N
        IP1 = I + 1
875     GHN(IP1) = 0.0
877     DO 960 I=1,22
        DO 880 J=1,N
        JP1 = J+1
880     C(J)    = GHD(JP1) + GK(I) * GHN(JP1)
        IF(NEXP)890,900,910
890     DO 895 J=1,N
895     C(J) = C(J)/GK(I)
        GO TO 910
900     DO 905 J=1,N
905     C(J) = C(J)/(1.0+GK(I))
910     IF(N-2)920,920,930
920     A1SAVE(1) = C(1)
        A2SAVE(1) = C(2)
        GO TO 940
930     CALL A86FPS
940     GKS = GK(I)
        CALL A86RTS
960     CONTINUE
        PRINT 970
970     FORMAT(1H1,32HEND OF COMPUTATION OF ROOT LOCUS)
        STOP
        END
```

```
TITLFE11TRN        101   J.B.VERNON
C       THIS PROGRAM COMPUTES THE INVERSE LAPLACE TRANSFORM OF A FUNCTION OF  S
C AND THE RESPONSE TO A FORCING FUNCTION.  THE FUNCTION OF  S  IS STORED ON
C TAPE 1 BY PROGRAM D91PRE.  FACTORS IN THE DENOMINATOR OF THE FUNCTION MAY BE
C REPEATED.  SEE PROGRAM D91PRE FOR ADDITIONAL COMMENTS.  OUTPUT OF THIS PROGRAM
C IS IN THE FORM OF ANALYTIC EXPRESSIONS OR NUMERICAL DATA POINTS DEPENDING
C ON THE VALUE OF AN INDEX, INVS.  IF  INVS  IS NEGATIVE, ONLY THE ANALYTIC
C EXPRESSION FOR THE INVERSE IS GIVEN.  IF  INVS  IS ZERO, BOTH THE ANALYTIC
C EXPRESSION AND THE NUMERICAL RESPONSE TO A UNIT IMPULSE ARE GIVEN.  IF  INVS
C IS POSITIVE, THESE ITEMS AND ALSO THE RESPONSE TO AN INPUT FORCING FUNCTION
C IS GIVEN.  INVS  IS OBTAINED FROM INPUT TAPE, AS ARE THE VALUES OF  TSRT,
C TSTP,  NTIME, TAU( ), AND F( ).  THE RESPONSE IS COMPUTED AT TIMES BEGINNING
C WITH TSRT, AND ENDING WITH  TSTP,  AND AT OTHER TIMES CORRESPONDING TO BREAK-
C ING THIS TIME INTERVAL UP INTO  NTIME  INCREMENTS.  THE FORCING FUNCTION F( )
C MUST BE SPECIFIED AT TIMES, TAU( ).  LINEAR INTERPOLATION FOR  F( ) IS
C ASSUMED BETWEEN THESE VALUES OF  TAU( ), BUT OTHERWISE THE CALCULATION
C CONTAINS NO APPROXIMATIONS.  AT DISCONTINUITIES USE TWO CARDS, EACH WITH THE
C SAME VALUE  OF  TAU, BUT TWO DIFFERENT VALUES OF  F.  FOLLOWING THE LAST DATA
C CARD SHOULD BE A CARD WITH A POSITIVE NUMBER IN COLUMN 37 TO SIGNIFY END OF
C DATA.   IT IS ASSUMED THAT THE FORCING FUNCTION REMAINS CONSTANT AFTER THIS.
        DIMENSION FACT(50),TDG(20),QGDS(20),QGDSS(20),NTX(10),NQX(10)
        DIMENSION GN(100),GD(100),A(20,10),B(20,10),C(20,10)
        DIMENSION G(500),X(500),T(500),TAU(502),F(502)
        DIMENSION FDR(20),FDI(20),FNR(20),FNI(20)
        DIMENSION FQR(20),FQI(20),FZR(20),FZI(20)
        COMMON P,AP,C1,C2,C3R,C3I,C4R,C4I,TOW,DUM1,DUM2,N,K,IX,IXLQ,I,
      1FACT,T
        CRMF(FK,AR,AI,BR,BI) = FK * (AR*BR - AI*BI)
        CIMF(FK,AR,AI,BR,BI) = FK * (AR*BI + AI*BR)
        DO 102 I=1,100
        GN(I) = 0.0
102     GD(I) = 0.0
        REWIND 1
        READ TAPE 1, GAING,NEXPG
```

```
        READ TAPE 1, NLDG,NQDG
        IF(NLDG)120,120,110
110     READ TAPE 1,(TDG(I),I=1,NLDG)
120     IF(NQDG)135,135,130
130     READ TAPE 1, (QGDS(I),QGDSS(I)  ,I=1,NQDG)
135     READ TAPE 1,NN,ND
        READ TAPE 1,(GN(I),I=1,NN)
        READ TAPE 1,(GD(I),I=1,ND)
        READ TAPE 1,ACC
        READ INPUT TAPE 5,140,INVS
140     FORMAT(I3)
        IF(INVS)188,150,150
150     READ INPUT TAPE 5,160,TSRT
        READ INPUT TAPE 5,160,TSTP
        READ INPUT TAPE 5,140,NTIME
160     FORMAT(2E17.9,I7)
        IF(INVS)188,180,165
165     DO 170 I=2,502
        READ INPUT TAPE 5,160,TAU(I),F(I),IEND
        IF(IEND)170,170,175
170     CONTINUE
175     NTAU=I
        TAU(1)=0.0
        F(1)=0.0
        TAU(NTAU) = 1.0E+30
        NL1 = NTAU - 1
        F(NTAU) = F(NL1)
180     T(1) = TSRT
        DELTT = '(TSTP - TSRT)/FLOATF(NTIME)
        DO 185 I=1,NTIME
        IP1=I+1
        T(IP1)=T(I)+DELTT
185     CONTINUE
188     IF(NEXPG)190,198,194
190     DO 192 I=1,ND
        NDL=ND-I-NEXPG+1
        NDI=ND-I+1
192     GD(NDL)=GD(NDI)
        ND=ND-NEXPG
        NT = -NEXPG
        DO 193 I=1,NT
193     GD(I) = 0.0
        GO TO 198
194     DO 196 I=1,NN
        NDL=ND-I+NEXPG+1
        NDI=ND-I+1
196     GN(NDL)=GN(NDI)
        NN=NN+NEXPG
        DO 197 I=1,NEXPG
197     GN(I) = 0.0
198     ACC=10.0*ACC
        NLDL = NLDG-1
        NQDL = NQDG-1
        IF(NLDG)202,202,199
199     DO 200 I=1,NLDG
200     TDG(I)=1.0/TDG(I)
202     IF(NQDG)212,212,204
204     DO 210 I=1,NQDG
        QGDS(I)=QGDS(I)/QGDSS(I)
210     QGDSS(I)=1.0/QGDSS(I)
212     IF(NLDL)222,222,214
214     DO 220 I=1,NLDL
        IP1=I+1
        DO 220 J=IP1,NLDG
        IF(TDG(I)-TDG(J))215,220,220
215     DUM=TDG(I)
        TDG(I)=TDG(J)
        TDG(J)=DUM
220     CONTINUE
222     IF(NQDL)234,234,224
224     DO 230 I=1,NQDL
        IP1 = I + 1
        DO 230 J=IP1,NQDG
        IF(QGDS(I)-QGDS(J))225,230,230
```

```
225    DUM=QGDS(I)
       QGDS(I)=QGDS(J)
       QGDS(J)=DUM
       DUM=QGDSS(I)
       QGDSS(I)=QGDSS(J)
       QGDSS(J)=DUM
230    CONTINUE
234    NTX(1) = 1
       IF(NLDG-1)323,3205,236
236    IST = 1
       IX = 0
270    K=1
       IX = IX + 1
       DO 300 I=IST,NLDL
       IP1=I+1
       DO 290 J=IP1,NLDG
       IF(ABSF((TDG(I)-TDG(J))/TDG(I))-ACC)280,280,295
280    K=K+1
290    CONTINUE
295    TDG(IX)=TDG(I)
       NTX(IX)=K
       IST = IST + K
       IF(IST-NLDG)270,310,320
300    CONTINUE
310    IX=IX+1
       TDG(IX)=TDG(NLDG)
       NTX(IX)=1
320    NLDG=IX
3205   IF(NEXPG)321,325,325
321    DO 322 I=1,NLDG
       NLI=NLDG-I+1
       NLI2=NLDG-I+2
       TDG(NLI2) =-TDG(NLI)
322    NTX(NLI2)=NTX(NLI)
       TDG(1)=0.0
       NTX(1)=-NEXPG
       NLDG=NLDG+1
       GO TO 325
323    IF(NEXPG)324,325,325
324    TDG(1) = 0.0
       NTX(1) = -NEXPG
       NLDG = 1
325    IF(NQDG-1)402,326,327
326    NQX(1) = 1
       GO TO 402
327    IST = 1
       IX=1
330    K=1
       DO 380 I=IST,NQDL
       IP1=I+1
       DO 360 J=IP1,NQDG
       IF(ABSF((QGDSS(I)-QGDSS(J))/QGDSS(I))-ACC)335,335,365
335    IF(ABSF(QGDS(I)/SQRTF(QGDSS(I)))-ACC)340,340,345
340    IF(ABSF(QGDS(J)/SQRTF(QGDSS(J)))-ACC)350,350,365
345    IF(ABSF((QGDS(I)-QGDS(J))/QGDS(I))-ACC)350,350,365
350    K=K+1
360    CONTINUE
365    QGDS(IX)=QGDS(I)
       QGDSS(IX)=QGDSS(I)
       NQX(IX)=K
       IST = IST + K
       IF(IST-NQDG)330,390,400
380    CONTINUE
390    IX=IX+1
       QGDS(IX)=QGDS(NQDG)
       QGDSS(IX)=QGDSS(NQDG)
       NQX(IX)=1
400    NQDG=IX
402    PRINT 405
405    FORMAT(1H1,1H )
       PRINT 410
410    FORMAT(1H0,12HSTART E11TRN )
       PRINT 415
415    FORMAT(1H0,79HINVERSE TRANSFORM OF G IN ANALYTICAL FORM FOLLOWS.
      1ADD ALL OF THE TERMS SHOWN.    )
```

```
      FACT(1)=1.0
      FACT(2)=1.0
      DO 420 I=2,49
      IP1=I+1
420   FACT(IP1)=FACT(I)*FLOATF(I)
      NNL1=NN-1
      NDL1=ND-1
      IXLQ = 0
      IF(NLDG)490,490,421
421   DO 423 I=1,NLDG
      N = NTX(I)
      SR = TDG(I)
      SI = 0.0
      GO TO 424
422   TDG(I) = SR
423   CONTINUE
      GO TO 490
424   NT2 = N*2
      DO 426 LH=1,NT2
      FDR(LH) = 0.0
      FDI(LH) = 0.0
      FNR(LH) = 0.0
      FNI(LH) = 0.0
      DO 426 LX = LH,ND
      LXLH = LX - LH
      FK = 1.0
      AR = 1.0
      AI = 0.0
      IF(LXLH)4251,4251,4248
4248  DO 425 IEX=1,LXLH
      AD = CRMF(FK,AR,AI,SR,SI)
      AI = CIMF(FK,AR,AI,SR,SI)
425   AR = AD
4251  FK = FACT(LX)/FACT(LXLH+1) * GD(LX)
      FDR(LH) = FDR(LH) + FK*AR
      FDI(LH) = FDI(LH) + FK * AI
      FK = FACT(LX)/FACT(LXLH+1) * GN(LX)
      FNR(LH) = FNR(LH) + FK*AR
      FNI(LH) = FNI(LH) + FK*AI
426   CONTINUE
      DO 427 LG = 1,N
      LGPN = LG + N
      FK = FACT(LG)/FACT(LGPN)
      FQR(LG) = FK * FDR(LGPN)
427   FQI(LG) = FK * FDI(LGPN)
      FZR(1) = FQR(1)/(FQR(1)*FQR(1) + FQI(1)*FQI(1))
      FZI(1) =-FQI(1)/(FQR(1)*FQR(1) + FQI(1)*FQI(1))
      IF(N-1)434,434,428
428   DO 433 LJ = 2,N
      FZR(LJ) = 0.0
      FZI(LJ) = 0.0
      DO 430 LR=2,LJ
      LJLR = LJ - LR
      FK = FACT(LJ)/FACT(LR-1)/FACT(LJLR+2)
      AR = FQR(LJLR+2)
      AI = FQI(LJLR+2)
      BR = FZR(LR-1)
      BI = FZI(LR-1)
      FZR(LJ) = FZR(LJ) + CRMF(FK,AR,AI,BR,BI)
      FZI(LJ) = FZI(LJ) + CIMF(FK,AR,AI,BR,BI)
430   CONTINUE
      AR = FZR(LJ)
      AI = FZI(LJ)
      BR = FZR(1)
      BI = FZI(1)
      FK = 1.0
      FZR(LJ) =-CRMF(FK,AR,AI,BR,BI)
433   FZI(LJ) =-CIMF(FK,AR,AI,BR,BI)
434   DO 485 K=1,N
      NLK = N-K+1
      DUMR = 0.0
      DUMI = 0.0
      DO 435 L=1,NLK
      NLKL = NLK - L
```

```
          FK  = 1.0/FACT(L)/FACT(NLKL+1)/FACT(K)
          AR  = FNR(NLKL+1)
          AI  = FNI(NLKL+1)
          BR  = FZR(L)
          BI  = FZI(L)
          DUMR = DUMR + CRMF(FK,AR,AI,BR,BI)
435       DUMI = DUMI + CIMF(FK,AR,AI,BR,BI)
          IF(IXLQ)440,440,470
440       C(I,K) = DUMR * GAING
          KL1 = K-1
          PRINT 460,C(I,K),KL1,TDG(I)
460       FORMAT(1H0,E17.9,7H * (T** I1, 8H * EXP( E17.9, 5H * T))
          GO TO 485
470       A(I,K) = 2.0*DUMR*GAING
          B(I,K) =-2.0*DUMI*GAING
          KL1 = K-1
          PRINT 480,KL1,SR,A(I,K),SI,B(I,K),SI
480       FORMAT(1H0,4H(T** I1,7H * EXP( E15.8,7H*T) * (  E15.8, 8H*COSINE(
         1E15.8,5H*T) +  E15.8,6H*SINE( E15.8,4H*T))   )
485       CONTINUE
          IF(IXLQ)422,422,510
490       IXLQ = 1
          IF(NQDG)551,551,500
500       DO 520 I=1,NQDG
          SR=-0.5*QGDS (I)
          SI=0.5*SQRTF(4.0*QGDSS(I)-QGDS(I)*QGDS(I))
          N = NQX(I)
          GO TO 424
510       QGDS(I) = SR
          QGDSS(I) = SI
520       CONTINUE
551       IF(INVS)552,555,555
552       STOP
555       PRINT 560
560       FORMAT(1H0,116HNUMERICAL RESULTS, WHERE T = TIME, F(T) = FORCING F
         1UNCTION, G(T) = RESPONSE TO UNIT IMPULSE, X(T) = RESPONSE TO F(T))
          PRINT 570
570       FORMAT(1H0,86H  TIME, T       FORCING, F(T)        RESPONSE TO IMPULS
         1E, G(T)          RESPONSE TO F, X(T)   )
          FD = 0.0
          NTIME = NTIME + 1
          DO 745 I=1,NTIME
          G(I)=0.0
          X(I)=0.0
          IF(INVS)745,577,577
577       IF(NLDG)582,582,579
579       DO 580 J=1,NLDG
          NTXL=NTX(J)
          DO 580 JI=1,NTXL
          IF(JI-1)5793,5793,5792
5792      TIJ = T(I)**(JI-1)
          GO TO 5794
5793      TIJ = 1
5794      IF(ABSF(TDG(J))-1.0E-30)5796,5796,5795
5795      EXT = EXPF(TDG(J) * T(I))
          GO TO 5797
5796      EXT = 1.0
5797      TJEX = TIJ * EXT
580       G(I) = G(I) + C(J,JI) * TJEX
582       IF(NQDG)590,590,584
584       DO 586 J=1,NQDG
          NQXL=NQX(J)
          DO 586 JI=1,NQXL
          IF(JI-1)5843,5843,5842
5842      TIJ = T(I)**(JI-1)
          GO TO 5844
5843      TIJ = 1
5844      IF(ABSF(QGDS(J))-1.0E-30)5846,5846,5845
5845      EXT = EXPF(QGDS(J)*T(I))
          GO TO 5847
5846      EXT = 1.0
5847      TJEX = TIJ * EXT
5849      IF(T(I) - 1.0E-30)5851,5850,5850
5850      ACBS = A(J,JI)*COSF(QGDSS(J)*T(I))+B(J,JI)*SINF(QGDSS(J)*T(I))
```

```
         GO TO 586
5851    ACBS = A(J,JI)
586     G(I) = G(I) + TJEX * ACBS
590     IF(INVS)745,591,595
591     PRINT 592,T(I),FD,G(I)
        GO TO 745
592     FORMAT(1H ,E11.5,E17.5,2E26.5)
595     DO 740 J=1,NL1
        JP1=J+1
        IF(TAU(JP1) - 1.0E-30)740,740,600
600     IF(ABSF((TAU(JP1)-TAU(J))/TAU(JP1))-1.0E-07)740,740,605
605     IF(TAU(J)-T(I))610,741,741
610     IF(TAU(JP1)-T(I))620,620,630
620     F2 = F(JP1)
        T2=TAU(JP1)
        GO TO 635
630     T2=T(I)
        F2=F(J)+(F(JP1)-F(J))/(TAU(JP1)-TAU(J))*(T(I)-TAU(J))
        FD=F2
635     F1=F(J)
        T1=TAU(J)
        C1 = (T2*F1-T1*F2)/(T2-T1)
        C2=(F2-F1)/(T2-T1)
        IXLQ = 0
        IF(NLDG)737,737,640
640     IF(IXLQ)645,645,650
645     NGEN = NLDG
        GO TO 660
650     NGEN = NQDG
660     DO 735 JK=1,NGEN
        IF(IXLQ)665,665,670
665     P = 0.0
        AP = TDG(JK)
        NQXL = NTX(JK)
        GO TO 680
670     P=QGDSS(JK)
        AP=QGDS(JK)
        NQXL=NQX(JK)
680     PTI2 = P * (T(I) - T2)
        IF(ABSF(PTI2)-1.0E-30)682,681,681
681     SS2 = SINF(PTI2)
        CS2 = COSF(PTI2)
        GO TO 683
682     SS2 = 0.0
        CS2 = 1.0
683     PTI1 = P*(T(I)-T1)
        IF(ABSF(PTI1)-1.0E-30)685,684,684
684     SS1 = SINF(PTI1)
        CS1 = COSF(PTI1)
        GO TO 686
685     SS1 = 0.0
        CS1 = 1.0
686     SUM1 = 0.0
        SUM2=0.0
        APT2 = AP * (T(I)-T2)
        IF(ABSF(APT2)-1.0E-30)687,687,6861
6861    EAT2 = EXPF(APT2)
        GO TO 688
687     EAT2 = 1.0
688     APT1 = AP * (T(I)-T1)
        IF(ABSF(APT1)-1.0E-30)690,689,689
689     EAT1 = EXPF(APT1)
        GO TO 691
690     EAT1 = 1.0
691     DO 730 NQ = 1,NQXL
        IF(IXLQ)692,692,693
692     ANQJK = C(JK,NQ)
        BNQJK = 0.0
        GO TO 695
693     ANQJK = A(JK,NQ)
        BNQJK = B(JK,NQ)
695     N=NQ-1
        TOW=T1
        CALL E11C4
```

```
      SUM1=SUM1+((C4R*CS1-C4I*SS1)*ANQJK    +(C4I*CS1+C4R*SS1)*BNQJK)
      TOW=T2
      CALL E11C4
710   SUM2=SUM2+((C4R*CS2-C4I*SS2)*ANQJK    +(C4I*CS2+C4R*SS2)*BNQJK)
730   CONTINUE
      X(I) = X(I) + EAT2*SUM2 - EAT1*SUM1
735   CONTINUE
      IF(IXLQ)737,737,740
737   IXLQ = 1
      IF(NQDG)741,741,640
740   CONTINUE
741   PRINT 592,T(I),FD,G(I),X(I)
745   CONTINUE
      STOP
      END




      SUBROUTINE E11C4
      DIMENSION FACT(50),T(500)
      COMMON P,AP,C1,C2,C3R,C3I,C4R,C4I,TOW,DUM1,DUM2,N,K,IX,IXLQ,I,
     1FACT,T
      NP1=N+1
      C4R=0.0
      C4I=0.0
      IX = -1
      IF(N)805,805,700
700   DO 800 K=2,NP1
      NDUM = N-K+1
      CONST = (-1.0)**(K-1) *(T(I)**NDUM * (FACT(NP1)/FACT(NDUM+1)
     1/FACT(K) * C1 - FACT(NP1)/FACT(NDUM+2)/FACT(K-1) * T(I) * C2))
      IF(ABSF(AP)-1.0E-30)701,710,710
701   IF(ABSF(P)-1.0E-30)702,710,710
702   C4R = C4R + TOW**K/FLOATF(K)*CONST
      GO TO 800
710   DUM1 = 0.0
      DUM2 = 0.0
720   CALLE11SSB
      IF(IX)795,810,820
795   C4R = C4R - CONST * DUM1
      C4I = C4I - CONST * DUM2
800   CONTINUE
805   IX = 0
      K = 1
      IF(ABSF(AP) - 1.0E-30)806,809,809
806   IF(ABSF(P) - 1.0E-30)807,809,809
807   C4R = C4R + C1*T(I)**N*TOW
      GO TO 815
809   CALL E11SSB
810   IF(T(I)-1.0E-30)812,811,811
811   TIN = T(I)**N
      GO TO 813
812   TIN = 1.0
813   C4R = C4R - C1*C3R*TIN
      C4I = C4I - C1*C3I*TIN
815   IX = 1
      K = N+2
      IF(ABSF(AP) - 1.0E-30)816,819,819
816   IF(ABSF(P) - 1.0E-30)817,819,819
817   C4R = C4R + (-1.0)**N*C2*TOW**(N+2)/FLOATF(N+2)
      RETURN
819   DUM1 = 0.0
      DUM2 = 0.0
      CALL E11SSB
820   C4R = C4R - (-1.0)**N*C2*DUM1
      C4I = C4I -(-1.0)**N*C2*DUM2
      RETURN
      END
```

```
      SUBROUTINE E11SSB
      DIMENSION FACT(50),T(500)
      COMMON P,AP,C1,C2,C3R,C3I,C4R,C4I,TOW,DUM1,DUM2,N,K,IX,IXLQ,I,
     1FACT,T
720   DO 790 L=1,K
      LP2=(L+2)/2
      LP1=(L+1)/2
      C2R=0.0
      C2I=0.0
      IF(IXLQ)770,770,740
740   DO 750 M=1,LP2
      LDUM=L-2*M+2
      APL = AP**(L-2*M+2)
      PM = P**(2*M-2)
      C2R =   C2R + (-1.0)**(M-1) * FACT(L+1)/FACT(2*M-1)/FACT(LDUM+1)
     1*APL*PM
750   CONTINUE
      DO 760 M=1,LP1
      LDUM=L-2*M+1
      APL = AP**(L-2*M+1)
      PM = P**(2*M-1)
      C2I =   C2I + (-1.0)**(M-1) * FACT(L+1)/FACT(2*M  )/FACT(LDUM+1)
     1*APL*PM
760   CONTINUE
      DENOM=C2R*C2R+C2I*C2I
      C3R=C2R/DENOM
      C3I=-C2I/DENOM
      GO TO 775
770   C3R = 1.0/AP**L
      C3I = 0.0
775   IF(IX)780,792,780
780   KLL = K-L
      TKL = TOW**KLL
      DUM1 = DUM1 + FACT(K)/FACT(KLL+1) * C3R * TKL
      DUM2 = DUM2 + FACT(K)/FACT(KLL+1) * C3I * TKL
790   CONTINUE
792   RETURN
      END




TITLEA87CXSK        0101  J.B.VERNON
C THIS PROGRAM COMPUTES THE SHOCK SPECTRUM FOR A SYSTEM WITH ZERO DAMPING
C SUBJECTED TO A COMPLEX SHOCK INPUT.  INPUT DATA CARDS SHOULD HAVE TWO NUMBERS
C ON EACH CARD IN ACCORDANCE WITH  FORMAT(2E17.9).  THE FIRST NUMBER
C SHOULD BE THE TIME AND THE SECOND NUMBER THE ACCELERATION AT THAT INSTANT, IN
C CHRONOLOGICAL ORDER.  AT DISCONTINUITIES USE TWO DATA POINTS WITH THE SAME
C VALUE OF TIME.  LINEAR INTERPOLATION BETWEEN DATA POINTS IS ASSUMED.
C FOLLOWING THE LAST OF THESE DATA CARDS IS A CARD WHICH SHOULD HAVE TWO FIXED
C POINT NUMBERS PUNCHED IN COLUMNS 35-37 AND 38-40.  THE FIRST OF THESE PROVIDES
C AN UPPER LIMIT FOR THE VALUE OF BETA, THE NATURAL FREQUENCY, WHICH IS THE
C ABSCISSA FOR THE SHOCK SPECTRUM PLOT.  (A VALUE OF  4 MAY BE A REASONABLE
C ESTIMATE.)  THE SECOND OF THESE FIXED POINT NUMBERS SPECIFIES THE NUMBER OF
C POINTS ON THE PLOT.  (THE TOTAL NUMBER OF POINTS WILL BE THE FIRST NUMBER
C MULTIPLIED BY THE SECOND NUMBER.)
      DIMENSION T(100),AY(100)
      PRINT 10
 10   FORMAT(1H1,1H )
      PRINT 40
 40   FORMAT(55HDATA FOLLOWS, TIME AND CORRESPONDING INPUT ACCELERATION)
      PRINT 580
      PRINT 50
 50   FORMAT(34H         TIME            ACCELERATION  / )
      I = 1
100   READ INPUT TAPE 5,T(I),AY(I),NCYC,NB
110   FORMAT(2E17.9,2I3)
115   FORMAT(2E17.6)
      IF(NCYC)120,120,130
120   PRINT 115,T(I),AY(I)
      I = I+1
      GO TO 100
```

```
130 NY = I-1
    TF = T(NY)
    PRINT 580
    PRINT 140
140 FORMAT(55HPRIMARY RESPONSE SPECTRUM FOLLOWED BY RESIDUAL SPECTRUM)
    PRINT 580
    PRINT 150
150 FORMAT(65HNAT FREQ, CPS  TIME,MAX ACC  MAX ACCEL   TIME,MIN ACC   MI
   1N ACCEL   /)
    PI = 3.14159625
    NBF = NB * NCYC
    FNB = NB
    DB = 2.0 * PI/(FNB * TF)
    BETA = 0.0
    DO 600 I=1,NBF
    INDX = 0
    BETA = BETA + DB
    AXA = 0.0
    AXDA = 0.0
    N1 = 1
    N2 = NY - 1
200 AMAX = 0.0
    AMIN = 0.0
    TMAX = 0.0
    TMIN = 0.0
    DO 520 J=N1,N2
    JP1 = J + 1
    TB = T(JP1)
    TA = T(J)
    AYA = AY(J)
    AYB = AY(JP1)
    IF(ABSF(TB)-1.0E-30)520,520,210
210 IF(ABSF(TB-TA)/TB -1.0E-06)520,520,220
220 AYDA = (AYB-AYA)/(TB-TA)
    C1 = AXA-AYA
    C3 = AXDA-AYDA
    C2 = C3/BETA
    C4 = -C1 * BETA
    PLUS = ABSF(AXA) + ABSF(AYA)
    IF(PLUS-1.0E-30)230,230,225
225 IF(ABSF(C1)/PLUS - 1.0E-06)230,230,260
230 PLUS = (ABSF(AXDA) + ABSF(AYDA))/BETA
    IF(PLUS-1.0E-30)470,470,235
235 IF(ABSF(C2)/PLUS - 1.0E-06)470,470,240
240 PSI = PI*0.5
    GO TO 280
260 PSI = ATANF(-C2/C1)
    IF(PSI)270,270,280
270 PSI = PSI + PI
280 C3S = C3*C3
    C4S = C4*C4
    ADS = AYDA*AYDA
    DENOM = C3S + C4S - ADS
    PLUS = C3S + C4S + ADS
    IF(ABSF(DENOM)/PLUS - 1.0E-06)300,300,310
300 BTPSI = PI * 0.5
    IX = 0
    BTSV = BTPSI
    GO TO 317
310 IF(DENOM)470,470,315
315 BTPSI = ATANF(-AYDA/SQRTF(DENOM))
    IX = 0
    BTSV = BTPSI
317 IF(BTPSI)320,330,330
320 BTPSI = BTPSI + PI
330 BT = BTPSI - PSI
    IF(ABSF(BT)-1.0E-06)335,335,337
335 BT = 0.0
    GO TO 350
337 IF(BT)340,350,350
340 BT = BT + PI
350 IF(BT-PI)370,370,360
360 BT = BT - PI
370 IF(BT - BETA*(TB-TA))380,430,430
```

```
380 AX = AYA+AYDA*BT/BETA+C1*COSF(BT)+C2*SINF(BT)
    IF(AX-AMAX)400,400,390
390 AMAX = AX
    TMAX = T(J) + BT/BETA
400 IF(AX - AMIN)410,420,420
410 AMIN = AX
    TMIN = T(J) + BT/BETA
420 BT = BT + PI
    GO TO 370
430 IF(IX)440,440,470
440 BTPSI = -BTSV
    IX = 1
    GO TO 317
470 BT = BETA*(TB-TA)
    AX = AYA+AYDA*BT/BETA+C1*COSF(BT)+C2*SINF(BT)
    IF(AX-AMAX)490,490,480
480 AMAX = AX
    TMAX = T(JP1)
490 IF(AX-AMIN)500,510,510
500 AMIN = AX
    TMIN = T(JP1)
510 AXDA = AYDA + C3 * COSF(BT) + C4 * SINF(BT)
    AXA = AX
520 CONTINUE
    BCPS = BETA*0.5/PI
    PRINT 550,BCPS,TMAX,AMAX,TMIN,AMIN
550 FORMAT(6E13.4)
    IF(INDX)560,560,570
560 N1 = NY
    N2 = NY
    T(N2+1) = T(NY) + 2.0*PI/BETA
    INDX = 1
    GO TO 200
570 PRINT 580
580 FORMAT(1H )
600 CONTINUE
    PRINT 610
610 FORMAT(33HEND OF SHOCK SPECTRUM COMPUTATION )
    END
```

Index

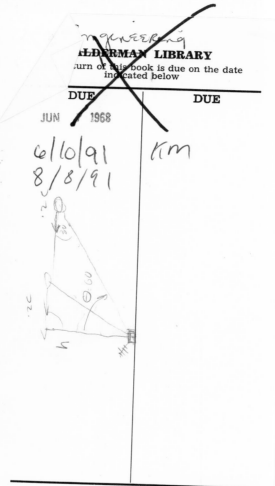